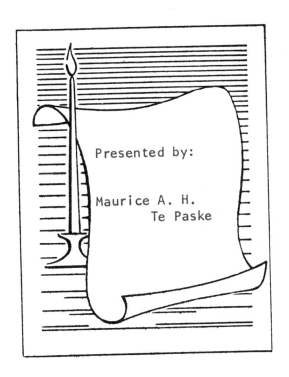

Presented by:

Maurice A. H.
Te Paske

TECHNIQUE OF ORGANIC CHEMISTRY

ARNOLD WEISSBERGER, *Editor*

Volume XIV

ENERGY TRANSFER AND ORGANIC PHOTOCHEMISTRY

TECHNIQUE OF ORGANIC CHEMISTRY
ARNOLD WEISSBERGER, *Editor*

TECHNIQUE OF ORGANIC CHEMISTRY
VOLUME XIV

Editors: P. A. Leermakers
A. Weissberger

ENERGY TRANSFER AND ORGANIC PHOTOCHEMISTRY

A. A. LAMOLA
N. J. TURRO

with chapters by

P. A. Leermakers and T. R. Evans

1969

INTERSCIENCE PUBLISHERS
a division of John Wiley and Sons, New York · London · Sydney · Toronto

Library of Congress Catalog Card Number 45–8533 SBN 471 932655

INTRODUCTION TO THE SERIES

Organic chemistry from its very beginning has used specific tools and techniques for the synthesis, isolation, and purification of compounds, and physical methods for the determination of their properties. Much of the success of the organic chemist depends upon a wise selection and a skillful application of these methods, tools, and techniques, which, with the progress of the science, have become numerous and often intricate.

The present series is devoted to a comprehensive presentation of the techniques which are used in the organic laboratory and which are available for the investigation of organic compounds. The authors give the theoretical background for an understanding of the various methods and operations and describe the techniques and tools, their modifications, their merits and limitations, and their handling. It is hoped that the series will contribute to a better understanding and a more rational and effective application of the respective techniques.

The field is broad and some of it is difficult to survey. Authors and editors hope that the volumes will be found useful and that many of the readers will let them have the benefit of their criticism and of suggestions for improvements.

A. WEISSBERGER

Research Laboratories
Eastman Kodak Company
Rochester, New York

TECHNIQUE OF ORGANIC CHEMISTRY

GENERAL PLAN OF THE SERIES

Volume I. (Third Edition—in four parts.) **Physical Methods of Organic Chemistry.** *Authors:* A. E. Alexander, D. H. Anderson, J. R. Anderson, J. C. Arthur, Jr., E. D. Bailey, N. Bauer, G. L. Beyer, E. R. Blout, L. O. Brockway, L. M. Corliss, A. H. Corwin, R. L. Custer, B. P. Dailey, G. Donnay, J. D. H. Donnay, K. Fajans, D. D. Fitts, G. K. Fraenkel, A. L. Geddes, H. S. Gutowsky, F. A. Hamm, W. D. Harkins, J. M. Hastings, W. Heller, E. E. Jelley, W. Klyne, C. G. Le Fevre, R. J. W. Le Fevre, S. Z. Lewin, W. N. Lipscomb, W. J. Mader, H. Mark, L. Meites, D. H. Moore L. D. Moore Jr., O. H. Muller, J. B. Nichols, W. C. Nixon, G. Oster, A. C. Parker, M. A. Peacock, R. B. Pontius, J. G. Powles, H. A. Scheraga, P. W. Selwood, T. Shedlowsky, R. Signer, D. R. Simonson, W. M. Siri, E. L. Skau, C. P. Smyth, M. Spire, D. W. Stewart, J. M. Sturtevant, W. Swietoslawski, J. F. Swindells, C. Tanford, G. W. Thomson, B. M. Tolbert, R. Ullman, M. J. Vold, R. D. Vold, R. H. Wagner, H. Wakeham, C. E. Waring, S. Wawzonek, W. West, N. B. Woodall, and N. Wotherspoon

Volume II. (Second Edition.) **Catalytic Reactions.** V. I. Komarewsky, C. H. Riesz, and F. L. Morritz; **Photochemical Reactions,** C. R. Masson, V. Boekelheide, and W. A. Noyes, Jr.; **Electrolytic Reactions,** S. Swann, Jr.

Volume III. (Second Edition.) **Part I. Separation and Purification.** C. M. Ambler, G. Broughton, D. Craig, L. C. Craig, A. B. Cummins, F. B. Hutto, Jr., A. L. Jones, K. Kammermeyer, F. W. Keith, Jr., E. MacWilliam, E. G. Scheibel, R. E. Stauffer, and R. S. Tipson. **Part II. Laboratory Engineering.** J. W. Axelson, R. S. Egly, R. F. Eisenberg, M. P. Hofmann, R. R. Kraybill, G. H. Miller, J. H. Rushton, and W. C. Streib

Volume IV. (Second Edition.) **Distillation.** *Editors:* E. S. Perry and A. Weissberger. *Authors:* C. S. Carlson, C. H. Deal, J. C. Hecker, D. E. Orgen, E. S. Perry, A. Rose, E. Rose, R. S. Tipson, F. E. Williams, and T. J. Williams

Volume V. **Adsorption and Chromatography.** H. G. Cassidy

Volume VI. **Micro and Semimicro Methods.** N. D. Cheronis. With contributions by A. R. Ronzio and T. S. Ma

Volume VII. **Organic Solvents.** A. Weissberger and E. S. Proskauer. Second Edition by J. A. Riddick and E. E. Toops, Jr.

Volume VIII. (Second Edition—in two parts.) **Investigations of Rates and Mechanisms of Reactions.** *Editors:* S. L. Friess, E. S. Lewis, and A. Weissberger. *Authors:* J. C. Balaceanu, M. L. Bender, S. A. Bernhard, C. E. Boozer, J. F. Bunnett, G. M. Burnett, B. Chance, L. DeMaeyer, M. Eigen, S. L. Friess, E. M. Grunwald, J. Higgins, F. M. Huennekens, J. C. Jungers, M. Kreevoy, E. S. Lewis, R. Livingston, A. Maccoll, E. F. MacNichol, Jr., H. W. Melville, B. K. Morse, R. M. Noyes, G. Porter, F. J. W. Roughton, G. A. Russell, W. H. Saunders, Jr., H. Strehlow, and A. Weller

Volume IX. (Second Edition.) **Chemical Applications of Spectroscopy.** *Editor:* W. West. *Authors:* Ralph S. Becker, A. B. F. Duncan, W. Gordy, R. N. Jones, F. A. Matsen, C. Sandorfy, D. R. Scott, and W. West

Volume X. **Fundamentals of Chromatography.** H. G. Cassidy

Volume XI. (in two parts). **Elucidation of Structures by Physical and Chemical Methods.** *Editor:* K. W. Bentley. *Authors:* B. Belleau, K. W. Bentley, K. Biemann, J. C. D. Brand, A. R. H. Cole, J. K. N. Jones, J. F. King, E. Leete, P. de Mayo, S. McLean, F. J. McQuillin, K. H. Overton, M. B. Perry, N. Polgar, K. T. Potts, A. I. Scott, E. Y. Spencer, J. B. Stothers, G. A. Swan, Z. Valenta, and B. C. L. Weedon

Volume XII. **Thin-Layer Chromatography.** Justus G. Kirchner

Volume XIII. **Gas Chromatography.** O. E. Schupp III

Volume XIV. **Energy Transfer and Organic Photochemistry.** *Editors:* P. A. Leermakers and A. Weissberger. *Authors:* T. R. Evans, A. A. Lamola, P. A. Leermakers, and N. J. Turro

vi

ENERGY TRANSFER AND ORGANIC PHOTOCHEMISTRY

PREFACE

Since 1948, when W. A. Noyes, Jr. and V. Boekelheide reviewed in a chapter of 62 pages the techniques used in the study of photochemical reactions, organic photochemistry has undergone very rapid development. New concepts and techniques have been introduced, and the number of photochemists has grown spectacularly. A second edition of the chapter on "Photochemical Reactions" by C. R. Masson, Boekelheide, and Noyes was published in 1956. This discussion, double the size of the first, retains its value, but very important further developments in concepts, techniques, and interpretations have taken place since. Although several treatises of photochemistry in general have been published in the meantime, a presentation of certain topics which are pertinent for a successful application of photochemical techniques is again needed. It was the plan of editors and authors to provide this discussion in a volume of this series, while duplicating as little as possible the treatments by Masson, Boekelheide, and Noyes, and by Calvert and Pitts (*Photochemistry*, Wiley, 1966).

The brief introductory Chapter I contains a discussion of fundamental photophysical and photochemical concepts, and is intended to lay a foundation for the later chapters. The material covers elementary spectroscopic, energetic, and photochemical concepts and definitions, as well as a brief summary of classes of photochemical reactions.

In Chapter II, A. A. Lamola has placed emphasis on energy transfer in organic photochemistry, an area with very substantial and rapid advance which has become a focus of photochemistry research. Sensitization and quenching by way of an electronic excitation transfer have been used to uncover new photoreactions, to control the course of photochemical reactions, and have been most useful in mechanistic studies. Electronic excitation transfer monitored through a subsequent photoreaction can lead to easy determination of the efficiencies and rates of photophysical processes not possible by spectroscopic means. Today there is hardly a photochemical investigation which does not make use of electronic energy transfer.

It is the purpose of Chapter II to review the various electronic energy transfer processes from both theoretical and phenomenological viewpoints and to review the scope and limitations of excitation transfer methods in photochemistry and spectroscopy. The emphasis is on excitation transfer in fluid solution. The approach is mainly that of the Hammond school. The author thanks Professor M. Guéron, Dr. M. Dillon, and Dr. P. Funabashi for helpful discussions and criticisms and the Bell Telephone Laboratories for the typing of manuscript and the drafting of figures.

In the third chapter, Nicholas J. Turro surveys the important areas of photochemistry of organic molecules by emphasizing the similarities and correlations between the photochemical behavior of different organic molecules. The primary photochemical processes are outlined so that formal reactivity analogies between groups are made obvious. Simple semiempirical models are proposed for most chromophores, and predictions of the expected photochemistry based on these models are explored. The energetic and dynamic relationships between electronically excited states and the ground state are reviewed and analyzed in relation to their crucial role in determining the efficiency of photoreactions.

The material presented is representative of the state of the art as of early 1968. An exhaustive compilation of reactions was neither desired nor possible. The author will appreciate comments and criticisms concerning the usefulness of the particular method of exposition employed.

In the final chapter, the advances in photochemical methods are reviewed by Ted R. Evans primarily for the organic chemists. Consequently the chapter deals only with liquid systems and the emphasis is on physical and preparative experimental techniques that require a minimum of specialized apparatus. Rather than describing a few experiments in detail, a more general approach has been taken using literature examples to illustrate the methods. Figures in Chapters I and IV were drafted by Lawrence D. Weis; typing and general editorial assistance were provided by Karen Branciforte and Lila Scoville, to all of whom the authors of these chapters are indebted.

Wesleyan University   PETER A. LEERMAKERS

Research Laboratories   A. WEISSBERGER
Eastman Kodak Company

ENERGY TRANSFER AND ORGANIC PHOTOCHEMISTRY

CONTENTS

Chapter III. PHOTOCHEMICAL REACTIONS OF ORGANIC MOLECULES.

CHAPTER I

FUNDAMENTAL CONCEPTS

PETER A. LEERMAKERS

*Department of Chemistry,
Wesleyan University, Middletown, Connecticut*

Historically, photochemistry has developed along two distinct lines: Organic chemists, with little theoretical background, used light to effect desired chemical transformations with synthesis as the primary emphasis. Physical chemists, primarily interested in fast reaction kinetics (usually in the vapor phase), studied the production and reactions of free radicals and other species generated photochemically. In the mid- to late 1950's the field of photochemistry began to change. Both the physical kineticist and the organic chemist began to relate their own interests to the relatively new field of molecular electronic spectroscopy, especially as workers in the latter field began using qualitative language and simplified models in describing excited states. At this point the general area of photochemistry and electronic spectroscopy almost literally exploded, with most of the enthusiasm rising from the organic and organically oriented physical chemist. The result has been a proliferation of concepts, theories, methods, and techniques relating to photochemical reactions.

Although initially the organic chemist relied heavily on the spectroscopist for such important considerations as the relationship of phosphorescence to the triplet state, the definition and nature of n,π^* and π,π^* states, and the determination of energy levels by spectroscopic methods, the spectroscopist can now benefit in return. Most spectacularly, the organic chemist can now, entirely by chemical means, determine energy levels in some molecules which are not determinable by direct spectroscopic means. In addition, perhaps more importantly, he can deduce information regarding types of excited states and examine various radiationless processes, including energy transfer from chemical observation alone.

It is now obvious that the importance of photochemistry, both as a synthetic and mechanistic tool, is enormous. Along with his intimate partner the spectroscopist, the photochemist has opened up entire vistas of new research problems and answers relating to some of the most fundamental and fascinating areas of chemistry and physics. This first section will attempt to give a general introduction to the basic concepts and terminology of photochemistry. Many of the topics introduced will be elaborated upon in more detail in subsequent sections.

I. MOLECULAR EXCITATION (1)

Basic to any photoprocess is absorption of a quantum of light—a photon. Obviously, if a molecule does not absorb radiation in the visible or near ultraviolet, it cannot undergo a *direct* photochemical reaction with light of these wavelengths. We will defer to a later time a discussion of *sensitized* reactions.

"Useful" wavelengths for electronic excitation extend from 2000 Å (corresponding to 142 kcal/mole) to 7000 Å (41 kcal/mole), although it will be seen in later sections that the conventionally inaccessible vacuum ultraviolet (wavelengths shorter than 2000 Å), requiring special optics and light sources, is a region where much interesting photochemistry takes place. The reason for the lower limit of 2000 Å, actually closer to 1850 Å, is that the atmosphere absorbs the light of shorter wavelength and quartz does not transmit it.

1. Absorption

Assume, then, that a molecule possesses an absorption band in the visible or near UV. A photon of the appropriate energy or wavelength corresponding to the absorption band may cause an electronic transition to take place. This usually involves promotion of an electron in a bonding or nonbonding molecular orbital (MO) to an antibonding molecular orbital. The molecule is thus raised to an excited state electronically, and usually vibrationally as well, from which a photochemical or any one of a number of photophysical processes may take place. In general, there will be a number of such possible excited states for a molecule. As an example, naphthalene possesses two distinct absorption bands in the near UV corresponding to two different electronic transitions. (A transition of *higher* energy, as contrasted with one of lower energy, simply means that the promoted electron arose from a more stable bonding molecular orbital to a given antibonding MO, or that from a given bonding MO it was promoted to a less stable antibonding MO.) The ground state of naphthalene, or nearly any molecule, has all electron spins paired, a multiplicity of one,* and is thus a singlet, designated S_g. Since spin must nearly always be conserved in an electronic transition the resulting excited states will also be singlets with no net spin, and be designated S_1, S_2, and S_3.

2. The Triplet State

Once the molecule is in an excited state, however, it is possible that spin inversion may take place (known as *intersystem crossing*) producing an excited state with a net spin of 1 and a multiplicity of 3, thus designated a *triplet* state. This, according to Hund's first rule, will be lower in energy than the corresponding excited singlet. And it is obvious that for every *excited* singlet electronic level there will be a corresponding triplet level. Figure 1 is a schematic diagram of the energy levels (below 200 K/cal) of naphthalene. Obviously there will be many possible vibrational states for each electronic state. Only the ground vibrational levels are shown in Figure 1.

3. Excitation Pathways

Let us now, in Figure 2, trace the various pathways upon excitation to an upper vibrational level of S_2, keeping in mind that direct excitation into the triplet manifold is formally forbidden. At this point, the fate of the excitation depends upon whether the molecule is in the solid, liquid, or vapor phase. In condensed phases, in which there are always neighboring molecules to

---

* The multiplicity of a state is given by the formula $2|S| + 1$. If all electrons are spin-paired, S, the net spin will be zero and thus the multiplicity will be *one*, hence the designation *singlet*. If two electrons become spin-unpaired (i.e., have parallel spins), which can occur in an excited state without violating the Pauli exclusion principle, the net spin will be ± 1, so that $2|S| + 1 = 3$ and the state is thus designated a *triplet*.

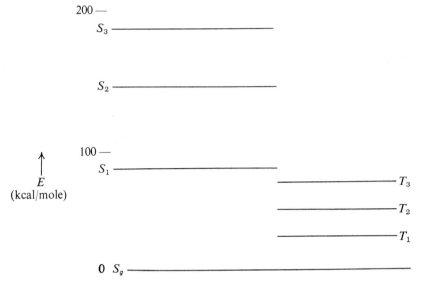

Fig. 1. Singlet and triplet energy levels for naphthalene (approximate).

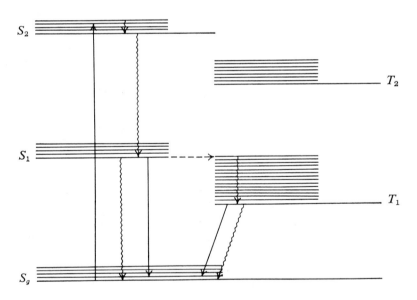

Fig. 2. Jablonski diagram. The fine horizontal lines represent vibrational levels. Solid arrows represent absorption or emission of radiation, wavy arrows are nonradiative pathways, and the dotted arrow represents intersystem crossing.

help in the dissipation of thermal energy, vibrational decay to the zero vibrational level of S_2 will be very fast, of the order of 10^{-13} sec; likewise nonradiative *internal conversion* leading to S_1 will be fast (of the order of 10^{-11} sec). In the vapor phase both of these processes will be much slower, opening up the possibility of photodecomposition as a competing pathway. In any case, direct return from S_2 to S_g by reemission of a photon is exceedingly unlikely for most organic compounds.

Once the molecule is in the S_1 state it has a lifetime in the range 10^{-9} to 10^{-6} sec, depending upon a number of competing factors including the "natural fluorescence lifetime" (see below). It may (at this point) radiate a photon and return to the ground state by a process called *fluorescence*, it may nonradiatively return to the ground state by internal conversion, it may photochemically react, or it may undergo intersystem crossing to the triplet state.

The triplet, T_1, has a lifetime that can be a million times that of the corresponding S_1 state. The reason for this is that any transition to the ground state will be strongly forbidden since spin cannot be conserved. Nevertheless the T_1 state will not live indefinitely, and thus may emit a photon in a "forbidden" radiative process called *phosphorescence*, usually observed only at very low temperatures in a solid glass; it may undergo nonradiative inter-system crossing and internal conversion to the ground state, it may react photochemically, or it may donate its triplet excitation to a neighboring molecule if the neighbor has a triplet energy equal to or lower than that of the donor. This latter phenomenon, known as the triplet–triplet energy transfer, is enormously important both theoretically and practically, and will be extensively discussed by Lamola.

II. THE NATURES OF EXCITED STATES

1. General Considerations

Before entering into any meaningful discussion of photochemical reactions in themselves, it is necessary and important that we know as much as possible about electronic configurations of the excited states responsible for the photoreactions (2).

In a typical organic molecule there can, in general, be three "kinds" of electrons, namely those residing in sigma bonds, those in pi bonds, and if a heteroatom is present, those residing in nonbonding atomic orbitals (3). (In the following discussion the terms "bond" and "molecular orbital" will be used interchangeably.) Excitation of one of these electrons will place it in a higher energy orbital; in the case of polyatomic molecules this will usually be a σ^* or π^* molecular orbital (the asterisk connotes antibonding). Quite clearly a difference in the "kind" of electron promoted (and to which higher energy orbital) will have a profound effect on the electronic distribution of the excited state as well as the energy of the excited state.

2. The Formaldehyde Molecule

Figure 3 depicts very approximately the orbitals of formaldehyde with energy increasing vertically in the diagram. The C—H σ bonds are essentially ignored. In the ground state the σ, π, and n (nonbonding oxygen 2py) orbitals are filled with two electrons each. The others are vacant. The following types of transitions can reasonably be expected to occur: σ–σ^*, i.e., an electron in the σ bonding orbital being promoted to the σ^* antibonding orbital (this would be a very high energy transition, expected to occur at energies corresponding to wavelengths shorter than 1600 Å), π–π^*, n–π^*, and n–σ^*. The latter three transitions have been observed, the n–π^* at 2900 Å, n–σ^* at 1900 Å, and the π–π^* at 1650 Å (3). The corresponding excited states produced would be S_1, S_2, and S_3, respectively.

It should be pointed out that we have arbitrarily chosen one system of designating transitions. The reader is referred to a more complete discussion by Pitts, Wilkinson, and Hammond (4).

3. Benzophenone and Other Molecules

Although the photochemistry of formaldehyde is by no means uninteresting, let us focus our attention on a more complicated carbonyl compound

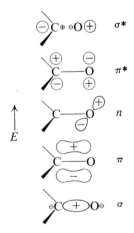

Fig. 3. Relative energies and approximate orbital descriptions of the bonding, non-bonding and antibonding orbitals of a non-conjugated carbonyl chromophore.

which has its $n-\pi^*$ and $\pi-\pi^*$ transitions in the "useful" ultraviolet (keeping in mind the orbital diagram in Fig. 3). For the present we shall not be concerned with $n-\sigma^*$ transitions.

A molecule such as benzene, naphthalene, etc., with no heteroatoms, can and does have only $\pi-\pi^*$ transitions in the near ultraviolet. Benzophenone, on the other hand, contains a carbonyl group and possesses an $n-\pi^*$ transition at about 3450 Å and a $\pi-\pi^*$ transition at about 2450 Å (leading to states S_1 and S_2, respectively). Even though the carbonyl group is formally conjugated to the two phenyl rings, one can still consider that excitation involving the carbonyl function is mostly localized in the carbonyl, and that Figure 3 is still an approximate representation of the carbonyl orbitals.

In $\pi-\pi^*$ excitation, there is no significant net change in the carbonyl dipole since the electron is removed from a region between the two atoms and promoted to an orbital shared by both, but not between them. On the other hand $n-\pi^*$ excitation removes an electron from the oxygen atom and promotes it to the same π^* orbital which is shared by both atoms, leaving *formally* a $\frac{1}{2}$ positive charge on oxygen. In fact, the C=O dipole is not reversed, only diminished, but the reasoning applies nevertheless. As important as the change in dipole moment accompanying an $n-\pi^*$ transition is the fact that oxygen, now possessing an odd number of electrons, acts very much like a free radical and indeed much of the chemistry of n,π^* states can be explained on this basis.

Thus far in the discussion of the benzophenone molecule we have ignored the fact that internal conversion from S_2 (π,π^*) to S_1 (n,π^*) is very rapid, and thus we would not expect chemical reactions from the π,π^* state even with appropriate excitation (2450 Å). Secondly, it will be noted in Section III that benzophenone undergoes intersystem crossing very efficiently, so that the chemically active state is actually T_1 (n,π^*), not S_1. This fact in no way affects the *basic* arguments advanced concerning the electronic distribution in n,π^* and π,π^* states, although, in fact, electronic distributions in singlet and triplet states of the same type do differ somewhat.

In the above discussion, the carbonyl group was selected to demonstrate n,π^* states. Actually, any π system containing an adjacent heteroatom with nonbonding electrons can have n,π^* states, aromatic amines and nitro compounds being only two of an extremely great number of examples.

III. ENERGY TRANSFER

Photosensitized reactions differ from direct photochemical reactions in that the photosensitizer absorbs the light but some other species in the system reacts. In general, most photosensitized reactions involve excitation energy transfer where the photosensitizer is the donor and the reacting molecule is the acceptor:

$$D + h\nu \rightarrow D^*$$
$$D^* + A \rightarrow D + A^*$$
$$A^* \rightarrow \text{products (or } h\nu \text{ or heat)}$$

Energy transfer can and does take place between singlet states, but often this is not chemically important in solution due to the usually short lifetimes of singlets and other restricting circumstances. Triplet–triplet energy transfer, on the other hand, is much more important and useful. A quantitative treatment of the mechanism(s) will be given in Chapter II; we shall introduce the subject qualitatively here.

Historically, mercury vapor photosensitization has been a classic technique, employed in the photodissociation of many kinds of substances, including hydrocarbons and ketones, for over 30 years. The strongest emission line in a low-pressure mercury arc is at 2537 Å; the corresponding *absorption* by Hg atoms produces the ^3P states with 112.5 kcal/mole of energy. These excited atoms can then collide with a suitable substrate (acceptor) usually producing the latter in the triplet state:

$$Hg + h\nu \rightarrow (^3P)Hg$$
$$(^3P)Hg + A \rightarrow Hg + {}^3A$$

Much novel and interesting photochemistry of acceptor molecules has been observed.

The concept of triplet–triplet energy transfer between organic molecules arose rather slowly in the 1950's from the spectroscopic work of Terenin and Ermolaev (5). These workers observed that if an ether–pentane–alcohol (EPA) glass at 77°K containing benzophenone and naphthalene were irradiated at a wavelength primarily absorbed by benzophenone, there was significant phosphorescent emission from naphthalene. The triplet level of benzophenone lies above that of naphthalene, and apparently where triplet benzophenone and ground-singlet naphthalene were nearest neighbors, energy transfer occurred to produce the naphthalene triplet which subsequently emitted phosphorescence. It was subsequently shown by Gilmore, Gibson, and McClure (6) and Hammond and Moore (7) that excited singlet benzophenone very efficiently crosses over to the triplet state; thus ordinary excitation of benzophenone produces triplet states in high yield. Benzophenone would seem, then, to be a "good" sensitizer to excite acceptors in situations different from that of Terenin and Ermolaev (5), namely, in liquid solution. This has been shown to be the case; since 1961, benzophenone and many other compounds with high intersystem-crossing efficiencies have been employed to sensitize a wide variety of chemical reactions (8).

According to workers who have studied triplet energy transfer in solid, liquid, and vapor phase, the process requires virtual collision, but is effective

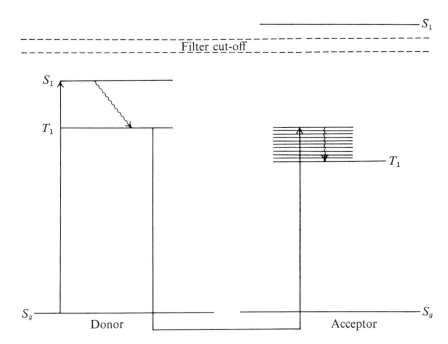

Fig. 4. Sensitized excitation of acceptor. Note that if the acceptor S_1 state is above S_1 of the donor, even though T_1 of the acceptor is below T_1 of the donor (not an unusual circumstance), then a filter cutting off energies above the dotted lines will insure that all acceptor triplets were formed via energy transfer, and that the acceptor singlet manifold was in no way involved.

upon nearly every encounter in condensed phases if the triplet energy of the donor is above that of the acceptor. One then observes what is called a coupled transition, i.e., simultaneous deactivation of donor and excitation of acceptor (Fig. 4). It is still not clear what the collision cross section really is, and in certain cases it has been postulated that the *spectroscopic* T_1 of the acceptor may indeed lie *above* T_1 of the donor, although the transfer efficiency falls off rapidly in this case (9).

IV. PHOTOCHEMICAL REACTIONS

1. Photoionization and Predissociation

In the present book, the focus is on photoprocesses that do *not* lead to photoionization, which usually occurs in the vacuum ultraviolet (below 1850 Å). In photoionization a photon of very high energy promotes an electron not to an antibonding orbital, but rather completely out of the molecular sphere of influence, thus creating a positive ion. The term "non-ionizing radiation" then means light in the visible and UV of energy insufficient to cause ionization.

Two-photon photoionization could be very important in biological systems and has been observed for many compounds in glasses.

$$X \xrightarrow{h\nu} X^*$$
$$^3X^* \xrightarrow{h\nu} X^+ + e$$

Predissociation, which is usually not important in condensed phases although it is important in the vapor phase under certain circumstances, involves excitation to an electronic level that does not contain a Morse curve type of minimum. It is also defined by some workers as excitation to a vibrational level of an upper electronic state which is above the bond dissociation energy of that electronic state. Figure 5 illustrates these processes, the net result of which is nearly always bond cleavage rather than a return to the ground state.

2. The Primary Process

The term primary photochemical process means different things to different workers. Noyes, Porter, and Jollye (10) define it as "comprising the series of events beginning with absorption of a photon by a molecule and ending either

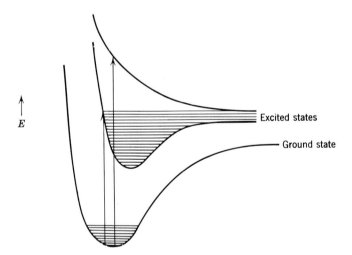

Fig. 5. Predissociation, as opposed to normal deexcitation, in Franck-Condon excitation. The Morse curves shown, for simplification, are for a diatomic molecule. The left-hand arrow leads to a "predissociative" vibrational level of an "ordinary" excited state, the right-hand arrow to a typically predissociative electronic level.

with the disappearance of that molecule or with its conversion to a state such that its reactivity is statistically no greater than that of similar molecules in thermal equilibrium with their surroundings." This definition, while thoughtful and reasonable, is probably too general since it involves the various photophysical processes such as fluorescence, internal conversion, intersystem crossing, and phosphorescence. Perhaps, then, a better definition of the primary photochemical process is the initial photo*chemical* act, be it homolysis of a bond, concerted decomposition into another molecular species, concerted unimolecular rearrangement, predissociation (see above), etc.

An understanding of the primary photochemical process is the aim of most physical photochemical research. It is relatively easy to irradiate material and obtain product amenable to rigorous characterization. However, such product may often be the result of secondary (thermal) reactions of photochemically generated intermediates. In order to understand the mechanism that converts substrate to photoproduct, it is necessary to possess as much knowledge as possible about the primary photochemical act. Toward such an end it is important to know something of the nature of the chemically active excited state. Often it is necessary to do careful quantum yield measurements under controlled conditions. Various methods for scavenging chemical intermediates are also routinely used. The point to be stressed at this time is that the science of photochemistry demands, above all, study and characterization of the primary process by any or all of the available tools.

3. The Concept of Quantum Yield

The overall chemical quantum yield, almost universally designated by the symbol ϕ, may be defined as the number of molecules reacting per photon absorbed. This will be the quantum yield for disappearance of reactant. One may also talk about quantum yield for formation of a given product, which may or may not be the same as the above quantity depending upon the stoichiometry and complexity of the reaction. In general, quantum yields will vary between zero and unity (or slightly above unity when a reactive intermediate consumes starting material). However, for chain reactions where the photon acts as only a "catalyst" to promote the initiation step, as for instance in the formation of HBr from H_2 and Br_2 by photolysis of a Br—Br bond, the quantum yield may be extremely large (on the order of tens or hundreds).

It is clear, then, that the usefulness of light to carry out a given reaction depends directly on the quantum yield for the process. Thus, a typical 450-W lamp that puts out on the order of 10^{18} quanta/sec of near-ultraviolet light may, per day, produce hundreds of grams of material in a chain process, tens of grams of material by an efficient nonchain process ($\phi \sim 1$), and perhaps milligrams or less when the quantum yield is very low (< 0.001).

Quantum yields apply also to photophysical processes, such as intersystem crossing, fluorescence, and phosphorescence. These values can never be larger than unity, and quantum yields of the two radiative processes are obviously competitive with photo*chemical* quantum yields.

Another kind of quantum yield of major theoretical importance is the *primary photochemical quantum yield*, which is the number of molecules undergoing a primary process, by our definition, per photon absorbed. This, of course, may never exceed unity. Only the initiation step of a photo-induced chain reaction, for instance, would be included in this definition. Also, in a process in which radical recombination regenerates starting material, the *primary* quantum yield might be high while the overall quantum yield, as previously defined, might be small or even zero.

4. Classes of Photochemical Reactions

Succeeding chapters of the book will deal extensively with a large number of specific photochemical reactions, both with respect to mechanism and practice. Here we will consider very briefly some of the various *classes* of photoreactions, utilizing simple molecules as typical examples, to illustrate the scope of the field of photochemistry.

A. PHOTOLYSIS

This must be the most general of photoreactions, since, by definition, it involves simple bond cleavage induced by absorption of a photon. Virtually every kind of molecule will undergo bond homolysis if irradiated at appropriate wavelengths, especially in the vacuum UV. Perhaps the two most widely studied examples are the photolysis of acetone (Eq. (1)) and iodine (Eq. (2)), the quantum yields [and ultimate fate of the fragments in Eq. (1)] of

$$CH_3COCH_3 \xrightarrow[\text{vapor phase}]{h\nu} CH_3\overset{\overset{\displaystyle O}{\|}}{C}\cdot + \cdot CH_3 \qquad (1)$$

$$I_2 \xrightarrow[\substack{\text{solution or} \\ \text{vapor}}]{h\nu} 2I\cdot \qquad (2)$$

both being temperature and wavelength dependent. Other, rather useful, examples of photolytic cleavages occurring at readily accessible wavelengths include photolysis of diazo compounds to yield carbenes (Eq. (3)), decom-

$$R_2C = N = N \xrightarrow{h\nu} R_2C\text{:} + N_2 \qquad (3)$$

position of azo compounds, ketenes, diketones, ketoesters, epoxides, peroxides, aryl iodides, azides, and many, many other classes of compounds. Although photolytic reactions can and do occur readily in solution for some systems, it is much more likely that such reactions occur in the vapor phase. Collisional deactivation is much slower in the vapor phase, this enhances the lifetime of the excited state, and hence the probability for chemical destruction.

B. PHOTOREDOX REACTIONS

Again, this is an enormously large class of reactions encompassing both inorganic and organic examples. Dye-sensitized photooxidation by molecular oxygen of various olefinic compounds is one example that will be treated later. Two classic examples of photoredox reactions are the light-induced oxidation of uranium oxalate (Eq. (4)) and the photoreduction of (certain) ketones (Eq. (5)). In the former case, apparently uranium does not change in

$$2H^+ + UO_2^{2+}C_2O_4^{2-} \xrightarrow[\text{H}_2\text{O solution}]{h\nu} UO_2^{2+} + CO_2 + CO + H_2O \qquad (4)$$

$$2R_2C{=}O + 2R'H \xrightarrow[\text{solution}]{h\nu} R_2\overset{\overset{\text{OH}}{|}}{C}{-}\overset{\overset{\text{OH}}{|}}{C}R_2 + R'{-}R'$$

$$(+ \text{ some } R_2\overset{\overset{\text{OH}}{|}}{C}{-}R') \qquad (5)$$

oxidation state. Other metals such as Fe(III) may be substituted for uranium, but in the specific case of iron, the metal does change oxidation state to Fe(II). Oxalic acid alone does not photoreact at wavelengths above 2000 Å.

Photoreduction of ketones (Eq. (5)) has for many years been the traditional example of photochemical synthesis on a preparative scale. It is clearly the method of choice for the laboratory-scale production of benzpinacol from benzophenone in the presence of a suitable hydrogen donor (R'H). Specific requirements for the donor, as well as the mechanism of the reaction, will be discussed in later chapters.

C. PHOTOREARRANGEMENT AND PHOTOISOMERIZATION

Some of the most interesting, highly strained hydrocarbon systems have been prepared by photochemical means, often involving isomerization of appropriate olefinic starting materials. Equations (6), (7), and (8) illustrate

$$\text{//}\diagdown\diagup\text{//} \xrightarrow{h\nu} \square\!\!\!\diagup \qquad (6)$$

$$\phi\text{—}C\text{=}CH_2 \xrightarrow{h\nu} \phi\text{—}\triangle \quad (7)$$

but three of the very many transformations of this type that have appeared in the recent literature. Photorearrangements or isomerizations are not limited to olefinic hydrocarbons, but these appear to afford the most striking examples. For instance, the first example of formation of a Dewar benzene was effected by direct irradiation of the 1,2,5-tri-*t*-butyl derivative of benzene.

Other widely studied examples in this class of reactions are photorearrangements of dienones, *cis–trans* isomerizations of olefins, various rearrangements of saturated cyclic ketones, and the enormous number of complex rearrangements in pigments, steroids, and other natural products.

D. PHOTOADDITION

Although this is a very diverse reaction class, most of the examples of photoaddition in the current literature involve photo*cyclo*addition, i.e., formation of substituted cyclobutanes. Equation (9) illustrates homodimerization indicating the four possible isomeric products. X can be virtually any

"activating" group (acyl, vinyl, cyano, etc.). The nature of X will be very influential on the stereochemical course and quantum yield of the reaction. Cross addition is also possible, as in the following example (Eq. (10)).

Hundreds of examples of photocycloaddition, including oxetane formation, photo-Diels-Alder reactions, and related additions, many of great synthetic value, have been reported in the recent literature. The scope and mechanisms of this class of reactions, as well as detailed *preparative* examples, will be treated in subsequent chapters.

E. MISCELLANEOUS

Obviously not all photochemical reactions can be categorized within the four classes listed above. For instance, the Norrish type II process (Eq. (11)) and the vapor photodecomposition of pyruvic acid (Eq. (12)) might formally be considered "photolyses" whereas mechanistically they must be in a special class of "photocycloelimination."

$$CH_3CCH_2CH_2CH_3 \xrightarrow{h\nu} \left[\begin{array}{c} O \\ \parallel \\ H_3C \end{array} C-CH_2-CH_2 \begin{array}{c} H \\ | \\ CH_2 \end{array} \right] \longrightarrow$$

$$CH_3\overset{OH}{\underset{|}{C}}=CH_2 + CH_2=CH_2 \quad (11)$$

$$CH_3CC-OH \xrightarrow[\text{vapor}]{h\nu} \left[CH_3C \overset{O}{\underset{O}{\overset{H}{\diagup}}} \overset{C}{\underset{O}{\diagup}} O \right] \longrightarrow CO_2 + \left[CH_3\overset{OH}{\underset{|}{C}}: \right] \longrightarrow CH_3CH \quad (12)$$

We have not discussed processes such as light-induced solvolysis reactions which presume solvated ionic intermediates. Such processes might be considered photolyses proceeding by heterolysis rather than homolysis, but due to the somewhat complex nature of such processes they really belong in a special category.

References

1. For recent and relevant reviews, see: (a) N. J. Turro, *Molecular Photochemistry*, Benjamin, New York, 1965; (b) G. S. Hammond and N. J. Turro, *Science*, **142**, 1541 (1963); (c) P. A. Leermakers and G. F. Vesley, *J. Chem. Educ.*, **41**, 535 (1964); (d) J. G. Calvert and J. N. Pitts, Jr., *Photochemistry*, Wiley, New York, 1966; (e) D. C. Neckers, *Mechanistic Organic Photochemistry*, Reinhold, New York, 1967; (f) S. P. McGlynn, T. Azumi and M. Kinoshita, *Molecular Spectroscopy of the Triplet State*, Prentice-Hall, Englewood Cliffs, N.J. 1969.
2. (a) J. N. Murrell, *The Theory of the Electronic Spectra of Organic Molecules*, Wiley, New York, 1963; (b) H. H. Jaffe and M. Orchin, *Theory and Applications of Ultra-violet Spectroscopy*, Wiley, New York, 1962.
3. M. Kasha, *Light and Life*, W. D. McElroy and B. Glass, Eds., Johns Hopkins Press, Baltimore, Md., 1961, pp. 31–64.

4. J. N. Pitts, F. Wilkinson, and G. S. Hammond, in *Advances in Photochemistry*, Vol. 1, W. A. Noyes, Jr., G. S. Hammond, and J. N. Pitts, Eds., Interscience, New York, 1963, pp. 1–22.
5. A. Terenin and V. Ermolaev, *Trans. Faraday Soc.*, **52**, 1042 (1956).
6. E. H. Gilmore, G. E. Gibson, and D. S. McClure, *J. Chem. Phys.*, **20**, 829 (1952); **23**, 399 (1955).
7. G. S. Hammond and W. M. Moore, *J. Am. Chem. Soc.*, **81**, 6334 (1959).
8. Cf. G. S. Hammond, P. A. Leermakers, and N. J. Turro, *J. Am. Chem. Soc.*, **83**, 2395 (1961); G. S. Hammond, N. J. Turro, and A. Fischer, *J. Am. Chem. Soc.*, **83**, 4674 (1961); and many other papers in this series. Other workers include R. B. Cundall, F. J. Fletcher and D. G. Milne, *J. Chem. Phys.*, **39**, 3536 (1963); and other authors too numerous to name at this stage in this monograph.
9. G. S. Hammond, J. Saltiel, A. A. Lamola, N. J. Turro, J. S. Bradshaw, D. O. Cowan, R. C. Counsell, V. Vogt, and C. Dalton, *J. Am. Chem. Soc.*, **86**, 3197 (1964).
10. W. A. Noyes, Jr., G. Porter, and V. G. Jolley, *Chem. Rev.*, **56**, 49 (1956).

CHAPTER II

ELECTRONIC ENERGY TRANSFER IN SOLUTION: THEORY AND APPLICATIONS

ANGELO A. LAMOLA

Bell Telephone Laboratories, Murray Hill, New Jersey

I. INTRODUCTION

Intermolecular transfer of electronic energy has become a powerful tool for uncovering new photochemical reactions, for directing the course of photochemical reactions, for elucidating mechanisms of photochemical reactions, and for obtaining information about molecular excited states not obtainable by ordinary spectroscopic methods. Without electronic energy transfer, the photosynthetic process in plants could not be nearly as efficient as it is, or might not operate at all. Excitation transfers are probably important controlling factors in the radiation chemistry and photochemistry of nucleic acids and proteins, and may play an important part in such processes as vision and phototaxis.

Several general papers or reviews concerning the theoretical (1–3,6,9,12, 13) or experimental (2,4,5,9,12,13) aspects of excitation transfer have appeared during the last decade but only recently have extensive discussions of its applications to photochemistry and spectroscopy (7,8,10) been published.

It is the purpose of this chapter to review those aspects of the theories of electronic energy transfer which are especially germane to photochemistry and molecular photobiology, and to discuss in some detail the experimental aspects. A large portion of the chapter deals with various applications of electronic energy transfer with detailed examples.

Pitts, Wilkinson, and Hammond have pointed out (11) that the term energy transfer or excitation transfer as used in photochemistry refers to any transfer of energy from an excited molecule to other species. The energy acceptor may itself be promoted to an excited electronic state or the electronic energy may be donated to a host system as vibrational, rotational, or translational energy. Here we will be concerned primarily with those cases in which the energy is transferred as electronic energy. That is, the acceptor is promoted to a higher electronic state as a consequence of the transfer.

Most of the cases of electronic energy transfer that are considered in this chapter can be described by Eq. (1).

$$D^* + A \rightarrow D + A^* \qquad\qquad (1)$$

In the initial state the donor D is electronically excited; in the final state the donor has been demoted to a lower electronic state and the acceptor A has been promoted to a higher electronic state. The electronic energy transferred is denoted by the asterisk. The energy-transfer process may involve two steps with the intermediacy of a photon (radiative transfer) or may be a one-step radiationless process requiring some direct interaction of the excited donor with the acceptor. Processes involving electron transfers will not be considered. Emphasis will be placed on those cases of radiationless excitation transfer where the donor and acceptor are chemically different species in condensed and disordered media and the excited states involved are low lying, so that, in general, the rates of the excitation transfers are slow compared to the rates of vibration relaxation in the donors and acceptors (see below).

II. RADIATIVE TRANSFER (THE TRIVIAL PROCESS)

Radiative transfer of electronic energy involves the possibility of reabsorption of donor emission. The process requires two steps with the intermediacy of a photon (Eqs. (2) and (3)).

$$D^* \rightarrow D + h\nu \tag{2}$$

$$h\nu + A \rightarrow A^* \tag{3}$$

No direct interaction of the donor with the acceptor is involved. Obviously only energies corresponding to that part of the emission spectrum of the donor that overlaps with the absorption spectrum of the acceptor can be transferred. The efficiency of the transfer is governed by the quantum yield of emission from the donor and by the Beer–Lambert law regarding the absorption of this radiation by the acceptor. The transfer can, of course, occur over very large distances (relative to molecular diameters) and the probability that an acceptor molecule reabsorbs the light emitted by a donor at a distance R varies as R^{-2}.

Radiative energy transfer may be characterized (2) by the invariance of the donor emission lifetime,† a change in the emission spectrum of the donor which can be accounted for on the basis of the acceptor absorption spectrum, and a lack of dependence of the transfer efficiency upon the viscosity of the medium.

Gaviola and Pringsheim (15) have pointed out that radiative transfer is usually of little importance when the donor and acceptor are similar molecules due to the usually small overlap of the emission and absorption spectra for this case. Consequently, the process was termed "trivial." However, quite efficient radiative transfer can take place if the donor and acceptor are different species and the spectral overlap is large. This can lead to quite serious "internal filter" effects plaguing spectroscopic studies of various sorts (16). Even in the case of self-absorption where the efficiency may be low, serious distortion of the emission spectrum can occur. There is one reported case where radiative transfer of excitation may be the controlling factor in the photochemistry of a system (17). Of course, one can always point out that

---

† This is correct unless the donor and acceptor are identical molecules. In the latter case there could be a lengthening of the sample emission lifetime due to "imprisoning" of the radiation if multiple reabsorptions and reemissions occur (14).

life on earth depends upon radiative transfer of energy from the sun. It is better, then, to take Livingston's point of view (3) in referring to radiative excitation transfer as "trivial," not because it is unimportant but because it is easy to explain.

III. RADIATIONLESS TRANSFER

Radiationless transfer of electronic energy involves the simultaneous de-excitation of the donor and excitation of the acceptor: a one-step process which does not involve the intermediacy of a photon. Some interaction of the donor and acceptor is necessary and the virtual transitions in the donor and acceptor must be very close in energy. Efficient transfer may occur even with a very small donor–acceptor interaction so that quite long-range transfers are possible.

It is the purpose of this section to introduce, one at a time, the several concepts basic to a discussion of the theory of radiationless electronic energy transfer; to review the various theoretical treatments in a qualitative manner, emphasizing the limit where the rate of transfer is slow compared to vibrational relaxation in the donor and acceptor; and finally to review some of the experimental aspects of electronic energy transfer in solution.

1. Theoretical Preliminaries

A. RESONANT OR COUPLED TRANSITIONS

In all of the mechanisms for radiationless excitation transfer considered here, close resonance between the initial ($D^* + A$) and final ($D + A^*$) states is required. This condition is fulfilled if the transition in the donor ($D^* \rightarrow D$) and the transition in the acceptor ($A \rightarrow A^*$) involve nearly the same energy, the excitation transfer being the simultaneous occurrence of the two coupled or resonant transitions. If there is a difference in the electronic energy gaps for the two transitions, it may be made up by including vibrational levels in the donor and acceptor, and (in condensed phase) lattice or solvent vibrational levels if the vibrations are sufficiently coupled to those of the donor and/or acceptor. Such a case is represented schematically in Figure 1.

If the energy transfer is slower than vibrational relaxation in the donor excited state and the temperature is not too high, the initial state has both the excited donor and the acceptor in vibrationless states. And if the energy-transfer process is a vertical one, that is, the transitions in both the donor and acceptor proceed in accordance with the Franck–Condon principle, the energy transferred must correspond to a frequency which is common to the

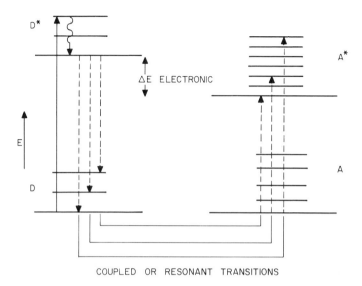

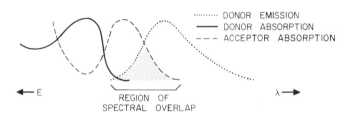

Fig. 1. Coupled transitions for a donor–acceptor pair with an electronic energy difference and their relation with the overlap of donor emission and acceptor absorption spectra.

appropriate emission spectrum of the donor and the appropriate absorption spectrum of the acceptor. That is, it belongs to the region of overlap of the two spectra. With increasing overlap, the number of possible coupled transitions (the number of possible final states) increases and so also the probability for excitation transfer (see Section III–1–C).

A spectral overlap integral J may be defined by

$$J = \int_0^\infty F_D(\nu)\mathscr{E}_A(\nu)\,d\nu \tag{4}$$

in which $F_D(\nu)$ is the spectral distribution of the donor emission and $\mathscr{E}_A(\nu)$ is the spectral distribution of the acceptor absorption, each expressed in quanta and *normalized to unity* on a wave number scale (Eq. (5)).

$$\int_0^\infty F_D(\nu)\, d\nu = \int_0^\infty \mathscr{E}_A(\nu)\, d\nu = 1 \tag{5}$$

The spectral distributions $[F_D(\nu)$ and $\mathscr{E}_A(\nu)]$ of the donor and acceptor transitions are, of course, chiefly determined by the associated Franck-Condon factors. Thus the spectral overlap integral as defined by Eq. (4) is a measure of the number of possible final states together with the "Franck-Condon factors" associated with the virtual transitions in the donor and acceptor that give rise to the various possible final states. It is important to note that the spectral overlap integral, as defined here, has nothing to do with the oscillator strengths of the transitions involved.

B. DONOR–ACCEPTOR INTERACTIONS

Radiationless excitation transfer can occur only if the initial (D* + A) and final (D + A*) states are degenerate or nearly so and if they are coupled by a suitable donor–acceptor interaction. The total interaction, β, is given as the matrix element of a perturbation between the initial and final states,† Eq. (6), and includes all the electrostatic interactions of the electrons and nuclei of the donor with those of the acceptor. The total interaction can be expressed as a sum of "coulomb" and "exchange" terms.‡

$$\beta = \int \Psi_i \hat{H}'\Psi_f\, d\tau = \int \Psi_{D^*}\Psi_A \hat{H}'\Psi_D \Psi_{A^*}\, d\tau \tag{6}$$

† β is a *resonance* integral between the configurations with D excited and with A excited, and the term *resonance excitation transfer* is used quite often in the literature.

‡ The second integral in Eq. (6) is not proper. The properly antisymmetrized initial and final state wave functions can be written as

$$\Psi_i = \frac{1}{\sqrt{2}}\{\Psi_{D^*}(1)\Psi_A(2) - \Psi_{D^*}(2)\Psi_A(1)\}$$

and

$$\Psi_f = \frac{1}{\sqrt{2}}\{\Psi_D(1)\Psi_{A^*}(2) - \Psi_D(2)\Psi_{A^*}(1)\}$$

(if only two electrons are considered), so that

$$\beta = \int \Psi_{D^*}(1)\Psi_A(2)\hat{H}'\Psi_D(1)\Psi_{A^*}(2)\, d\tau$$

$$- \int \Psi_{D^*}(1)\Psi_{A^*}(2)\hat{H}'\Psi_D(2)\Psi_{A^*}(1)\, d\tau.$$

In the last equation, the first term is the coulomb term and the second the exchange term.

The electrostatic potentials in the coulomb term can be replaced by a multipole expansion, the first term of which gives the dipole–dipole interactions, the second the dipole–quadrupole interaction, etc. (19). It then becomes a matter of evaluating each term. Since the wave functions (Ψ'_i and Ψ'_f) are not known such calculations are not possible. However, it can be shown that the dipole–dipole term represents the interaction between the transition dipole moments $\overline{M}_D$ and $\overline{M}_A$ of both molecules (Eq. (7)), the squares of which are proportional to the oscillator strengths of the radiative transitions in the isolated donor and acceptor molecules. Thus, the dipole–dipole

$$\beta(\text{dipole–dipole}) \sim \overline{M}_D \overline{M}_A / R^3 \qquad (7)$$

term can be obtained experimentally from the appropriate absorption and emission spectra or emission lifetimes. It can also be shown that if the transitions in the donor and acceptor are allowed and the distance of separation is not too small, the dipole–dipole term predominates and the higher multipole terms can be neglected. The dipole–dipole interaction falls off as the inverse third power of the distance, R in Eq. (7), separating the interacting centers and can lead to excitation transfer over distances many times the molecular diameters (see Section IV).

The exchange interaction is a quantum-mechanical effect arising from the symmetry properties required of electronic wave functions with regard to the interchange of the space and spin coordinates of any two electrons in the donor–acceptor system. This kind of exchange-symmetry requirement, for example, is what leads to singlet–triplet splittings in isolated molecules.

$$\beta(\text{exchange}) = \int \phi_{D^*}(1)\phi_A(2) \frac{e^2}{r_{12}} \phi_D(2)\phi_{A^*}(1) \, d\tau \qquad (8)$$

The space part of the exchange term is of the form given by Eq. (8) where r_{12} is the distance between electrons (1) and (2). Here only one of the possible pairs of electrons is considered; the complete term is a sum over all electrons taken two at a time. Two characteristics of the exchange interaction are of special importance to the problem of electronic energy transfer. First, the integral (Eq. 8)) simply represents the electrostatic interaction between two charge clouds $Q_i(1) = \phi_{D^*}(1)\phi_{A^*}(1)$ and $Q_f(2) = \phi_D(2)\phi_A(2)$. Since the Q's are vanishingly small unless there is spatial overlap of the donor and acceptor wave functions, the interaction is necessarily of short range (on the order of collision diameters). Also, a very sharp fall-off with donor–acceptor separation is expected due to the approximately exponential fall-off of electron density outside the boundaries of the molecules. Secondly, the magnitude of the exchange interaction is not at all related to the oscillator strengths of the transitions in the donor and acceptor. If the virtual transitions in the donor and acceptor are strongly forbidden the dipole–dipole term is very small and the exchange term usually predominates at close approach of donor and acceptor. However, when the transitions are fully allowed, the dipole–dipole term predominates.

Higher order terms in the coulombic interaction (electric dipole–electric quadrupole, electric dipole–magnetic dipole) become important at close approach of the donor and acceptor. But at these small donor–acceptor distances the exchange interaction will always contribute significantly to the total interaction if allowed by the spin selection rules (1) (see below).

For nearest neighbors the dipole–dipole term can range from 10^4 cm^{-1}, if the transitions in the donor and acceptor are both fully allowed, to 0.01 cm^{-1} or less if both transitions are spin forbidden. The nearest neighbor exchange interaction for low-lying excited states in aromatic crystals, for example, is on the order of 10 cm^{-1} (37,43).

C. RATES, EFFICIENCIES, AND SPIN SELECTION RULES

For almost all cases in which electronic energy transfer is slow compared to vibrational relaxation in the donor and acceptor,† the rate $n_{D^* \to A}$ for transfer is given by Eq. (9) according to time-dependent perturbation theory and based upon an interaction-of-continua model (40).

$$n_{D^* \to A} = \frac{2\pi}{\hbar} \beta^2 \rho_E \qquad (9)$$

In Eq. (9), β is the interaction matrix element between the initial and final states discussed in the previous section, and ρ_E is the density of states (number of resonant states per energy interval) and is related to the number of possible final states and thus to the extent of spectral overlap.

Transfer via Dipole–Dipole Interaction. Förster (2,21,27,28) and later Dexter (1), and Robinson and Frosch (6), taking different approaches, have shown that the rate constant for (vibrational–relaxation) excitation transfer in which the initial and final states are coupled through a dipole–dipole interaction is given by Eq. (10) (combine Eqs. (7) and (9))

$$k_{D^* \to A}(\text{dipole–dipole}) = \frac{2\pi}{\hbar} C\rho_E \left(\frac{\overline{M}_D \overline{M}_A}{R^3} \Theta(\theta) \right)^2 \sum (\langle \chi_{D^*}|\chi_D\rangle\langle\chi_{A^*}|\chi_A\rangle)^2 \qquad (10)$$

in which C is a constant, $\Theta(\theta)$ is the angular dependence of the dipole–dipole

---

† These include almost all cases of electronic-energy transfer between chemically different solute molecules in solution, many cases of transfer between identical solute molecules and between solvent molecules in noncrystalline states, many cases of transfer between nonconjugated chromophores within the same molecule, and some cases of transfer between host molecules in mixed crystals if the temperature is not too low (see below).

interaction, and the $\langle\chi'|\chi\rangle^2$ are Franck-Condon factors. The latter are summed over all possible final resonant states and a Boltzman distribution of initial states. Appropriate transformation of Eq. (10) leads to an expression (Eq. (11)) in which all the terms are related to experimentally obtainable parameters. In Eq. (11)

$$k_{D^*\to A}(\text{dipole–dipole}) = \frac{2\pi}{h}\, C' \,\frac{f_D f_A}{R^6\bar{\nu}^2}\,\Theta(\theta)^2 J \tag{11}$$

C' is a constant, f_D and f_A are the oscillator strengths for the donor and acceptor transitions, respectively, $\bar{\nu}$ is an "average" wave number for the transitions, and J is the spectral overlap integral. Thus the "selection rules" for electronic energy transfer via dipole–dipole interaction are the same as those for the corresponding electric dipole transitions in the isolated molecules (see Table 1). The spin selection rule is, then, $M_{D^*} = M_D$ and $M_A = M_{A^*}$,

TABLE 1

Donor and Acceptor Transitions and Dipole–Dipole Resonance Transfer

Donor transition	Acceptor transition	Relative transfer rate[a]	Relative transfer efficiency[a]
Fully allowed	Fully allowed	1.0	1
Symmetry forbidden	Fully allowed	∼0.1	∼1
Symmetry forbidden	Symmetry forbidden	∼0.01	∼0.1
Spin forbidden	Fully allowed	∼10^{-6}	∼1
Spin forbidden	Spin forbidden	∼10^{-12}	∼10^{-6}

[a] R, Θ, and J assumed to be constant.

where M denotes the multiplicity of the state. The two spin-allowed processes of interest for organic systems are given by Eqs. (12) and (13).

$$D^*(\text{singlet}) + A(\text{singlet}) \to D(\text{singlet}) + A^*(\text{singlet}) \tag{12}$$

$$D^*(\text{singlet}) + A(\text{triplet}) \to D(\text{singlet}) + A^*(\text{triplet}) \tag{13}$$

If the consequences of the energy transfer are important, the *efficiency or number of transfers per donor lifetime* ($\tau_D k_{D^*\to A}$) may be more critical than the rate of the transfer. Since, neglecting radiationless deactivation paths, $\tau_D \propto 1/f_D$, and since $k_{D^*\to A} \propto f_D$, the efficiency ($\tau_D k_{D^*\to A}$) of the excitation transfer should be nearly independent of the nature of the *donor* transition. Thus transfers involving spin-forbidden transitions in the donors (Eqs. (14) and (15)) should be as *efficient* as those in which the donor transitions are allowed (Eqs. (12) and (13)) (see Table 1).

$$D^*(\text{triplet}) + A(\text{singlet}) \rightarrow D(\text{singlet}) + A^*(\text{singlet}) \qquad (14)$$

$$D^*(\text{triplet}) + A(\text{triplet}) \rightarrow D(\text{singlet}) + A^*(\text{triplet}) \qquad (15)$$

Transfer via Exchange Interaction.   Dexter (1) has derived an expression (Eq. (16)) for the rate of (vibrational–relaxation) excitation transfer in which the initial and final states are coupled through the exchange interaction. In Eq. (16),

$$k_{D^* \rightarrow A}(\text{exchange}) = \frac{2\pi}{\hbar}\,(Ke^{-2R/L})J \qquad (16)$$

R is the distance of separation of the donor and acceptor, L is an effective average orbital radius for the initial and final electronic states of the donor and acceptor, J is the spectral overlap integral, and K is a quantity with the dimensions of energy. The latter cannot be directly related to experimentally obtainable quantities. Thus, the Dexter equation gives only an approximate distance dependence of the transfer rate, and the expected dependence on the extent of spectral overlap.

It has already been pointed out that the rate of excitation transfer by the exchange mechanism should have nothing to do with the spatial selection rules for the transitions in the donor and acceptor. Dexter (1) gives the spin part of the exchange term as the integral (Eq. (17)) where the $\sum$'s are spin wave functions.

$$\int \sum\nolimits_{D^*}(1) \sum\nolimits_{A}(2) \sum\nolimits_{D}(2) \sum\nolimits_{A^*}(1)\, d\tau \qquad (17)$$

Unless $\sum_{D^*} = \sum_{A^*}$ and $\sum_{D} = \sum_{A}$ the integral vanishes. So that, according to Dexter, the spin selection rule for excitation transfer by the exchange mechanism is $M_{D^*} = M_{A^*}$ and $M_D = M_A$, but M_{D^*} need not equal M_D. Multiplicity is conserved in the donor–acceptor pair but not necessarily in the individual molecules. Thus the case described by Eq. (18), although doubly forbidden by dipole–dipole interaction, is allowed by the exchange interaction. The processes shown in Eqs. (12) and (13) are, of course, spin allowed by exchange.

$$D^*(\text{triplet}) + A(\text{singlet}) \rightarrow D(\text{singlet}) + A^*(\text{triplet}) \qquad (18)$$

Others (7,22), however, have pointed out that transfer by the exchange interaction should follow Wigner's spin rule (23) from which follows: S_D and S_{A^*} are allowed final spin quantum numbers if there is at least one common number in the two series $|S_D + S_{A^*}|$, $|S_D + S_{A^*} - 1|$, ..., $|S_{D^*} - S_A|$ and $|S_{D^*} + S_A|$, $|S_{D^*} + S_A - 1|$, ..., $|S_{D^*} - S_A|$ where S_{D^*} and S_A are the initial spin quantum numbers. Spin, but not necessarily multiplicity, is conserved. Thus the triplet–triplet annihilation processes (19), (20), and (21) are also spin allowed by the exchange mechanism (see Section VIII).

$$D^*(\text{triplet}) + A(\text{triplet}) \rightarrow D(\text{singlet}) + A^*(\text{quintet}) \qquad (19)$$

$$D^*(\text{triplet}) + A(\text{triplet}) \rightarrow D(\text{singlet}) + A^*(\text{triplet}) \qquad (20)$$

$$D^*(\text{triplet}) + A(\text{triplet}) \rightarrow D(\text{singlet}) + A^*(\text{singlet}) \qquad (21)$$

But, on the basis of "spin statistics" (22) alone, the triplet–triplet annihilation process shown in Eq. (20), for example, is predicted to be about an order of magnitude less probable than the process shown in Eq. (18). Processes, such as that shown in Eq. (22), which do not conserve spin are forbidden by both exchange and dipole–dipole mechanism.

$$D^*(\text{singlet}) + A(\text{singlet}) \rightarrow D(\text{singlet}) + A^*(\text{triplet}) \qquad (22)$$

A magnetic or relativistic (spin–orbit) perturbation is required for such a process to occur with any efficiency. In what may be the only reported example of a rapid process with such spin changes, the acceptor contained bromine atoms (24).

D. STRONG, WEAK, AND VERY WEAK COUPLING

It has been pointed out (Section III–1–B) that the magnitude of the interaction (β) coupling the initial and final states can vary over a large range depending on the nature of the interaction, donor–acceptor distances and orientations, oscillator strengths, etc. It has also been indicated that the expression (Eq. (9)) for the rate of transfer which has been used throughout the last section is valid only for energy transfers which are slow compared to vibrational relaxation. This case has been termed vibrational–relaxation energy transfer or, more recently, the very weak interaction case. Vibrational–relaxation excitation transfer is expected to be (see below) operative for the great majority of cases of transfer between solute molecules in solution, especially when the donor and acceptor are chemically different, the solution is dilute, and the temperature is near room temperature. On the other hand, electronic energy "transfer" between molecules in molecular aggregates or in molecular crystals, for example, is often very much faster than vibrational relaxation, suggesting a relatively strong interaction. These systems also exhibit absorption and emission spectra which are quite different from those of the components. The very fast "transfer" rates and the spectral changes can be accounted for quite adequately by "exciton" theory, first described by Davydov (25) and expanded by Simpson and Peterson (26) and others. According to exciton theory, the rate of excitation "transfer" for the strong interaction case is not given by Eq. (9) but by Eq. (32).

Förster (27,28) has shown that "exciton" theory and his treatments (2,21) and those by Dexter (1) of vibrational–relaxation excitation transfer are closely related, arising from the same basic considerations but simply dealing

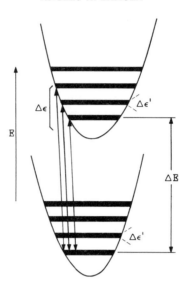

Fig. 2. Schematic interpretation of $\Delta\epsilon$ and $\Delta\epsilon'$ (after Förster, ref. 27).

with different limiting cases. More usefully, he showed that the various cases can be well defined in terms of the relative magnitudes of the donor–acceptor interaction energy β, and two experimentally obtainable energy parameters inherent to the isolated molecules; these are the Franck-Condon bandwidth $\Delta\epsilon$, and the widths of the individual vibronic levels $\Delta\epsilon'$ (see Fig. 2). A typical Franck-Condon bandwidth for aromatic compounds, for example, is about 3000 cm^{-1}. Individual vibronic bandwidths for molecules in condensed phase are determined mainly by the redistribution of vibrational energy and are environmental and temperature dependent. At room temperature a typical value would be 100 cm^{-1}; a lower limit of about 3 cm^{-1} is suggested (28) for organic molecules at liquid helium temperature. Depending on the magnitude of the donor–acceptor interaction, three cases arise, defined by the inequalities (23), (24), and (25). These have been designated the strong, weak, and very weak interaction cases, respectively. Similar classifications have been considered by others (26,29). Especially illuminating discussions concerning these limits from both theoretical and phenomenological viewpoints have been given by Förster (27,28), Kasha (30), and by Guéron

$$\beta \gg \Delta\epsilon \gg \Delta\epsilon' \quad \text{strong} \tag{23}$$

$$\Delta\epsilon \gg \beta \quad \gg \Delta\epsilon' \quad \text{weak} \tag{24}$$

$$\Delta\epsilon \gg \Delta\epsilon' \gg \beta \quad \text{very weak} \tag{25}$$

et al. (158). More recently, Robinson and Frosch (6) have discussed the problem in more detail and have developed a classification scheme which includes the additional limits $\Delta E \gg \beta$, and $\Delta E \ll \beta$, where ΔE is the electronic energy gap (see Fig. 1) between the excited states of the donor and acceptor. Some of the more salient features of each case are given below. It is assumed that the donor–acceptor system is in a medium; and the donor has the higher excitation energy.

$\beta \gg \Delta E,\ \beta \gg \Delta\epsilon \gg \Delta\epsilon'$ **(strong interaction case).** These conditions lead to profound changes in both the emission and absorption characteristics of the "donor–acceptor" system relative to those of the components. This is because there is quite complete delocalization of the excitation over the components and it is impossible to excite one component alone. The system may be described by the two stationary states given in Eqs. (26) and (27) (exciton theory). For the case of identical "donor" and "acceptor" ($\Delta E = 0$) $c = c' = 1/\sqrt{2}$,

$$\Psi_I = c\phi_{D^*}\phi_A + c'\phi_D\phi_{A^*} \tag{26}$$

$$\Psi_{II} = c'\phi_D\phi_A - c\phi_D\phi_{A^*} \tag{27}$$

and the *exciton splitting* is $2\beta_{el}$ (β_{el} is the purely electronic interaction matrix element, i.e., $\beta = \beta_{el}\cdot$vibrational factors) (Fig. 3). Accompanying the exciton splitting is a change in the shape of the spectrum (Fig. 4). This is because of a change in vibrational frequencies in the excited state of the dimer relative to the monomer since the excitation is distributed over both molecules in the former. The excitation would be spread over many molecules in the hypothetical infinite polymer so that the excited-state geometry is nearly identical to that of the ground state.† This leads to a very narrow spectrum

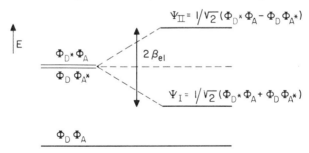

Fig. 3. Exciton model in the strong coupling limit for a dimer of identical molecules.

† The electronic structures of the low lying states of several real molecular crystals are well understood in terms of exciton theory, and extension to the question of mixed crystals is now receiving much attention. The dynamics of exciton motion in crystals is still very much an open question. None of these topics are discussed in any detail in this chapter. The interested reader is directed to several reviews and papers (25,26,32–37,43).

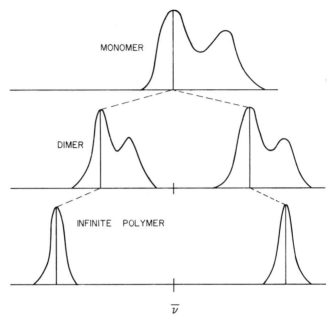

Fig. 4. Spectral effects expected for the exciton model in the strong coupling limit (after Kasha, ref. 30).

since only the 0–0 transition has a nonzero Franck-Condon factor and only transitions to one of the borders of the exciton band is allowed.

One may determine a "transfer rate" in the dimer by considering the wave functions including the time. A general nonstationary eigenfunction for the system can then be constructed (Eq. (28)), where Ψ_I and Ψ_{II} are the stationary functions given above, and E_0 is the unperturbed energy.

$$\Psi(t) = \frac{1}{\sqrt{2}} \{ \Psi_I \exp\left(-i\beta_{el}t/\hbar\right) + \Psi_{II} \exp\left(+i\beta_{el}t/\hbar\right) \} \exp\left(-iE_0 t/\hbar\right) \quad (28)$$

The squared modulus of the nonstationary function (if at $t = 0$, $\Psi^*(t)\Psi(t) = \phi_{D^*}^2\phi_A^2$) is given by Eq. (29) and the coefficients by Eqs. (30) and (31). This is a well-known result of first-order perturbation theory (38),

$$\Psi^*(t)\Psi(t) = a^*(t)a(t)\phi_{D^*}^2\phi_A^2 + a'^*(t)a'(t)\phi_D^2\phi_{A^*}^2 \quad (29)$$

$$a^*(t)a(t) = \cos^2\left(\beta_{el}t/\hbar\right) \quad (30)$$

$$a'^*(t)a'(t) = \sin^2\left(\beta_{el}t/\hbar\right) \quad (31)$$

and corresponds to an "oscillation" of the excitation between the "donor" and "acceptor" with a period $t = h/4\beta_{el}$. The reciprocal of the oscillation period may be considered the "transfer rate," Eq. (32). A β_{el} of 10,000 cm^{-1} corresponds to a "transfer rate" of 10^{15} sec^{-1}.

Operationally, however, it is meaningless to consider a "transfer rate" for the strong interaction case since to observe the oscillations ("transfers") a measuring process which is rapid compared to the oscillation period (10^{-15} to 10^{-14} sec) would be required. A more important reason why it is meaningless to speak of a "transfer" is because one cannot define a "donor" and "acceptor," since it is impossible to excite one component alone.

$$n_{D^* \to A} = 4\beta_{el}/h \tag{32}$$

$\Delta E \gg \beta$; $\beta \gg \Delta\epsilon \gg \Delta\epsilon'$. When the electronic energy gap is larger than the interaction energy, the relative magnitudes of the coefficients (c and c') in Eqs. (26) and (27) are quite different, that is, the excitation is mostly located on one component. Also, transitions between vibronic states of the system eventually lead to complete localization of the excitation on the acceptor. Thus there is the possibility of excitation transfer; that is, the excitation may initially be delocalized but be mostly on the donor, and eventually it becomes localized on the acceptor. Estimates of the rates of such localizations are given by Katsuura (39). It should be pointed out that this case is experimentally unimportant and is included only for completeness.

$\beta \gg \Delta E$, $\Delta\epsilon \gg \beta \gg \Delta\epsilon'$ (weak interaction case). For the strong interaction case the interaction is sufficiently great (exceeding the transition bandwidth) that all vibronic sublevels of the initial state are in resonance with those of the final state, and vibrational quantization may be neglected. Not only is the "rate of transfer" fast compared to vibrational relaxation, it is also fast compared to nuclear motion. In the weak interaction case, defined by the limits shown above, excitation transfer is still fast compared to vibrational relaxation, but is slow enough so that following excitation the nuclei of the component can perform several vibrations before transfer takes place. Since the interaction energy is less than vibrational separations, only individual vibronic levels of the components are in resonance. This requires the inclusion of vibrational overlap integrals in the expression for the transfer rate, Eq. (33).

$$n_{D^* \to A} = \frac{4\beta_{el}}{h} \sum \langle \chi_{D^*} | \chi_D \rangle \langle \chi_{A^*} | \chi_A \rangle \tag{33}$$

The sum is taken over all possible final resonant vibronic states and the appropriate distribution of initial states. In the case where the "donor" and "acceptor" are identical molecules and the temperature is sufficiently low, only the 0–0' transition comes into play, Eq. (34).

$$n_{D^* \to A} = \frac{4\beta_{el}}{h} \langle \chi_{0'} | \chi_0 \rangle^2 \tag{34}$$

The weak interaction limit does not lead to profound spectral changes but only to small, second-order effects such as hypochromism or hyperchromism and small splittings of certain vibronic bands ("Davydov splitting").

As implied above, in the case of weak coupling the excitation is temporarily entirely localized on one or the other component of the "donor–acceptor" pair. That is, there is a genuine oscillatory transfer of the excitation back and forth between the components. This goes on until the excited state is destroyed in one or the other of the components by emission, an internal conversion or intersystem crossing, chemical reaction, etc.

$\Delta E \gg \beta; \Delta\epsilon \gg \beta \gg \Delta\epsilon'$. In this case the excitation is shuttled between the donor and acceptor at a rate faster than vibrational relaxation, but since the electronic energy gap is larger than the interaction energy, the excitation eventually becomes permanently localized on the acceptor (unless the temperature is such that $kT \approx \Delta E$). That is, rapid transfer of the excitation between the donor and acceptor takes place as described for the previous case, but *vibrational relaxation* in the acceptor localizes the excitation there. The net transfer (localization), then, depends upon the rate of vibrational relaxation in the acceptor.

$\Delta E \gg \beta; \Delta\epsilon \gg \Delta\epsilon' \gg \beta$ (**Very weak interaction case; vibrational–relaxation transfer**). When the interaction energy is smaller than the vibronic bandwidths, the resonance is very sharp and only small regions of the vibrational sublevels are in resonance. The interaction of continua model (40) is appropriate here, for which time-dependent perturbation theory gives Eq. (35)

$$n_{D^* \to A} = \frac{2}{\hbar} \frac{\beta_{el}^2}{\Delta\epsilon'} \sum \langle \chi_{D^*} | \chi_D \rangle^2 \langle \chi_{A^*} | \chi_A \rangle^2 \tag{35}$$

(compare to Eqs. (9) and (10)) where the sum is over all possible final resonant states and a Boltzman distribution of initial states. Robinson and Frosch (6,41) arrive at the same result using a similar but physically more meaningful model.

No observable alterations in the spectra of the system are expected since the splittings are smaller than the vibrational bandwidths. The excitation is certainly entirely localized on the donor before transfer and on the acceptor afterwards. Furthermore, thermal equilibrium is attained in the donor before transfer since transfer is slow compared to vibrational relaxation. Vibrational relaxation in the acceptor prevents back transfer (unless $kT \approx \Delta E$). Finally, the transfer rate falls off more drastically with donor–acceptor distance for the very weak coupling case than for the weak coupling case because of the dependence of the rate in the former case on the *square* of the interaction energy.

$\beta \gg \Delta E; \Delta\epsilon \gg \Delta\epsilon' \gg \beta$. Slow transfer of excitation between identical molecules ($\Delta E = 0$) is of chief interest here.

Förster (27,28) and others (9) have claimed that as long as the width of the vibrationless level is larger than the interaction energy the transfer rate is given by Eq. (36).

$$n_{D^* \to A} = \frac{2\pi}{\hbar} \frac{\beta_{el}^2}{\Delta\epsilon'} \langle \chi_0 | \chi_0 \rangle^4 \tag{36}$$

That is to say, Eq. (35) is valid for both $\beta \gg \Delta E$ and $\beta \ll \Delta E$ as long as $\Delta\epsilon' \gg \beta$. Thermal and solvent broadening lead to 0–0 bandwidths on the order of 100 cm^{-1} for most molecules of interest in solution, even at liquid nitrogen temperature. Thus, one would expect to find many cases of excitation transfer between identical molecules in solution or even in mixed or single crystals (at higher temperatures) for which β_{el} is sufficiently small and Eq. (36) valid.

Robinson and co-workers (6,42) have taken a different view. They claim that only lifetime broadening is important. Thus, since it is rarely the case in systems of interest that transfer times are shorter than the lifetimes of the zeroth vibrational levels, they feel that it is almost *always* appropriate to use Eq. (34) (weak coupling limit) when considering excitation transfer between identical molecules, and that Eq. (35) obtains only when there is some important quenching process associated with the zeroth vibrational level of the excited acceptor. Sternlicht, Nieman, and Robinson (42) have made general use of Eq. (34) to estimate transfer rates for their tunneling model for transfer between identical solute molecules present at low concentrations in an inert solvent.

E. ELECTRONIC ENERGY TRANSFER IN SOLUTION

Phenomenological Types. It is useful to categorize electronic energy transfer processes in solution in the following way (2,3,7):

1. Radiative or "trivial" transfer

2. Long-range, single-step radiationless transfer

3. Collisional transfer

4. Excitation migration among donor (solvent) molecules followed by transfer to acceptor (solute)

By long-range, single-step transfer is meant radiationless transfer from the donor to the acceptor over distances large compared to molecular diameters. This would necessitate a coulombic (dipole–dipole) interaction mechanism.

By collisional transfer is meant an excitation transfer process which requires close approach (on the order of collisional diameters) of donor and acceptor in order to obtain efficient transfer. This would be the case, for instance, if only the exchange interaction mechanism were operating. If every collision between excited donor and acceptor molecules leads to transfer, the

transfer rate will be the diffusion-controlled rate.* That is, the rate of transfer
is governed by the rate of diffusion together of excited donor and acceptor
molecules. Approximate bimolecular rate constants for diffusion-controlled
reactions can be obtained from the simplified Debye (47)† expression (Eq.
(37), in which η is the viscosity of solvent in poise). For typical organic

$$k(\text{diffusion-controlled}) = \frac{8RT}{3000\eta} \; (\text{liter mole}^{-1} \text{ sec}^{-1}) \qquad (37)$$

solvents at room temperature, diffusion-controlled rate constants are 10^9 to
10^{10} liter mole^{-1} sec^{-1}. Table 2 lists values for solvents of widely different
viscosities.

TABLE 2

Viscosities and Diffusion-Controlled Bimolecular
Rate Constants at 20°C [a]

Solvent	Viscosity (0.001η)	k (diffusion-controlled) $(1 \text{ mole}^{-1} \text{ sec}^{-1})$
Hexane	3.26	2.0×10^{10}
Benzene	6.47	1.0×10^{10}
Cyclohexane	9.65	6.9×10^{9}
Water	10.05	6.5×10^{9}
Ethanol	11.94	5.4×10^{9}
Ethylene glycol	173.0	3.8×10^{8}
Glycerol	10690.0	6.0×10^{6}

[a] Calculated using Eq. (37).

An interesting case arises when the concentration of donor molecules is
very high, especially if the donor is the solvent with the acceptor present at
low concentration. Efficient and fast transfer of excitation to an acceptor
molecule far from an initially excited donor molecule (or region of collectively
excited donor molecules) could take place if the donor molecules interact
sufficiently. Fast multistep migration from donor (solvent) molecule to donor
molecule occurs until the excitation is on a donor molecule which is sufficiently close to the acceptor for energy transfer to the latter to take place (see
Section VII).

---

* This is true even if every encounter leads to transfer. An encounter is that period
during which the donor–acceptor pair are nearest neighbors. The two partners are
surrounded by a solvent "cage" at the moment of encounter and will suffer from 10 to
100 collisions with one another before they diffuse apart (45,46).

† Modifications of the Debye equation have been given by Beckett et al. (49), and by
Dubois (50).

Experimental differentiation of these phenomenological types can be
accomplished by examining the concentration dependence of the energy
transfer and the several items listed in Table 3.*

TABLE 3

Characteristics of Some Excitation Transfer Types

	(1) "Trivial" radiative transfer	(2) Long-range radiationless transfer	(3) Transfer requiring collision	(4) Excitation migration
Dependence of rate on increasing viscosity	None	Slightly decreased[a]	Decreased[b]	?
Donor lifetime	Unchanged	Decreased	Decreased	Decreased
Donor emission spectrum	Changed	Unchanged	Unchanged	Depends on magnitude of donor–donor interaction
Donor absorption spectrum	Unchanged	Unchanged	Unchanged	Small change depending on magnitude of donor–donor interaction
Dependence of efficiency on increasing volume	Increased	None	None	None

[a] Decrease observed only at sufficiently low acceptor concentrations.
[b] May not be decreased if the transfer is collision controlled and a number of encounters can occur during the lifetime of the excited donor.

Solvent Effects. There are several ways in which the solvent might
influence the rate or efficiency of an electronic energy transfer process. These
include viscosity effects which were mentioned above, and solvent effects on
the energy levels of the donor and acceptor. The effect on the transfer process
of solvent shifting of energy levels (and so also the spectra) of the donor
and/or acceptor should be, for the most part, explicable in terms of the
dependence of the transfer process on the donor–acceptor energy gap and the
spectral overlap integral, all of which has been discussed. Another possibility
is some effect of the solvent on the excited-donor lifetime. This would be
expected to be due most often to an effect on some radiationless deactivation
process, for example a reversible photochemical reaction between excited
donor and solvent, such as a proton transfer, which leads to quenching of the
donor.

* A scheme like this was first presented by Förster (2).

The solubility of the donor and acceptor can be important. Whereas a "good" solvent for the donor–acceptor system leads to a random distribution of donor and acceptor molecules, a "poor" solvent might lead to a non-statistical distribution with clumping together of donor molecules, acceptor molecules, or donor and acceptor molecules. These sorts of non-statistical distributions could lead to anomalously high or low transfer rates and efficiencies. It should be pointed out that solubility is an especially important and often overlooked factor in experiments dealing with rigid glasses at low temperatures.

If the donor–acceptor interaction is coulombic, one must correct for the field in a dielectric medium (solvent). In the Förster formulation for long-range transfer due to coulombic interaction this is accomplished by inclusion of the solvent index of refraction (see below).

Finally, Robinson (6) has pointed out that excitation transfer between solvent-separated donor and acceptor may take place directly, or it may take place indirectly through virtual states of the solvent. Furthermore, when the solvent electronic states are low lying, transfer *through* solvent states in rigid media may very well be faster than direct transfer. Sternlicht, Nieman, and Robinson (42) have developed a model for excitation transfer between identical solute molecules in rigid media (crystalline or glassy) making use of solvent virtual states (the tunneling mechanism). The one-dimensional case is described by Eq. (38), in which β_N is the donor–acceptor interaction energy,

$$\beta_N = (f_\beta \beta_0)^2 (f_\beta' \beta_0')^{N-1} (-\Delta E)^{-N} \tag{38}$$

β_0 is the donor–solvent interaction energy, β_0' is the solvent–solvent interaction energy, the f's are Franck-Condon factors, ΔE is the donor–solvent electronic energy gap, and N is the number of solvent molecules separating the donor from the acceptor. If one estimates transfer rates using Eq. (38), and takes $f_\beta \beta_0 = f_\beta' \beta_0 = 12$ cm^{-1} (a typical value for an exchange inter-action) and $\tau_D = 1$ sec efficient transfer through four solvent molecules is predicted if $\Delta E = 34$ kcal/mole and through 12 solvent molecules if $\Delta E = 0.3$ kcal/mole! It must be pointed out, however, that the interesting and large effect of donor–solvent energy gap predicted by this tunneling model, although sought, has not been found (52,53).

A mechanism for transfer between solute molecules making use of low-lying solvent states, which has been shown to operate, involves sufficient vibrational excitation of the excited solute so as to match the solvent-excitation energy. For example (53), triplet-energy transfer from phenanthrene-d_{10} to naphthalene, both present at low concentration in a crystal of biphenyl, is an activated process with an activation energy nearly equal to the difference in the vibrationless triplet levels of phenanthrene-d_{10} and biphenyl. Vibrational excitation of the excited solute allows energy transfer to the solvent where the energy migrates until it becomes trapped on an acceptor molecule. An example of this type of solvent participation in amorphous systems has not yet been reported.

2. Long-Range Transfer via Dipole–Dipole Interaction: The Förster Formulation

Förster (2,27,28) has developed a quantitative expression (Eq. (39)) for the rate of electronic energy transfer due to dipole–dipole interactions in terms of experimentally obtainable parameters. In Eq. (39)

$$k_{D^* \to A} = \frac{8.8 \times 10^{-25} K^2 \phi_D}{n^4 \tau_D R^6} \int_0^\infty F_D(\nu) \epsilon_A(\nu) \frac{d\nu}{\nu^4} \tag{39}$$

ν is the wave number, $F_D(\nu)$ is the spectral distribution of the donor emission in quanta normalized to unity, $\epsilon_A(\nu)$ is the molar extinction coefficient for the acceptor absorption, n is the refractive index of the solvent, K is an orientation factor which equals $(2/3)^{1/2}$ for a random distribution of donor and acceptor molecules, Φ_D is the quantum yield of donor emission, τ_D is the actual donor emission lifetime (in seconds) ($\Phi_D \tau_D^0 = \tau_D$, where τ_D^0 is the true radiative lifetime), and R is the distance between the donor and acceptor molecules (in centimeters). Casual inspection by the reader will show that Eq. (39) is, of course, identical to Eq. (11) since $\Phi_D/\tau_D \bar{\nu}^2 \propto f_D$, and

$$\int_0^\infty F_D(\nu) \epsilon_A(\nu)\, d\nu \propto f_A J$$

As has already been stated, this formulation is based upon the very weak interaction model where the energy transfer is much slower than vibrational relaxation in the donor and acceptor, and considers only the dipole–dipole term in the coulombic interaction. The Förster relationship (Eq. (39)) applies strictly only to those cases where the donor and acceptor are well separated (20 Å, at least) and are immobile, the donor and acceptor exhibit broadened, relatively unstructured spectra, the spectral overlap is significant (39), there are no important medium or solvent interactions, and the solvent-excited states lie much higher than those of the donor and acceptor.

The efficiency of Förster-type energy transfer is usually expressed in terms of a "critical radius" R_0, the distance of separation of the donor and acceptor at which the rate of intermolecular energy transfer is equal to the sum of the rates for all other donor deexcitation processes (Eq. (40)). The expression

$$k_{D^* \to A}(\text{at } R_0) = 1/\tau_D \tag{40}$$

$$R_0^6 = \frac{8.8 \times 10^{-25} K^2 \Phi_D}{n^4} \int_0^\infty F_D(\nu) \epsilon_A(\nu) \frac{d\nu}{\nu^4} \tag{41}$$

(Eq. (41)) for R_0† follows by combining Eqs. (39) and (40). The "critical concentration" of acceptor $C_A{}^0$ (55) at which the transfer is 50% efficient (the donor fluorescence is half quenched) is given by Eq. (42). An approximate relationship between R_0 and $C_A{}^0$ is given by Eq. (43).

$$C_A{}^0(\text{moles/liter}) = \frac{4.8 \times 10^{-10}n^2}{K} \left[\Phi_D \int_0^\infty F_D(\nu)\epsilon_A(\nu) \frac{d\nu}{\nu^4} \right]^{-\frac{1}{2}} \qquad (42)$$

$$R_0(\text{Å}) = \frac{7.35}{(C_A{}^0)^{\frac{1}{3}}} \qquad (43)$$

It has already been shown that the efficiency of excitation transfer by dipole–dipole interaction is predicted to be independent of the strength of the donor transition. Thus R_0 and $C_A{}^0$ do not depend on the donor transition strength. The inclusion of the donor emission quantum yield Φ_D accounts for competition with the energy transfer by all other radiationless deactivation processes in the donor. For a strong ($\epsilon_{max} \sim 10{,}000$) transition in the acceptor, significant spectral overlap, and donor emission yields of 0.1–1.0, R_0 values of 50–100 Å are predicted from Eq. (41). Thus the theory predicts efficient long-range energy transfer for the four cases described by Eqs. (12)–(15) for the appropriate donor–acceptor pairs. In fact, examples of all four cases have been observed and in many instances excellent quantitative agreement with Förster theory was found. Some of the experimental details connected with examples of each case now follow.

A. D*(SINGLET) + A(SINGLET) → D(SINGLET) + A*(SINGLET)

Long-range transfer of singlet excitation was first invoked by Perrin (55) to explain several cases of fluorescence depolarization found to occur in very viscous solvents. The early investigations of singlet-excitation transfer between dissimilar molecules involved measurements of fluorescence quenching or fluorescence sensitization in fluid solutions. In one of the first studies of this kind, Förster (56) argued that inclusion of long-range excitation transfer was necessary to explain the rates of transfer between unlike dye molecules in water solution.

The first studies in which it was attempted to clearly separate other modes of transfer (the trivial process, donor–acceptor complex formation, collisional

---

† If the donor emission is very weak so as to be very difficult or impossible to detect, one can calculate an approximate value for R_0 by using Eq. (44), in which the donor emission spectrum is expressed in terms of its absorption, ϵ_D is the molar extinction coefficient for donor absorption, ν_0 is the wavelength for the 0–0 band in the donor spectrum, and τ_D is the actual donor lifetime. The latter must be independently determined

$$R_0{}^6 \approx \frac{10^{-24}\tau_D}{\nu_0{}^2} \int_0^\infty \epsilon_A(\nu)\epsilon_D(2\nu_0 - \nu)\,d\nu \qquad (44)$$

transfer, and excitation migration among donor molecules) were those of Bowen, Livingston, and Brocklehurst (57,58). The contribution of the trivial process was kept low by choosing a donor (1-chloroanthracene) which has a small fluorescence yield. Donor–acceptor (perylene) complex formation was discounted on the basis of absorption measurements. Finally, the measured transfer rates were found to be greater than diffusion controlled and unchanged on going from fluid solutions at room temperature ($k_t = 1.4$–2.5×10^{11} liter mole^{-1} sec^{-1}) to a rigid glass at $-180°C$ ($k_t = 1.5 \times 10^{11}$ liter mole^{-1} sec^{-1}). These studies clearly demonstrated that efficient, long-range, radiationless singlet-excitation transfer occurs from 1-chloroanthracene to perylene over distances on the order of 50 Å, in qualitative agreement with the result predicted by Eq. (41).

Ware (59) was the first to extensively investigate singlet-excitation transfer by measuring the shortening of the donor fluorescence lifetime. This approach has the merit of being free of complications due to trivial transfer since the latter does not affect the donor lifetime. His data are shown in Table 4. It

TABLE 4

Long-Range Singlet Energy Transfer in Solution[d]

Donor	Acceptor	R_0(theoret.)[a] Å	k_t^{b}(theoret.) liter mole^{-1} sec^{-1}	k_t^{c}(theoret.) liter mole^{-1} sec^{-1}	k_t(found)[e] liter mole^{-1} sec^{-1}
Anthracene	Perylene	31	2.3×10^{10}	3.0×10^{10}	1.2×10^{11}
Perylene	Rubrene	38	2.8×10^{10}	3.8×10^{10}	1.3×10^{11}
9,10-Dichloro-anthracene	Perylene	40	1.7×10^{10}	3.8×10^{10}	8.0×10^{10}
Anthracene	Rubrene	23	7.7×10^{9}	2.0×10^{10}	3.7×10^{10}
9,10-Dichloro-anthracene	Rubrene	32	8.5×10^{9}	2.7×10^{10}	3.1×10^{10}

[a] Calculated using Eq. (41).
[b] Calculated using Eqs. (41) and (42).
[c] Calculated using Eq. (45).
[d] Benzene solution at room temperature.
[e] Data of Ware (59).

must be pointed out, however, that these data may be deficient in certain cases since the lifetimes were measured using the phase-shift technique so that decay curves (see below) were not obtained.

Before proceeding to a discussion of the only complete quantitative investigations of long-range coulombic transfer of singlet excitation, it is important to discuss the effect of molecular diffusion on the Förster transfer rate. It is important to remember that Eq. (39) is valid only for rigid systems, and must be modified for mobile systems to account for molecular diffusion. The lack of such a modification of the theory led experimentalists to contrive experiments designed to determine the significance of diffusion in systems in which long-range, singlet-excitation transfer was operating. However, contradictory results ensued. Hardwick (60) found similar transfer efficiencies on going from the liquid methyl methacrylate to the polymerized solid for the system naphthalene–anthracene. Bowen and co-workers (57,58) found similar specific rates in a rigid glass and in fluid benzene for the system 1-chloranthracene–perylene. On the other hand, Weinreb (61) found a marked effect by changing the viscosity of his solvent system for the transfer of energy from naphthalene to anthracene. However, his experiments are subject to question because the lifetime of the naphthalene increases with increasing viscosity. Melhuish (62), working with a different donor–acceptor system, also found an appreciable change in the transfer rate with viscosity changes. In the systems studied by Ware, the excitation-transferring species had time to diffuse as far as 20–30 Å (benzene solvent) during the donor lifetime. There is no wonder that the rates calculated using Eq. (41) differ from the experimental ones by as much as a factor of five (see Table 4). Several investigators have attempted to modify Förster's equations to take diffusion into account, but they have used inadequate or erroneous treatments. For example, a common error is to equate the Förster critical radius R_0 with the encounter distance in the Smoluchowski equation.

TABLE 5

Long-Range Singlet Energy Transfer in Rigid Media

Donor	Acceptor	R_0(theoret.)[a] (Å)	R_0(found) (Å)
Bis(Hydroxyethyl)-2,6-naphthalenedicarboxylate	"Sevron" Yellow GL	26	27 ± 1 [b]
Pyrene	"Sevron" Yellow GL	39	42 ± 2 [b]
Pyrene	Perylene	36	36 ± 2 [c]

[a] Calculated using Eq. (41) with $K^2 = 0.6$.
[b] Data of Bennett (64).
[c] Data of Povinelli (63).

Povinelli (63) has recently undertaken a more exact treatment which gives for the specific rate of long-range resonance transfer in mobile systems (at steady state) Eq. (45), where N is Avogadro's number, R_0 is the Förster critical distance, τ is the lifetime of the donor in the absence of the acceptor, and D is the mutual diffusion coefficient. The rates predicted from Eq. (45) for

$$k_t(\text{moles liter}^{-1}\text{ sec}^{-1}) = \frac{8}{3}\pi\frac{NR_0^{3/2}D^{3/4}}{1000\tau^{1/4}}$$ (45)

the systems studied by Ware are also listed in Table 4. Povinelli has measured the rates of singlet-excitation transfer from pyrene to perylene in hydrocarbon solvents of various viscosities by two methods, sensitized-acceptor fluorescence and donor-emission decay curves (Table 6). The agreement of the results was excellent and the R_0 values calculated using the measured rates and Eq. (45) were found to be 36 ± 2 Å.

TABLE 6

Specific Rates of Singlet Energy Transfer from Pyrene to Perylene in Fluid Solutions of Varying Viscosity at Room Temperature[a]

Viscosity η(cP)	Specific rate k_t(mole liter^{-1} sec^{-1})
0.88	1.33×10^{10}
2.88	6.67×10^9
8.38	4.57×10^9
71.06	2.02×10^9
256.1	1.11×10^9

[a] Data of Povinelli (63).

It has been only recently that long-range, singlet-excitation transfer through coulombic interaction has been studied under conditions where Eq. (41) is supposed to be valid. These studies, carried out by Bennett (64), are the only complete quantitative test for the Förster formulation. Precise donor (pyrene) fluorescence decay curves were obtained for various acceptor concentrations in rigid matrices (clear plastic films) where the donor–acceptor distance and orientation were random but fixed. Nonfluorescent dyes were used as acceptors. The decay curves were fitted to Eq. (46) using γ as the variable parameter. In Eq. (46) τ is the donor emission lifetime in the absence of acceptor and $\gamma = C_A/C_A^0$, where C_A is the acceptor concentration and C_A^0 is the "critical" concentration (Eq. (42)). The effect of the acceptor on the yield of donor

$$I_f = I_f^0 \exp\{-[t/\tau - 2\gamma(t/\tau)^{1/2}]\}$$ (46)

fluorescence was measured independently. C_A^0 values extracted from both sets of measurements were found to be in excellent agreement and to be constant to 12% for changes in acceptor concentrations over an order of magnitude. The R_0 values 27 ± 1 Å were found to agree exactly with that calculated from spectral data using Eq. (41). Data for another system examined by Bennett, and for the pyrene–perylene system on which a similar study was made by Povinelli, are given in Table 5. These results clearly demonstrate the R^{-6} distance dependence expected for vibrational–relaxation transfer through dipole–dipole interaction, and the accuracy of the Förster formulation.

The spectacular experiments of Kuhn and co-workers (65,66), who studied singlet-energy transfer between monolayers of dyes separated by an inert paraffin layer of uniform and controllable thickness, must not go unmentioned. The results of these experiments were found to be in exact agreement with Förster's theory. Finally, the results of the studies by Latt, Cheung, and Blout of singlet transfer from one chromophore to another within the same molecule and held at fixed distance by conformational restraints were also found to agree with the predictions of Förster's theory. The details of these experiments are found in Section III–8.

B. D*(SINGLET) + A(TRIPLET) → D(SINGLET) + A*(TRIPLET)

Very elegant experiments by Bennett (67) afford the only reported example of this case. He was able to demonstrate the quenching of perylene fluorescence by long-range radiationless transfer to the lowest triplet state of phenanthrene-d_{10}, i.e., perylene (S_1) + phenanthrene-$d_{10}(T_1)$ → perylene (S_0) + phenanthrene-$d_{10}(T_x)$. The compounds were incorporated in cellulose acetate films and the experiments carried out at 77°K. The very long lifetime of the phenanthrene-d_{10} triplet state under these conditions makes it possible to achieve a suitably high concentration of the latter. The fluorescence spectrum of perylene and the triplet–triplet absorption spectrum of phenanthrene overlap significantly. Trivial complications were eliminated through carefully designed experiments. The observed variation of the perylene fluorescence as a function of the phenanthrene-d_{10} triplet concentration could be predicted quantitatively by the Förster theory.

C. D*(TRIPLET) + A(SINGLET) → D(SINGLET) + A*(SINGLET)

The first observation of the long-range radiationless excitation transfers of this type were those of Ermolaev and Sveshnikova (68). They measured the reduction in the phosphorescence lifetime of the donor (triphenylamine), under pulsed excitation, as a function of the concentration of various acceptors having appropriate singlet–singlet absorption spectra, chrysoidin, chlorophyll a and b, and pheophytin a and b. The donor–acceptor systems were dissolved in rigid organic glasses at 77°K. They were able to estimate experimental R_0 values near 55 Å for all the cases. In subsequent experiments (69) using several donor–acceptor pairs, the intensity of the delayed fluorescence of the acceptor was measured along with the shortening of the donor lifetime. The expected correspondence between the two was found.

The first quantitative measurement for such a case were performed by Bennett, Schwenker, and Kellogg (70). They determined the phosphorescence decay curves for the donor phenanthrene-d_{10} under pulsed excitation for various concentrations of the acceptor rhodamine B. The donor–acceptor system was incorporated into a plastic film. Fitting the decay curves to Eq. (46) yielded $C_A{}^0$ values which were constant within 10% for a tenfold variation in acceptor concentration. For the experimental R_0 values, 47 Å was found to agree quite well with the value 45 Å obtained from spectral data using Eq. (41).

Spence and Ludwig (71) have examined several other systems. They worked with rigid glassy solutions at 77°K and determined donor triplet ESR signal decay curves upon shutting off the exciting light after steady state conditions were achieved. The form of the decay curves for these conditions is much more complicated than that given by Eq. (46). This may explain why the agreement between the experimental and theoretical R_0 values is not as good as that found by Bennett and co-workers. Spence and Ludwig found 47 Å for the triphenylene triplet–rhodamine B system and 46 Å for the triphenylene triplet–acridine yellow system; the theoretical values calculated from spectral data are 37 Å and 49 Å, respectively.

D. D*(TRIPLET) + A(TRIPLET) → D(SINGLET) + A*(TRIPLET)

In a very elegant study, Kellogg (72) demonstrated that radiationless transfer of excitation from the triplet state of phenanthrene-d_{10} to the triplet state of a second phenanthrene-d_{10} leading to excitation of the latter to a higher triplet state can occur with high efficiency at distances of 40 Å. The triplet–triplet absorption spectrum and the phosphorescence spectrum of phenanthrene overlap significantly. Triplet–triplet annihilation, which presumably occurs by an exchange mechanism, could be discounted on the basis of the large donor–acceptor distances involved and the fact that no delayed fluorescence expected from triplet–triplet annihilation could be detected. Long-range transfer through a dipole–dipole interaction is the only mechanism which explains the results. The degree of triplet–triplet self-quenching observed was smaller by about a factor of two than that predicted by Förster theory. Kellogg attributes this difference to the fact that transfer between nearest neighbors in this case destroys only one excitation of the pair and leads to a nonstatistical distribution of triplets in such a manner as to inhibit the total effect.

Kellogg and Bennett have pointed out (67,72) that under conditions leading to high steady-state triplet concentration ($> 10^{-3} M$) long-range singlet–triplet and triplet–triplet interactions can lead to serious errors in luminescence yield measurements. Kellogg has also noted that most aromatic hydrocarbons have overlapping phosphorescence and triplet–triplet absorption bands.

3. Triplet–Triplet Transfer

The process described by Eq. (18) has come to be known as triplet–triplet excitation transfer. The first example of such a process was provided by the classic experiment of Terenin and Ermolaev (73), in which they demonstrated that the phosphorescence of naphthalene in a rigid solution at 77°K could be excited by 3660 Å light, which naphthalene itself does not absorb, provided one adds to the solution benzophenone which does absorb the exciting light. The relative dispositions of the excited-state levels of naphthalene and benzo-phenone makes the interpretation that the sensitized phosphorescence is due to triplet–triplet transfer from benzophenone to naphthalene unambiguous (Fig. 5). Furthermore, simultaneous quenching of the benzophenone phos-phorescence was observed. Subsequent studies (74,75) have extended con-siderably the number of donor–acceptor pairs for which sensitized phosphorescence due to triplet–triplet transfer in rigid solutions occurs (Table 7). In all cases the triplet level of the donor lies higher than that of the acceptor.

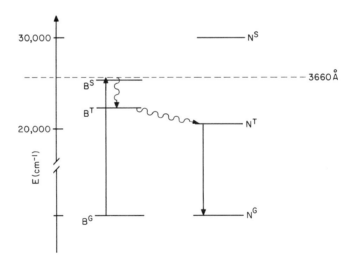

Fig. 5. Energy level scheme showing the ground (G), lowest excited singlet (S), and lowest triplet (T) states of benzophenone (B) and naphthalene (N). Excitation of the benzophenone by 3660-Å light is followed by intersystem crossing to the triplet state which may be transferred to the naphthalene and detected by the phosphorescent emis-sion of the latter.

TABLE 7

Sensitized Phosphorescence in Rigid Solution at 77°K

Donor	Acceptor	$R_c(\text{Å})$
Benzaldehyde	Naphthalene	12
	1-Chloronaphthalene	12
	1-Bromonaphthalene	12
Benzophenone	Naphthalene	13
	1-Chloronaphthalene	13
	1-Bromonaphthalene	13
	1-Iodonaphthalene	13
m-Iodobenzaldehyde	Naphthalene	11
	1-Bromonaphthalene	11
Triphenylamine	Naphthalene	13
Carbazole	Naphthalene	15
Phenanthrene	Naphthalene	13
	1-Chloronaphthalene	14
	1-Bromonaphthalene	14

It was shown by Terenin and Ermolaev (74) that the variation of donor-phosphorescence quenching with acceptor concentration is very well described by Eq. (47), where I_0 is the phosphorescence intensity in the absence of the acceptor, I_A is the intensity with acceptor present at concentration C_A, and α is a constant with the dimensions of reciprocal concentration. This equation was first derived by Perrin (76) and later by Vavilov (77) to describe some

$$I_0/I_A = e^{\alpha C_A} \qquad (47)$$

cases of fluorescence quenching in rigid media and is based upon the "spheres of quenching action" model. In this model, an excited molecule possessing a quencher within its "sphere of quenching action" is "instantaneously" deactivated without emitting, but a quencher molecule located outside the "sphere" exerts no influence. The model assumes a very viscous or rigid medium so that those excited molecules which contain no quencher within their "sphere" may emit. If Perrin's model is an appropriate one for triplet–triplet transfer in rigid solution, the donor emission lifetime should be independent of the acceptor concentration. Investigations have shown that, in fact, very small or no lifetime changes are observed for both components of a number of donor–acceptor pairs (73–75). The Perrin model also assumes a random distribution of donor and acceptor molecules. Complications due to the possibility that random distribution is not achieved in glassy solutions at low temperature because of clustering, or due to the possibility of donor–acceptor "complex" formation especially in poor solvents, have been found to be negligible (78,79).

$$V_c(\text{cc}) = \frac{1000 \ln I_0/I_A}{N C_A(\text{moles/liter})} \qquad (48)$$

The volume V_c of the Perrin "sphere" can be obtained from the quenching data by using Eq. (48) in which N is Avogadro's number. The corresponding critical radii R_c for a number of donor–acceptor pairs are given in Table 7. The values are all in the range 11–15 Å or slightly more than the van der Waals radii expected for donor–acceptor collision complexes. At these short donor–acceptor distances and for these multiplicity changes, the exchange mechanism must be considered operative. A dipole–dipole mechanism may be excluded for two reasons. Calculated donor–acceptor distances for effective triplet–triplet transfer by the dipole–dipole mechanism are one to two orders of magnitude smaller than the R_c values. For example, the Förster R_0 value for triplet-excitation transfer from benzophenone to naphthalene ($R_c = 13$ Å) is calculated to be 0.18 Å (83). Furthermore, the R_c values do not depend on the strength of the $S_0 \rightarrow T_1$ absorption in the acceptor. For example, the R_c value for triplet–triplet transfer from benzophenone to all the 1-halonaphthalenes is 13 Å despite the nearly thousandfold change in the $S_0 \rightarrow T_1$, oscillator strengths in the series of acceptors. Transfer through higher multipole–multipole interactions could operate at such close approach of donor and acceptor, but according to Dexter (1) the probabilities for such processes should be small compared to that for exchange when the latter is fully allowed by the spin selection rules. Furthermore, Smaller and co-workers (80) have shown that the "sharpness" of the interaction sphere for triplet–triplet transfer from phenanthrene to naphthalene [a tenfold variation in the transfer rate occurs in a shell thickness (δR_c) of 1.3 Å] is consistent with an exchange interaction.

It should be emphasized that studies of intermolecular triplet–triplet transfer in rigid media yield no information about the rates of the transfers except that they are fast compared to the decay rates (10^3–0.1 sec^{-1}) of the donors when an acceptor is within its "sphere of quenching action."

The first studies of triplet–triplet transfer in fluid solution are due to Bäckström and Sandros (81,82) and Porter and Wilkinson (83). The first pair of investigators took advantage of the fact that biacetyl exhibits relatively strong phosphorescence in fluid solution. They measured the bimolecular rate constants for the quenching (quenching rate = $k_q[D^*][A]$) of this phosphorescence in benzene solution at 20°C for a large number of quenchers (acceptors) for which the quenching mechanism was assumed to be excitation transfer.† A plot of the measured quenching constants versus the lowest triplet–state excitation energy of the acceptors is shown in Figure 6.

In their very detailed and extensive study, Porter and Wilkinson measured

---

† Bäckström and Sandros found that for many of the quenchers which are good hydrogen donors, alcohols, amines, aldehydes, etc., the quenching mechanism is probably a chemical one, namely hydrogen abstraction from the quencher by the biacetyl triplet. Only nonchemical quenchers are considered in the present discussion.

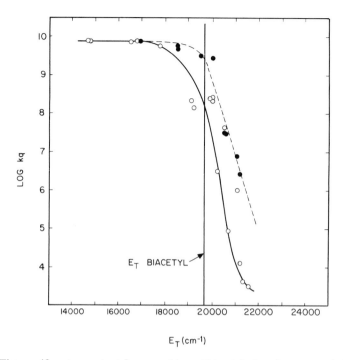

$E_T \, (cm^{-1})$

Fig. 6. The specific rate constant for quenching of biacetyl phosphorescence in benzene solution at room temperature due to energy transfer to the quencher as a function of the energy of the lowest triplet state of the quencher. The open circles are the observed rates and the full circles are the rates corrected for back transfer. These data are from refs. 81, 82, and 84.

the rates of quenching of a variety of triplet donors in fluid solution at room temperature by the flash photolysis technique. For most of the systems studied, the mechanism of quenching was unequivocally established as triplet–triplet transfer by observation of the appearance of the triplet–triplet absorption spectrum of the acceptor concomitant with the disappearance of that of the donor. Some of their results are listed in Table 8.

It is evident from both sets of data that the values of the quenching constants fall into three groups:

1. When the triplet level of the donor lies higher than that of the acceptor by 3–4 kcal/mole or more, the transfer rate is very nearly the diffusion-controlled rate, that is, transfer occurs on nearly every encounter of an excited donor with an acceptor.

2. As the acceptor triplet level approaches that of the donor, the quenching rates drop very quickly and are nearly two orders of magnitude smaller than

TABLE 8

Acceptor	Solvent	ΔE_T(kcal/mole)	k_q, liter mole^{-1} sec^{-1}
1,2-Benzanthracene	Benzene	9.15	3.0×10^9
Naphthalene	Benzene	8.85	2.0×10^9
	Hexane	6.30	1.3×10^9
1-Iodonaphthalene	Hexane	3.15	7.0×10^9
	Ethylene glycol	3.15	2.1×10^8
	Ethylene glycol	2.30	2.8×10^8
1-Bromonaphthalene	Hexane	2.60	1.5×10^8
	Ethylene glycol	2.60	1.5×10^7
1-Iodonaphthalene	Ethylene glycol	0.55	8.0×10^8
Naphthalene	Hexane	0.85	2.9×10^6
	Ethylene glycol	0.85	2.3×10^6

Upper limits for the quenching rate could be established for the following systems:

Phenanthrene	Hexane	-0.85	2×10^4
	Ethylene glycol	-0.85	1×10^5
	Ethylene glycol	-2.60	5×10^4
Triphenylene	Hexane	-6.30	5×10^4
Benzophenone	Benzene	-8.85	1×10^4
Biacetyl	Benzene	-9.15	5×10^4
1-Iodonaphthalene	Ethylene glycol	-16.60	2×10^4
Naphthalene	Hexane	-18.85	4×10^4
1-Iodonaphthalene	Ethylene glycol	-19.70	5×10^3

the diffusion-controlled rate when the donor and acceptor levels are iso-energetic.

3. When the triplet excitation energy of the acceptor becomes greater than that of the donor by 3–4 kcal/mole or more, the quenching rates become at least a million times slower than diffusion controlled.

Similar results have been reported by Hammond and co-workers, who used chemical reactions of the excited donor or acceptor to monitor the transfer rates. All of the results indicate that triplet–triplet transfer in fluid solution takes place during an encounter between the donor and acceptor at nearly normal collisional distances, entirely consistent with the studies in rigid media. The falloff in rate from near the diffusion-controlled rate to much lower rates, as the donor triplet level approaches that of the acceptor, may be partly rationalized in terms of the spectral overlap integral in the Dexter formulation (Eq. (16)) for the rate of transfer due to exchange. If the donor and acceptor triplet levels are equal in energy, only the 0–0 bands overlap. As the donor level rises with respect to that of the acceptor, the spectral overlap increases; consequently, the transfer rate increases also. No decrease in rate is observed as the donor-triplet energy becomes much greater than the acceptor lowest triplet energy, even though the spectral overlap between the corresponding transitions again becomes small, probably because higher acceptor triplets come into play.

Transfer still occurs, albeit at much lower rates, when the triplet energy of the donor is less than that of the acceptor by a small amount (2–3 kcal/mole). This endothermic transfer requires vibrational activation. That is, the difference in electronic energies is made up by vibrational excitation of the donor and/or acceptor. Another way of expressing this is in terms of the spectral overlap integral which, of course, involves a summation over a Boltzman distribution of initial states. Endothermic triplet-energy transfer of this sort, then, should proceed as an activated process with an activation energy equal to the difference in the triplet energies of the donor and acceptor. That is, the slope of the transfer rate versus triplet-energy curve such as shown in Figure 6 should be given by Eq. (49). At room temperature the slope should be -0.73 kcal^{-1}.

$$\frac{\Delta \log k}{\Delta E_T} = -\frac{1}{2.303RT} \tag{49}$$

Indeed, values close to this are found (84,85). However, the data obtained in many cases, e.g., Figure 6, are rather scattered. Sandros (84) proposed and demonstrated that the discrepancies were due to back transfer. That is, when the "donor" and "acceptor" energies are close and the acceptor triplet exhibits a lifetime comparable to that of the donor back transfer can occur. He corrected the quenching data for the system of biacetyl in benzene solution for such back transfer and obtained a very good linear quenching plot with a slope of -0.7 kcal^{-1}.

In the earlier report by Bäckström and Sandros it was concluded for the system of biacetyl as donor and the halonaphthalenes as acceptors that the rate constant for energy transfer increased with the increasing oscillator strength of the acceptor. The energies of the triplets of the halonaphthalenes are nearly identical. However, this bothersome finding disappears when the apparent transfer rates are corrected for back transfer. This is because the triplet lifetime decreases as one goes from the chloro to the iodo derivative and back transfer becomes less important.

It has been stated above that triplet–triplet excitation transfer is nearly diffusion controlled when the donor's energy is higher than that of the acceptor by a few kilocalories per mole. Actually many triplet-energy transfer rates agree very well with the diffusion-controlled rate calculated using the simplified Debye expression (Eq. (37)). But at the same time there are many cases of exothermic transfer for which the measured rates are smaller by factors of two or three and sometimes more than the calculated diffusion-controlled rate (83,86). For most of the latter cases it is not known whether, in fact, the transfer rate is less than diffusion controlled or if the calculated diffusion-controlled rate is too high. Thus, our ignorance is covered over in the vague statement that, in general, exothermic triplet-excitation transfer is nearly diffusion controlled. There are systems, however, for which the transfer has been definitely shown to be slower than the encounter rate. One of the better authenticated examples has been supplied by Wager (87) for transfer from valerophenone ($E_T \approx 73$ kcal/mole) to 2,5-dimethyl-2,4-hexadiene ($E_T \approx 60$ kcal/mole). He showed that for a series of inert solvents the transfer rate was not a linear function of viscosity. For example, for the 15-fold decrease in viscosity on going from hexadecane to pentane, less than a four-fold increase in the transfer rate was observed. Thus, there is a good indication that the transfer of triplet excitation is sufficiently inefficient in the non-viscous solvents to allow the diffusion apart of the donor and acceptor to compete.

Why should different cases of equally exothermic triplet-energy transfer exhibit rates varying by as much as a factor of ten? Back transfer may be ruled out when the donor's energy exceeds that of the acceptor by more than 4 or 5 kcal/mole (84). One possibility is steric hindrance to good overlap of the appropriate molecular wavefunctions (88–91). Another possibility involves restrictive Franck-Condon factors which would apply to those cases where the donor and/or acceptor possess very structured spectra.

4. Singlet Excitation Transfer Requiring Collision

If the absorption of the acceptor is sufficiently weak so that the Förster critical distance R_0 approaches the collision diameter for the donor–acceptor pair, then the rate of singlet energy transfer in fluid solution cannot be faster than the diffusion-controlled rate. Furthermore, the Förster relationship (see Section III–2) cannot be employed to predict rates in this case since it is invalid at such small donor–acceptor distances. In addition, the exchange mechanism probably always contributes significantly to the transfer at these distances.

Almost all of the quantitative experimental data with regard to collisional transfer of singlet excitation is due to Dubois, Wilkinson, and co-workers (92,93). They measured the rates of singlet-energy transfer from a number of donors to a common acceptor in hexane and cyclohexane solutions at room temperature by monitoring the donor and acceptor fluorescence. The acceptor used in all the studies was biacetyl. Its lowest energy absorption bands are weak ($n \to \pi^*$ transitions) and it does fluoresce in solution. The stronger phosphorescence of biacetyl was eliminated in these studies by working in aerated solutions. A number of aromatic hydrocarbons and aliphatic ketones were employed as donors. Both the quenching of the donor fluorescence and the sensitization of the biacetyl fluorescence were measured as a function of the biacetyl concentration. From the data they obtained sensitization and quenching rates in terms of the quantities K_s and K_q, respectively. The latter are defined (92,93) by Eqs. (50) and (51), where Φ_A^0 and Φ_D^0 are the intensities

$$\frac{-d(\Phi_A/\Phi_A^0)}{d[D]} = \frac{\epsilon_D}{\epsilon_A} \left\{ \frac{K_s}{1 + K_s[A]} \right\} \tag{50}$$

$$\frac{d(\Phi_D^0/\Phi_D)}{d[A]} = \frac{K_q}{1 + K_q[D]} \tag{51}$$

of fluorescence from the isolated acceptor (biacetyl) and donor, and Φ_A and Φ_D are the intensities of fluorescence from mixtures of the two. Equations (50) and (51) are valid for solutions of low optical density and only if the quenching and sensitization involve singlet-energy transfer. If the latter is true, then K_s should equal K_q and should be equal to $\tau_D k_t$, the product of the donor lifetime and the specific rate constant for energy transfer. Some of the results are listed in Table 9. The good agreement between the K_s and K_q values

TABLE 9

Donor	K_q (M^{-1})	K_s (M^{-1})	τ_D (sec $\times$ 10^9)	k_t (M^{-1} sec^{-1} $\times$ 10^{-10})
In cyclohexane				
Benzene	200	270	12.2	1.9
Naphthalene	180	175	15.0	1.2
Phenanthrene	128	131		
Chrysene	243	244	14.0	1.7
Acetone	26	14		
Cyclopentanone	25	19		
In hexane				
Benzene	190	190	5.7	3.3
Toluene	214	197	5.8	3.5
o-Xylene	208		6.0	3.5
Naphthalene	186		8.3	2.2

is gratifying. A few τ_D values for hexane and cyclohexane solutions saturated with air have been measured (94,95), and so k_t can be obtained for those cases. The calculated k_t values are also listed in Table 9. The k_t values in cyclohexane are very closely grouped about 2×10^{10} liters mole^{-1} sec^{-1} and those in hexane about 3×10^{10} liters mole^{-1} sec^{-1}. These are very close to the diffusion-controlled bimolecular rate constants for those solvents. Thus collisional encounter between the excited donor and biacetyl is necessary for transfer of excitation. This is, of course, expected because the Förster R_0

values for transfer to biacetyl calculated by using Eq. (41) are less than 7 Å for all the donors studied. The transfers occur upon every encounter and, as mentioned previously, most likely involve exchange as well as coulombic interactions. It is likely that in solution exothermic singlet transfer, that is, where the donor singlet lies higher than that of the acceptor, is no slower than diffusion controlled or nearly so for any donor–acceptor pair, since the exchange interaction is probably always sufficient to allow transfer during an encounter.

5. Excitation Migration in Solution

Migration of singlet excitation over large distances in the solvent by multiple nearest-neighbor transfers has been invoked to explain the large rates and efficiencies of excitation transfer from the solvent to a solute, present in a very small amount, for several fluid systems (96). The most extensively studied systems contained benzene or an alkylbenzene as solvent and a highly fluorescent solute (scintillator) such as p-terphenyl, anthracene, or 1,6-diphenylhexatriene. A brief review of some of the observations made on these systems follows.

The quantum yields for fluorescence from neat liquid benzene or alkyl-benzenes near room temperature are all less than 0.05. Addition of small amounts of the solutes mentioned above, for example, leads to strongly fluorescent systems (solute fluorescence) even if all the exciting light is absorbed by the solvent. Efficiencies of excitation transfer from the solvent to the solute is high. For instance, transfer efficiencies at $2 \times 10^{-3} M$ p-terphenyl are 0.72 for toluene, 0.81 for p-xylene, and extrapolate to unity at high terphenyl concentrations (103,104). Obviously radiative transfer of excitation from solvent to solute cannot account for the high transfer efficiency. Furthermore, the solvent emission lifetime decreases by the same factor that the solute intensity increases (105). It remains to determine the relative contributions of the three radiationless modes, long-range single-step transfer, molecular diffusion, and excitation migration, to the total transfer rate. Before proceeding, it must be pointed out that in most of the experiments concerning these systems, excitation of the solvent was by ionizing radiation (X-rays or γ-rays). But it has been conclusively demonstrated (104) that the same excited state of the solvent, namely the lowest excited singlet state, is involved in the transfer processes when either ionizing radiation or ultra-violet light (2537 Å) is employed.

Calculations using the Förster relationship reveal that long-range, single-step dipole–dipole transfer from initially excited solvent molecules to solute molecules cannot, in the absence of molecular diffusion or excitation migra-tion, account for the observed transfer efficiencies. For example, Lipsky (104) calculates that long-range dipole–dipole transfer would lead to a transfer efficiency of not more than 0.26 for $10^{-2} M$ p-terphenyl in xylene, whereas it is measured to be 0.96. The inclusion of molecular diffusion (63) raises the calculated transfer efficiency to 0.81. Comparable discrepancies are found for other solvents. That long-range transfer is not the chief mode in these systems is also indicated by the fact that the rate of tra.1sfer to oxygen is comparable to that for transfer to the scintillator. For example, Lipsky found the rate of singlet excitation transfer from neat benzene to p-terphenyl and to oxygen to be 7.8×10^{-10} and 11×10^{10} liter mole^{-1} sec^{-1}, respectively (104). Presumably the long-range resonance transfer mode cannot operate in the oxygen case.

Several studies have been undertaken to determine the relative importance of molecular diffusion and excitation migration (105–107). The experiments involved measuring solute fluorescence intensity or decay curves as a function of the dilution of the solvent with an inert cosolvent, such as cyclohexane, while keeping the solute concentration constant. From the results of the most detailed study of this kind, Dillon and Burton (105) concluded that excitation migration is at least as important as molecular diffusion of excited molecules for excitation transfer from neat benzene to a solute.

Because of the weakness of the intermolecular interaction, excitation migration in fluid benzene and alkylbenzenes most assuredly involves only nearest-neighbor molecules. The excitation should be localized in a single solvent molecule before and after each solvent–solvent transfer and the motion of the excitation should be a hopping one with a diffusive length of the order of a molecular diameter. Based on this model a diffusion coefficient for singlet excitation in pure liquid benzene of 4×10^{-5} cm^2/sec and a hopping time (time for one solvent–solvent transfer) of 10^{-11} sec can be calculated from the data of Dillon and Burton (105). The exact nature of the solvent–solvent transfer process is not known. Interestingly, the intermediacy of an excimer (see Section III-6) has been suggested for the case of benzene (105).

Amata (108) recently analyzed fluorescence decay curves for mixtures of benzene and cyclohexane with and without quencher (CCl$_4$) present. The fluorescence was monitored at wavelengths where either monomer or excimer emission is most important. It was found that the data could be fitted to a mechanism which includes steps for reversible excimer formation and the possibility that the CCl$_4$ can quench both monomer and excimer. One interpretation of the rate constants that were extracted is that excitation migration is not important compared to molecular diffusion, and that the increase in efficiency of excitation transport to a quencher or scintillator with increasing benzene concentration simply reflects the larger cross-section presented by the excimer compared to the monomer.

The possibility of triplet excitation migration in fluid acetone has been reported recently. Borkman and Kearns (109) demonstrated that the rate of triplet energy transfer from acetone to added pentene-2 or biacetyl† increases by a factor of 5 on going from dilute solutions of acetone in methanol to neat acetone. The difference could not be explained by a change in the rate of molecular diffusion. It was postulated that in neat acetone there are two mechanisms for transporting triplet excitation: by molecular diffusion and by triplet-excitation migration among acetone molecules. A hopping time for the triplet excitation in neat acetone at room temperature of about 10^{-11} sec can be estimated from the data. An alternative interpretation of the results due to Wagner (111) is that the lifetime of the acetone triplet is greater in neat acetone than in methanol because of more rapid chemical reaction (hydrogen abstraction) in the latter. A most interesting observation made by Borkman and Kearns was that the proposed acetone triplet–triplet transfer rate is temperature dependent, decreasing by a factor of about 60 on going from room temperature to $-78°C$. The suggested explanation for this effect is that there is a significant difference between the geometries of the ground and triplet states of acetone resulting in a small Franck-Condon factor (spectral overlap integral).‡ Vibrational excitation of either the ground state or excited molecule could lead to a much larger Franck-Condon factor resulting in a temperature-dependent rate for the transfer process.

6. Triplet–Triplet Annihilation

In general, the term triplet–triplet annihilation can be applied to any process in which the interaction of two triplet-state molecules leads to simultaneous transitions in both molecules and usually the destruction of their triplet characters. In this discussion only those cases in which the interaction of two molecules in excited triplet states leads to electronic energy transfer from one to the other are of concern. Specifically the processes described by Eqs. (52), (53), and (54) will be considered.

$$D^*(\text{triplet}) + A^*(\text{triplet}) \rightarrow D(\text{singlet}) + A^{**}(\text{singlet}) \qquad (52)$$

$$D^*(\text{triplet}) + A^*(\text{triplet}) \rightarrow D(\text{singlet}) + A^{**}(\text{triplet}) \qquad (53)$$

$$D^*(\text{triplet}) + A^*(\text{triplet}) \rightarrow D(\text{singlet}) + A^{**}(\text{quintet}) \qquad (54)$$

Of the three, that described by Eq. (52) is the most important.

---

† Triplet energy transfer to *cis* and *trans* pentene-2 was monitored by determination of the extent of the resultant *cis–trans* isomerization (see Section IV-3-C); excitation transfer to biacetyl was monitored by measuring the sensitized phosphorescence.

‡ The electronic interaction is, of course, the exchange interaction and is temperature independent.

All three processes (Eqs. (52), (53), and (54)) are spin allowed by the exchange mechanism and, in addition, the process described by Eq. (53) can occur by the long-range dipole–dipole interaction mechanism if the donor lifetime is sufficiently long. An example of the latter has been given in Section III–2–D. To the knowledge of this author no documented example of the process in Eq. (53) has been provided for fluid systems, although there should be many systems where it does operate.

The process in which two triplets give a singlet and quintet (Eq. (54)) conserves spin and multiplicity. No one has observed an excited quintet state of an organic compound and so it is not known whether they lie low enough in simple compounds so that they can be achieved in triplet–triplet annihilation. Interestingly, Robinson has speculated (113) that triplet–triplet annihilation leading to a quintet state may be important in chlorophyll aggregates since it is possible (113) that the lowest quintet state of chlorophyll lies lower than twice the triplet level. Birks (114) has suggested that the quintet state of pyrene is produced by triplet–triplet association.

There are a large number of examples of the process of Eq. (52). This is not surprising because both spin and multiplicity are conserved and because the process is energetically feasible for most organic systems. Furthermore, the "acceptor," which is usually the same as the "donor," ends up, after internal conversion if necessary, in the lowest excited singlet state. This may be followed by fluorescence so that the triplet–triplet annihilation process may be easily observed by way of a delayed fluorescence (Fig. 7). It is important to discuss this mechanism in more detail. A detailed and critical review has been contributed by Parker (116).

Delayed fluorescence does not always indicate triplet–triplet annihilation. There are other mechanisms which can give rise to "long-lived" fluorescence. For example, the simplest mechanism was first demonstrated by Lewis and co-workers (115) for fluorescein in boric acid glass. They showed that the triplet state of fluorescein can be thermally activated to the lowest singlet state from which fluorescence takes place. This delayed fluorescence has the same lifetime as does the triplet state. Parker (116) has termed this mechanism the E-type. It also operates for eosin (117) and proflavin hydrochloride.

Delayed fluorescence arising from triplet–triplet annihilation, P-type, was first clearly demonstrated by Parker and Hatchard. It had been previously observed by Porter and Wright (118) that a diffusion-controlled, second-order contribution (i.e., $-d[T]/dt = k_{\text{dif}}[T]^2$) to the decay rate is important for many excited-triplet species in fluid solution. Later, Stevens and Hutton (119) characterized the long-lived emission from pyrene solutions as delayed fluorescence. The latter workers proposed that the mechanism for delayed fluorescence involved the interaction of an excited singlet molecule with a ground-state molecule to give a long-lived, excited dimer which could, after

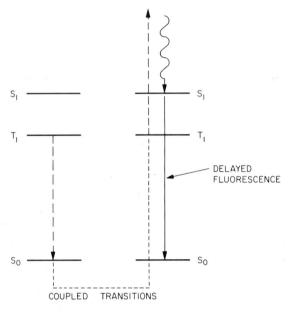

Fig. 7. The triplet–triplet annihilation mechanism for delayed fluorescence. Two molecules in the triplet state interact resulting in the excitation of one of them to a higher singlet state. After relaxation to the lowest excited singlet level, the "acceptor" molecule may emit fluorescence.

some delay, dissociate. However, Parker and Hatchard definitively related the two observations, triplet–triplet annihilation and delayed fluorescence, for several systems (116). The results for anthracene are briefly reviewed here (120).

Degassed dilute solutions of anthracene in cyclohexane exhibit a delayed fluorescence identical to the normal fluorescence. The ratio (ϕ_{DF}/ϕ_F) of the intensities of the delayed fluorescence and normal fluorescence under steady illumination could be accurately measured as a function of the anthracene concentration or the intensity of the exciting light. A mechanism involving triplet–triplet annihilation is given by Eqs. (55)–(60) in which f and β are

Rate

$$A \xrightarrow{h\nu} A^{*1} \qquad\qquad fI \qquad\qquad (55)$$

$$A^{*1} \longrightarrow A + h\nu' \qquad\qquad k_1[A^{*1}] \qquad\qquad (56)$$

$$A^{*1} \longrightarrow A^{*3} \qquad\qquad k_2[A^{*1}] \qquad\qquad (57)$$

$$A^{*1} \longrightarrow A \qquad\qquad k_3[A^{*1}] \qquad\qquad (58)$$

$$A^{*3} \longrightarrow A \qquad\qquad k_4[A^{*3}] \qquad\qquad (59)$$

$$A^{*3} + A^{*3} \longrightarrow A^{*1} + A \qquad\qquad \beta k_5[A^{*3}]^2 \qquad\qquad (60)$$

efficiency factors and I is the incident light intensity. If the light intensity is low, then $\beta k_5[A^{*3}]^2 \ll k_4[A^{*3}]$ and ϕ_{DF}/ϕ_F are given by Eq. (61), where ϕ_{isc},

$$\frac{\phi_{DF}}{\phi_F} = \frac{1}{2}(\beta f k_5 I)\left(\frac{\phi_{isc}}{k_4}\right)^2 \tag{61}$$

the quantum yield of triplets, is $(k_2/k_1 + k_2 + k_3)$. A mechanism involving an excited-singlet dimer (excimer) is shown by Eqs. (62)–(67). For slow dissociation of the excimer, ϕ_{DF}/ϕ_F is given by Eq. (68). For low concentrations

$$A \xrightarrow{h\nu} A^{*1} \qquad\qquad fI \tag{62}$$

$$A^{*1} \longrightarrow A + h\nu' \qquad\qquad k_1[A^{*1}] \tag{63}$$

$$A^{*1} \longrightarrow A \qquad\qquad k_3[A^{*1}] \tag{64}$$

$$A^{*1} + A \longrightarrow A_2^{*1} \qquad\qquad k_6[A^{*1}][A] \tag{65}$$

$$A_2^{*1} \longrightarrow A^{*1} + A \qquad\qquad k_7[A_2^{*1}] \tag{66}$$

$$A_2^{*1} \longrightarrow A + A \qquad\qquad k_8[A_2^{*1}] \tag{67}$$

$$\frac{\phi_{DF}}{\phi_F} = \left(\frac{k_7}{k_7 + k_8}\right)\frac{k_6[A]}{k_1 + k_3 + k_6[A]} \tag{68}$$

of anthracene $\phi_{DF}/\phi_F \propto [A]$. This is what is found. However, this is also consistent with the triplet–triplet annihilation mechanism since $_q \propto [A]$ for low concentrations. The appropriate test, of course, is to examine the dependence of ϕ_{DF}/ϕ_F on I, the light intensity. The excimer mechanism predicts no dependence, whereas the triplet–triplet annihilation mechanism predicts a linear dependence. The observed ϕ_{DF}/ϕ_F values as a function of I and for constant $[A] = 5 \times 10^{-4}M$ are listed in Table 10. The results are obviously consistent with the triplet–triplet annihilation mechanism. Of course, these results could also be accounted for by a mechanism involving the

TABLE 10

Light Intensity and Delayed Fluorescence from Anthracene ($5 \times 10^{-4}M$) in Cyclohexane (120)

Rel I	$10^4 \dfrac{\phi_{DF}}{\phi_F}$	$\dfrac{\phi_{DF}}{\phi_F I}$
1.000	93	0.009
0.290	36	0.012
0.112	17.5	0.016
0.081	12.9	0.016
0.032	4.5	0.014
0.010	1.4	0.014

absorption of a photon by triplet anthracene. However, delayed fluorescence from anthracene is not observed in rigid solution (in glasses at 77°K) pointing to the necessity for diffusion of the intermediates. Finally, the triplet–triplet annihilation mechanism predicts that at low light intensities the lifetime of the delayed fluorescence (τ_{DF}) should be just half the triplet lifetime (τ_T). τ_{DF} for anthracene in ethanol at room temperature is 4 msec; τ_T under similar conditions was found to be about 3 msec. Much better agreement between $2\tau_{DF}$ and τ_T is obtained for phenanthrene (116,120).

The involvement of excited-singlet dimers (124) ("excimers") in triplet–triplet annihilation was first demonstrated by Parker and Hatchard (121) for the system pyrene in ethanol. The term "excimer" was coined to describe the excited complex formed as a consequence of the interaction of an excited and ground-state molecule. It is to be distinguished from an excited complex obtained by excitation of a stable, ground-state complex. By definition, an excimer state is not observed in absorption. The "excimer" is stable only in the excited state, and after deexcitation the two partners repulse each other. Excimer fluorescence is characterized as being red-shifted from the monomer fluorescence and lacking in vibrational structure because of the repulsive ground state (see Fig. 8). Although excimer fluorescence lifetimes can be longer than monomer lifetimes, they are not on the order of triplet lifetimes (122,123). Furthermore, excimer binding energies are 10 kcal/mole or less (123), so that in fluid solution at room temperature excimer formation is reversible. Thus, as was stated above, excimer formation from excited-singlet monomer and ground-state monomer cannot lead to delayed fluorescence in fluid solution at room temperature.

Pyrene solutions exhibit excimer fluorescence (124). The ratio of excimer to monomer fluorescence, of course, increases with pyrene concentration (125). At $2 \times 10^{-6}M$ pyrene in ethanol there is no prompt excimer fluorescence, only monomer fluorescence, presumably because in such dilute solution an excited-singlet pyrene does not encounter a ground-state pyrene during its lifetime. Deoxygenated ethanol solutions of pyrene exhibit delayed fluorescence made up of both monomer and excimer bands. The intensities of both monomer and excimer bands were found to be proportional to the square of the intensity of absorbed light and thus consistent with a triplet–triplet annihilation process. Significantly, even at $2 \times 10^{-6}M$ the delayed fluorescence spectrum exhibits a large excimer band. It is suggested (125), therefore, that the triplet–triplet annihilation gives rise to the excimer which subsequently dissociates giving excited singlet monomer (Eq. (69)). Furthermore, fluores-

$$P^{*3} + P^{*3} \rightarrow P_2^{*1} \rightarrow P^{*1} + P$$
$$\downarrow \qquad \downarrow \qquad\qquad (69)$$
$$hv' \qquad hv$$

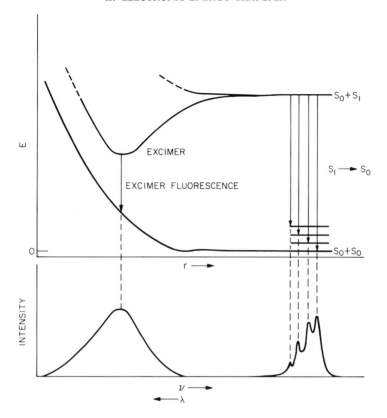

Fig. 8. A schematic representation of excimer formation and excimer fluorescence.

cence from both the monomer and excimer must occur faster than a monomer–excimer equilibrium is attained. Interestingly, Colpa (126) has suggested that concentration quenching of fluorescence goes by the reverse process (Eq. (70)).

$$X^{*1} + X \rightarrow X_2^{*1} \rightarrow X^{*3} + X^{*3} \tag{70}$$

There are many examples of mixed excimers formed by the interaction (Eq. (71)) of either partner in its excited-singlet state with the other in its

$$X^{*1} + Y \rightarrow (XY)^{*1} \leftarrow X + Y^{*1} \tag{71}$$

ground state (122,127). Parker proposed that mixed triplet–triplet annihilation can occur giving rise to delayed fluorescence from one of the partners (Eq. (72)). Specifically, it was shown (128) that strong, delayed napthacene

$$A^{*3} + N^{*3} \rightarrow (AN)^{*1} \rightarrow A + N^{*1}$$
$$\downarrow \tag{72}$$
$$h\nu$$

fluorescence can be obtained from a solution containing $5 \times 10^{-5} M$ anthracene and $4 \times 10^{-8} M$ naphthacene, whereas $10^{-6} M$ napthacene alone gives no delayed fluorescence. Singlet-energy transfer to naphthacene from singlet anthracene formed by ordinary triplet–triplet annihilation is precluded because of the low napthacene concentration.

7. "Nonvertical" Triplet Energy Transfer

Hammond (129) introduced the term "nonvertical excitation" (or "nonvertical triplet energy transfer") to describe energy transfer in cases in which available spectroscopic data do not lead to the expectation that transfer should occur with any efficiency. The term has become both very popular (129–139) and somewhat abused, and concepts associated with it are rather variable. Perhaps the term was a poor choice, but it is in use and one is hard put to find another. It is the purpose of this section to attempt to clearly describe the useful concepts which should be associated with the term "nonvertical triplet energy transfer."

As is shown below, nonvertical energy transfer may involve no concepts other than those described in the section on triplet–triplet transfer. However, its treatment is included in a separate section, partially because the term needs special clarification, but mainly because it is a useful phenomenological tool in that definitive conclusions can be drawn about the excited states of compounds which are able to participate in "nonvertical" transfers.

Two acceptor systems, the stilbenes (1a, b) and the α-methylstilbenes

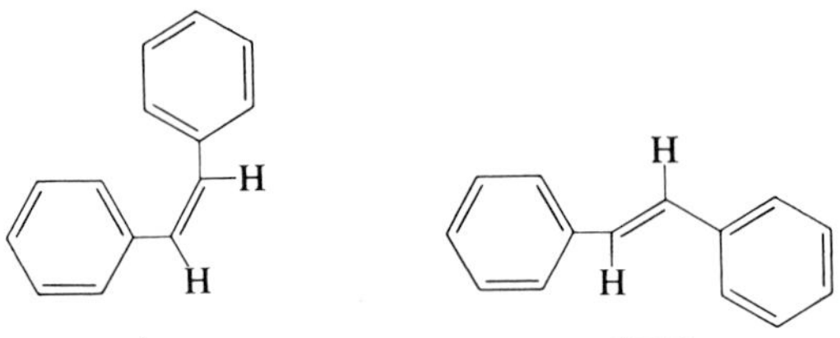

cis	trans
(1a)	(1b)

(2a, b) for which nonvertical energy transfer from triplet donors has been

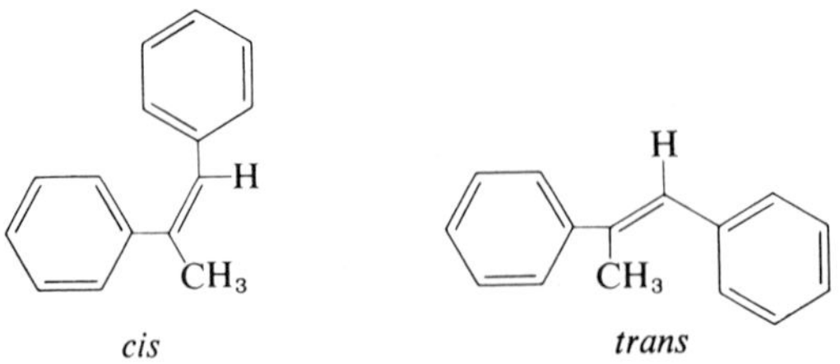

cis	trans
(2a)	(2b)

proposed, have been studied in great detail (129–131,140). These systems provide the clearest cases and so it is most useful to review them in detail as a basis for discussion.

Two kinds of measurements made on these systems are of prime importance. The result of exciting any of the four olefins to the triplet state is isomerization about the double bond. The first kind of measurements are of the photostationary ratio of isomers obtained by exciting either isomer of the *cis–trans* pair by energy transfer from a triplet donor. The second kind of measurements are of the rates of quenching of the triplet state of the donor by each isomer. These data were obtained by means of kinetic flash spectroscopy. In all the experiments the solvent was benzene, the temperature near room temperature, and the samples carefully degassed.

The results of the isomerization experiments are shown in Figures 9 and 10, which are plots of the photostationary isomer ratio versus the triplet excitation energy of the donor used. In these experiments the light was carefully filtered so that only the donors were excited directly. Points for donors which were found to form complexes with the olefins or which underwent some photodecomposition have been discarded (140). Finally, the data

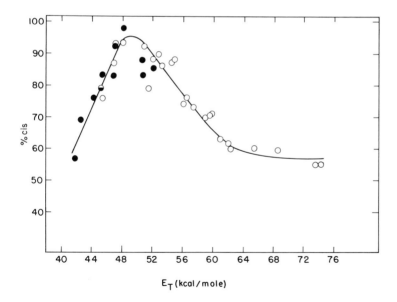

Fig. 9. A plot of the fraction of the *cis*-isomer in the photostationary mixture obtained in the triplet-sensitized isomerization of stilbene as a function of the triplet excitation of the sensitizer (open circles). The filled circles are predictions based on the rate constants for quenching of the sensitizer triplets by each isomer as measured by the flash photolytic technique. The data in this figure are from ref. 138.

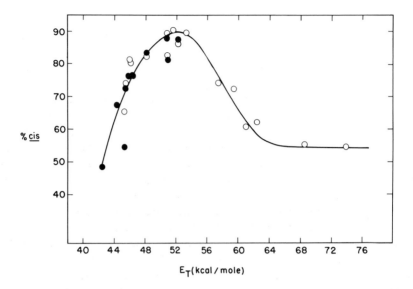

Fig. 10. A plot of the fraction of the *cis*-isomer in the photostationary mixture obtained in the triplet-sensitized isomerization of α-methylstilbene as a function of the triplet excitation energy of the sensitizer (open circles). The filled circles are predictions based on the rate constants for quenching of the sensitizer triplets by each isomer as measured by the flash photolytic technique. The data in this figure are from ref. 138.

shown have been corrected for any back transfer from the excited olefin to the donor.

These data can be accommodated by the simple mechanism shown by Eqs. (73)–(76).

$$S^{*3} + c \xrightarrow{k_1} S + T \qquad (73)$$

$$S^{*3} + t \xrightarrow{k_2} S + T \qquad (74)$$

$$T \xrightarrow{k_3} c \qquad (75)$$

$$T \xrightarrow{k_4} t \qquad (76)$$

where S is the sensitizer, c and t are the *cis* and *trans* isomers, respectively, and T is the triplet state of the olefin. The photostationary ratio of isomers is, then, given by the product of two ratios of rate constants (Eq. (77)).

$$(c/t)_{\text{pss}} = (k_2/k_1)(k_3/k_4) \qquad (77)$$

The ratio (k_3/k_4) may be called the decay ratio, that is, it is the ratio at which the two isomers are produced upon decay of the olefin triplet. It should be constant as long as the solvent and temperature remain the same and no new decay mode is activated. The ratio k_2/k_1 may be called the activation ratio.

It reflects the relative rates of energy transfer from the triplet sensitizer to each of the isomers. When the triplet energy of the sensitizer exceeds the vertical triplet energies of both isomers by at least 4 kcal/mole, $k_2 \cong k_1 \cong$ diffusion-controlled rate constant, and the photostationary ratio is simply the decay ratio. Thus, one can obtain the ratio (k_2/k_1) for any sensitizer by measuring $(c/t)_{\text{pss}}$ and using (k_3/k_4) obtained from a similar measurement employing a "high-energy sensitizer."

Vertical triplet excitation energies could be determined for the stilbenes and α-methylstilbenes from singlet–triplet absorption spectra. They are, cis-stilbene 57 kcal/mole, trans-stilbene 48 kcal/mole, cis-α-methylstilbene 56 kcal/mole, and trans-α-methylstilbene 50 kcal/mole.

Thus sensitizers with triplet energies above about 62 kcal/mole should be "high-energy sensitizers" for both systems, that is the photostationary cis/trans ratio should be the same for these sensitizers. This is observed (Figs. 9 and 10). In both cases the photostationary cis/trans ratio increases as the triplet energy of the sensitizer is lowered below 62 kcal/mole. This is in accord with the vertical triplet energies of the substrates. The cis-isomers have higher triplet energies than the trans-isomers and so the activation ratio should increase as the sensitizer energy is lowered. One might expect this trend to continue as the sensitizer energy is lowered with very cis-rich photostationary states achieved, although with less efficiency. However, the contrary is observed. As the triplet-excitation energy of the sensitizer drops below about 50 kcal/mole the photostationary cis/trans ratio begins to drop! At the same time the expected large drop in the isomerization efficiency is not observed. One interpretation of these results is that the activation ratio begins to fall for sensitizer energies below 50 kcal/mole despite the fact that the trans-isomers have lower excitation energies than do the cis-isomers. Nonvertical excitation transfer from these low-energy sensitizers to give twisted olefin triplets was invoked to explain these results. From the photostationary-state measurements quenching experiments with azulene, and available spectroscopic data, the potential energy diagrams shown in Figures 11 and 12 were derived for the stilbenes and α-methylstilbenes, respectively.

In the case of the stilbenes, the photostationary state achieved for sensitizers with energies less than about 53 kcal/mole were dependent upon the sensitizer concentration. The photostationary mixtures become more trans-rich as the concentration of the sensitizer is increased. (The data plotted in Fig. 9 were extrapolated to zero concentration of sensitizer.) Thus it appeared that back transfer from the stilbene triplet to sensitizer gives the trans ground state. If the sensitizer concentration is kept constant a similar increase in trans-isomer at the photostationary mixture is observed with increasing added azulene concentration. This "azulene effect" is independent of the sensitizer used, demonstrating that the same species is being quenched in all cases.

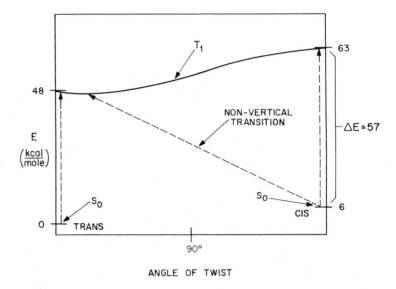

Fig. 11. The proposed potential-energy profile for the lowest triplet state of stilbene with regard to twisting about the central carbon–carbon bond.

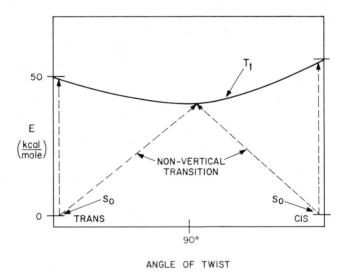

Fig. 12. The proposed potential-energy profile for the lowest triplet state of α-methyl-stilbene with regard to twisting about the central carbon–carbon bond.

Since deactivation to the *trans* ground state is the result of quenching by azulene and sensitizer, the geometry of the stilbene triplet was assigned as *trans* planar. That is, there is a minimum in the potential energy versus twist curve near the *trans*-planar geometry. The dependence of the efficiency of the proposed back transfer to sensitizer on the sensitizer triplet energy is consistent with this model. Since the α-methylstilbene system exhibits neither the sensitizer concentration effect nor the azulene effect, the minimum in the triplet potential energy function was placed at an angle of twist about the central bond of about 90°, where methyl group–phenyl group interaction would be least. If, for the stilbenes, there is also a minimum at 90°, the twisted state would have to be close to isoenergetic with the planar *trans* configuration and fast interconversion of the two possible. Thus, the curves of Figures 11 and 12 predict that excitation of *cis*-stilbene and both isomers of α-methylstilbene could be effected by sensitizers processing triplet energies far less than those necessary to achieve vertical excitation but that *trans*-stilbene should find no path for excitation with an energy requirement much lower than that for vertical excitation.

The support lent these potential energy models for the stilbene and α-methylstilbene systems by the flash photolysis experiments of Herkstroeter (138) is nothing less than spectacular. Herkstroeter measured the rate constants for quenching of the sensitizer lowest triplet state by each olefin isomer. These direct measurements which monitor the sensitizer lowest triplet state preclude the kinds of complications possible in the photostationary state measurements due to interactions with sensitizer singlet states (139) or to energy transfer from higher triplet states of the sensitizer (141). From his quenching data and the decay ratios Herkstroeter could predict photostationary mixtures. The predicted values are shown in Figures 9 and 10. The agreement with measured values leaves no doubt that the activation ratios determined from photostationary isomer ratios have meaning in terms of energy transfer from sensitizer lowest triplet states. Plots of the quenching rate constants as a function of sensitizer triplet energy are shown in Figures 13 and 14 for the stilbenes and α-methylstilbenes, respectively. As can be seen, only the plot for *trans*-stilbene exhibits "classical" behavior (see Section III-3). The straight line through the data has the slope predicted by Eq. (49). For *cis*-stilbene and both α-methylstilbene isomers the quenching rates for low-energy sensitizers (40–56 kcal/mole) are much greater than the "classical" rates.

The results for *cis*-stilbene and both isomers of α-methylstilbene are best explained by invoking excitations to twisted excited states (Figs. 11 and 12). Thus, the term "nonvertical excitation" is an appropriate one to describe the overall process (or more specifically the final states). However, whether a nonvertical transition (one which violates the Franck-Condon principle) ever

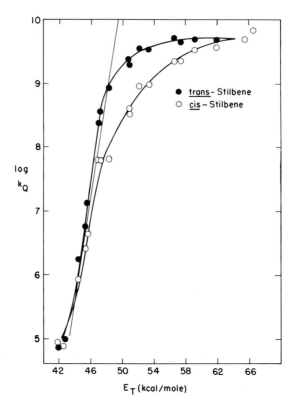

Fig. 13. The specific rate constants (bimolecular) for the quenching of the triplet states of various sensitizers by the two isomers of stilbene as a function of the triplet energy of the sensitizer. The line drawn through the data for *trans*-stilbene has a slope of 0.73 kcal^{-1}. The data in this figure are from ref. 138.

occurs during the triplet excitation transfers is a question. As will be shown below, such non-Franck-Condon processes are not required to explain the results. Furthermore, one can rationalize the results entirely on the basis of the "hot bands" expected in the absorption spectra of the acceptors. However, it is very doubtful that the isolated acceptor is an adequate model since the relatively long times (10^{-6} to 10^{-7} sec) required for these "nonvertical excitations" could allow for vibronic coupling of the donor and acceptor in the collision complex. Each of these possibilities is reviewed in more detail below.

What needs explanation is the behavior of acceptors *cis*-stilbene and both α-methylstilbenes as compared to *trans*-stilbene which exhibits "classical" behavior as an acceptor of triplet excitation energy from low energy sensitizers. For the case of "endothermic" energy transfer to well-behaved acceptors like

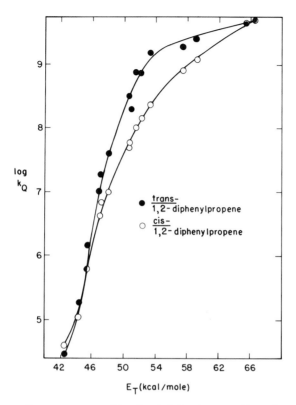

Fig. 14. The specific rate constants (bimolecular) for the quenching of the triplet states of various sensitizers by the two isomers of α-methylstilbene as a function of the triplet energy of the sensitizer. The data in this figure are from ref. 138.

trans-stilbene, it is proposed that the electronic energy discrepancy is made up by activating vibrations in the ground state of the acceptor and excited state of the donor (see Section III-3). The virtual transition in the vibrationally excited acceptor during the energy transfer corresponds to a "hot band" in its absorption spectrum. This kind of analysis can be applied to acceptors like *cis*-stilbene and leads to a rationalization of their special behavior if the potential surface for the excited state which was proposed above is assumed (142).

The proposed potential energy scheme for the stilbenes is shown again in Figure 15, including this time some activated vertical transitions (transitions originating from vibrationally excited ground states). The potential curve describes only one vibrational mode—the twisting vibration involving the central carbon–carbon double bond. Consider the *trans*-isomer. If the *trans*-triplet lies at a minimum with regard to all vibrational modes, then only the

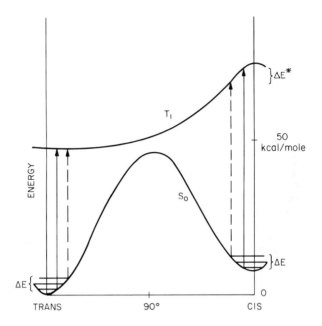

Fig. 15. A potential energy model for the ground and lowest triplet states of stilbene showing possible "hot band" transitions (dashed lines) (ref. 142).

vibrational excitation in the ground state contributes to the reduction (by ΔE) in energy needed for vertical electronic excitation. Excitation of any one of several modes (those coupled to the electronic transition) would be effective in this regard and excitation of the twisting mode is not especially effective. The situation is quite different for the *cis*-isomer. According to the model of Figure 14, the potential surface in the triplet state about the *cis* conformation is saddle-shaped since the *cis*-triplet is at a maximum with respect to twisting about the central carbon–carbon bond. Activation of this twisting mode in the ground state would be especially effective in reducing the energy required for vertical electronic excitation because this twisting leads to a lowering (by ΔE^*) of the excited state energy (see Fig. 15). Thus to the extent that this mode is activated, one would expect higher transfer rates than predicted by Eq. (49).

The other extreme in models, based on the isolated acceptor, involves actual nonvertical transitions. That is, concomitant with the electronic process. there is a geometry change during the energy transfer. As explained above, the potential curve in Figure 11 predicts that nonvertical transitions to twisted forms would be energetically advantageous for *cis*-stilbene but not for the *trans*-isomer.

The nonvertical transitions are of low probability because of the vanishing Franck-Condon factors associated with them. The "hot bands" would have normal Franck-Condon factors associated with them but have reduced intensities because of severe Boltzman factors. A detailed analysis of the red end of the singlet–triplet absorption spectrum of *cis*-stilbene, if it could be determined accurately enough, could show which of these descriptions would be the better. However, it is doubtful that such an analysis of the spectrum of the isolated acceptor would be sufficient to explain the energy transfer rates. This is because it is not certain that one can easily relate the optical intensities with specific rate constants for energy transfer. More importantly, it is doubtful that the isolated acceptor is a reliable model for the donor–acceptor collision complex.

The role of the donor may be far from being a passive energy source in these special endothermic transfers. The average time needed to effect these "nonvertical excitations" is relatively long ($\sim 10^{-6}$ to 10^{-7} sec). This is ample time for the donor–acceptor pair to explore many kinds of collisions. Some of these may be especially important in the transfer process. That is, the donor could in some way aid in the distortion of the acceptor. Hammond suggested this sort of role for the donor in some of the first papers dealing with the question of "nonvertical energy transfer." He suggested that triplet excitation transfer processes in which acceptors are not excited in accordance with the Franck-Condon principle should have some of the characteristics of both thermal and spectroscopic processes but are identical to neither. The processes are not spectroscopic since Franck-Condon restrictions are removed. The behavior should not be typical of thermal reactions because the donor–acceptor system does not come to equilibrium with its surroundings since the acceptor is released in an electronically excited state. The transfer may be effected by passage through "internal equilibrium states" of the donor–acceptor system which mix vibrational and electronic states. That is to say, the electronic systems of the donor and acceptor must interact and some vibrations of the two components must become strongly coupled. Thus, discussion of the configuration of the system at the time the energy is being transferred should resemble discussions of the transition states of ordinary thermal reactions.

To summarize, triplet-energy transfer between donors and acceptors whose spectra show no apparent overlap ("endothermic energy transfer") is especially fast for acceptors like *cis*-stilbene compared to others. In these peculiar endothermic excitations the acceptor arrives in the excited state with a geometry different than the geometry of the relaxed ground state. Details of the transfer process and in particular the exact role of the donor are not known. The simplest picture has the donor as a passive energy source and blames the exceptional transfer rate upon the peculiarities of the "hot band" transitions expected for the acceptors, but quantitative justification of this picture is lacking.*

No matter what the details of the transfer process are, energy conservation demands that the excited states of compounds which are acceptors in "nonvertical energy transfers" must have significantly different equilibrium geometries than do the respective ground states. Another nice example is provided by biphenyl. Spectroscopic studies clearly indicate that the triplet state equilibrium geometry is the planar geometry while in the ground state the dihedral angle formed by the planes of the two phenyl rings is about 40°. Wagner (143) has shown very clearly that biphenyl can accept triplet excitation from donors at rates in excess of the "classical rates."

In principle the geometry changes in the excited state can be more involved than simple rotations about essential single bonds. For example, the triplet state may be dissociative such as for the hydrogen molecule. The rare gas and mercury-sensitized photodissociation of hydrogen may involve nonvertical energy transfer. Triplet transfer to dissociative states has been invoked to explain the sensitized isomerization of 1,2-diphenylcyclopropane (134,135) and the sensitized conversion of quadricyclene to norbornadiene (135). However, it is now known that the excited singlet states of the sensitizers are involved in some of these reactions (143a, 184).

8. Intramolecular Electronic Energy Transfer

Any radiationless combination involving two excited states within a molecule may be considered an example of intramolecular electronic energy transfer (6). It is most useful to classify the various intramolecular excitation transfer processes with respect to the locale of the excitation before and after the transfer. Thus two main classifications arise: (1) transfer within a chromophore and (2) transfer between two chromophores. The latter is usefully split into two subgroups: (a) transfer between conjugated chromophores and (b) transfer between nonconjugated chromophores.

Excitation Transfer within a Chromophore. Most cases of internal conversions and intersystem crossings between *excited* states of a molecule involving the same chromophore compose this class of intramolecular excitation transfer. These processes are not discussed here.

Excitation Transfer between Chromophores. The absorption spectrum of a molecule containing two chromophores which are conjugated (in the broad sense, exhibiting a large overlap of wave functions) is often very different

---

*Note Added in Proof: For a certain *assumed* shape for the long-wavelength tail of the So → T₁ absorption spectra of the stilbenes A. Bylinda [*Chem. Phys. Letters*, **1**, 509 (1968)] has shown that the "hot band" model can accomodate the data.

from the combined spectra of the two chromophores alone in different mole-cules. This is because of the strong mixing of the electronic states of the two chromophores due to the overlapping of their wave functions which delocal-izes the electrons (resonance), and through electronic interactions which delocalize the excitation and which are independent of the overlapping of the wavefunctions. In molecules containing two chromophores which are not conjugated (that is, they are separated by insulating groups) only the latter interactions operate to change the absorption spectrum relative to the com-bined spectra of the two chromophores alone. For nonconjugated, dissimilar chromophores these changes are usually very small, especially in the long wavelength region of the spectrum; that is, the weak or very weak coupling limit obtains.

A. EXCITATION TRANSFER BETWEEN CONJUGATED CHROMOPHORES

Some molecules containing formally conjugated (by the organic chemists' definition) dissimilar chromophores exhibit absorption spectra which have long-wavelength regions that resemble very closely the combined spectra of the chromophores alone in different molecules. That is, there is little electron delocalization and only weak or very weak overlap independent interactions, and one may speak of excitation transfer from one chromophore to another. For example, Ermolaev and Terenin (144) noted that the long-wavelength region of the absorption spectrum of 4-benzoylbiphenyl 3 is very much like that of benzophenone, that is the $n \rightarrow \pi^*$ singlet state is of the same energy and is the lowest excited singlet state in both compounds. Absorption of light in this wavelength region results in a singlet excited state in which the excitation

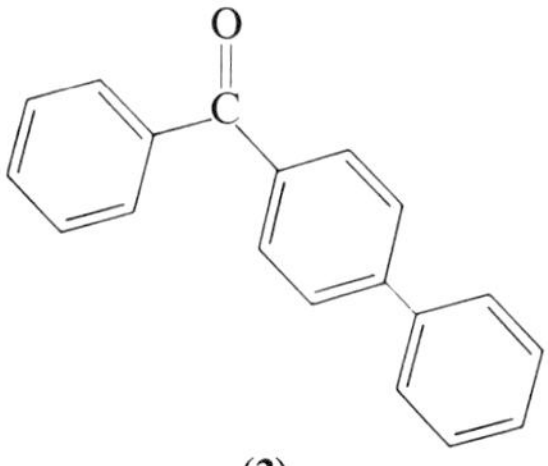

(3)

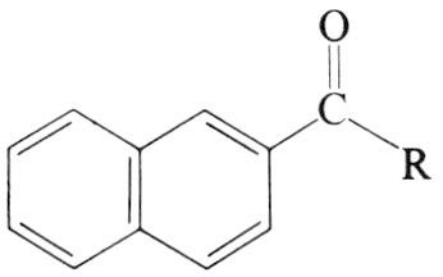

(4) 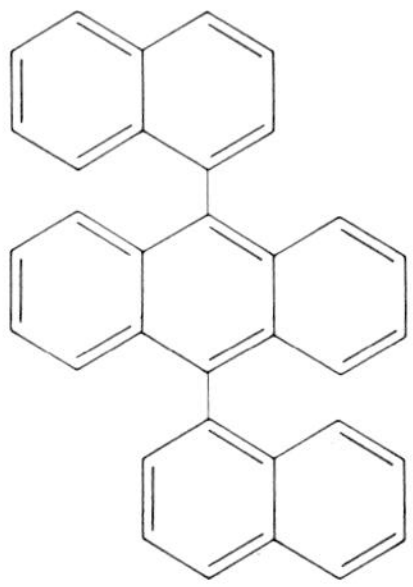   (5)

is fairly well localized to the carbonyl group. But the phosphorescent emission from 4-benzoylbiphenyl is very similar to that of biphenyl. The lowest triplet state of biphenyl lies lower than that of benzophenone, and so Ermolaev and Terenin interpreted this result in terms of intramolecular energy transfer from the carbonyl $n \rightarrow \pi^*$ triplet state to the lowest $(\pi \rightarrow \pi^*)$ triplet state of the biphenyl system by an exchange mechanism. There is no direct evidence for the intermediacy of the carbonyl $n \rightarrow \pi^*$ triplet, that is crossing from the carbonyl $n \rightarrow \pi^*$ singlet to the biphenyl $\pi \rightarrow \pi^*$ triplet is energetically feasible and could be operating. But the very fast intersystem crossing expected in the benzophenone grouping (145) should preclude the latter possibility.

Certain chelates of the rare-earth elements offer more straightforward examples of excitation transfer between conjugated chromophores. Crosby (146) first noted that excitation of the organic ligands leads to the line emission characteristic of the metal ion if the lowest triplet state of the ligand lies above the emitting state of the metal ion. If no ion excited state lies below the ligand triplet, ligand phosphorescence is observed. More recently, Bhaumik and El-Sayed (147) showed proof for the Crosby model. They were able to find compounds possessing high lying singlet states but with lowest triplet levels in between those of the ion and ligand for certain europrium and terbium chelates. These compounds acted to quench the emission from the chelated ion but not the free ion. Thus one mechanism for ion excitation in these chelates is by transfer of triplet excitation from the ligand.

Other systems (148) which present examples of excitation transfer between conjugated chromophores include the naphthyl ketones **4** and 9,10-di-naphthylanthracene **5**.

B. EXCITATION TRANSFER BETWEEN NONCONJUGATED CHROMOPHORES

The study of intramolecular energy transfer between chemically different, nonconjugated chromophores has been receiving much attention recently. This is an interesting area for a number of reasons. Molecular dimensions are well within the limits where some of the simplifying assumptions of the various theoretical treatments of excitation transfer break down. The saturated and supposedly insulating molecular link between the chromophores might play an important role in some cases. The study of excitation transfer between chromophores having known fixed spatial dispositions relative to one another is possible and limited only by difficulties in the syntheses of appropriate systems. Finally, important applications to biological macromolecules, which are composed of large numbers of nonconjugated chromophores, would follow. For instance, one might obtain information about the tertiary structure of an enzyme from a study of excitation transfer within the molecule.

Some of the first examples of intramolecular excitation transfer between isolated chromophores were provided by Weber (149–151). He found that the action spectrum for fluorescence from the naphthylamine grouping in 1-dimethylaminonaphthalene-5-(N-benzyl)-sulfonamide **6** followed its absorption spectrum exactly even in the wavelength region where some of the exciting

(6)   (7)

light was absorbed by the phenyl group. Evidently, efficient transfer of singlet excitation from the phenyl group to the naphthylamine group takes place. In the corresponding N-phenyl compound **7**, the action spectrum drops off significantly in the region where the aniline moiety absorbs. In this case excitation transfer cannot compete with other deactivation paths for the aniline group singlet state. Weber also reported that efficient singlet excitation transfer takes place from the adenine group to the nicotinamide moiety in dihydrodiphosphopyridine nucleotide (DPNH) and from the adenine group to the isoalloxazine moiety in flavin adenine dinucleotide (FAD).

Schnepp and Levy (152) reported that singlet excitation is transferred from the naphthalene groups to the anthracene groups in the homologous series of compounds **8a, b, c**. The efficiency of the transfer was found to be undiminished as the bridge is increased from one to three methylene groups. The investigators pointed out that lengthening the bridge does not significantly lengthen the distance between the chromophores because of the flexibility of the methylene chain. Thus it is not surprising that the same transfer efficiency was found in all three cases. Schnepp and Levy considered a Förster-type mechanism for the transfer and felt that the methylene bridge plays no part.

Latt et al. (153) reported a most elegant study of intramolecular singlet energy transfer between nonconjugated chromophores held at a relatively fixed distance. They made use of a steroid dimer as a stiff bridge to which they attached a donor–acceptor pair. Two such pairs were studied, **9** and **10**.

(8a) $n = 1$
(8b) $n = 2$
(8c) $n = 3$.

(9) $R_1 = $ MeO—⟨ ⟩—CH$_2$CO— $R_2 = $

(10) $R_1 = $ $R_2 = $

From the transfer efficiencies determined from fluorescence spectra and quantum yields, together with R_0 values for the donor–acceptor pairs calculated from the Förster equation (assuming random orientation), donor–acceptor distances in the two compounds were calculated. The value for the pair in **9** (21.3 Å) was found to agree very well with that obtained from measurements on molecular models (21.8 Å). The calculated value for the pair in **10** (16.7 Å) was found to be somewhat lower than the model indicated (21.5 Å). The discrepancy in the latter case may be due to non-random donor–acceptor orientations tending to increase transfer.*

---

* **Note added in proof:** See L. Stryer and R. P. Haugland, *Proc. Nat'l. Acad. Sci., U.S.*, **58**, 719 (1967) for an elegant example of Förster transfer between chromophores held at known fixed distances in a series of twelve compounds.

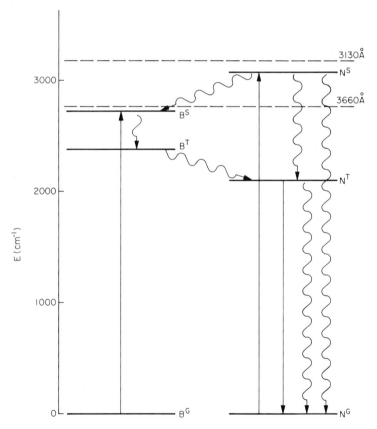

(11a) $n = 1$
(11b) $n = 2$
(11c) $n = 3$

Intramolecular transfer of both singlet and triplet excitation in the three compounds **11a, b, c** was studied in some detail by Lamola et al. (154). In addition to luminescence studies, chemical methods for detecting, characterizing, and counting triplet state molecules were employed. They found (see Fig. 16) that singlet excitation transfer from the lowest singlet state of

Fig. 16. The energy level scheme for compounds **11a, b, c**. It shows the ground (G), lowest excited singlet (S), and lowest triplet (T) states of the benzophenone (B) and naphthalene (N) moieties. Straight arrows represent the radiative transitions and wavy arrows the radiationless transitions observed in these compounds.

the naphthalene groups to the lowest $n \to \pi^*$ singlet state of the benzophenone chromophores occurs with high but not total efficiency (98% for
11a, 80% for **11b**, and 94% for **11c**). Totally efficient intersystem crossing
operates in the benzophenone moieties and the triplet excitation is transferred to the naphthalene groups with 100% efficiency in all three cases. Since
the efficiency of intersystem crossing for naphthalene is only about half that
for benzophenone (145), the overall effect of the transfers is an enhancement
of the yield of naphthalene triplets. From the effectiveness of a competing
intermolecular transfer process it was possible to determine a lower limit for
the triplet excitation transfer rate, $k > 10^{10}$ sec^{-1}. The exchange mechanism
can account for a rate on this order, since the distance between the centers of
the chromophores is about 10 Å in all three compounds. Rates for the singlet
transfers were calculated by the authors assuming that the competing processes are the normal deactivation processes for the naphthalene singlet state.
However, this assumption is in error since the residual fluorescence is not
only naphthalene fluorescence but originates in part from an excited state
complex (exciplex) between the naphthalene and benzophenone moieties
(155,156). Amplification and confirmation of the studies of Lamola et al. has
been provided by Breen and Keller who studied triplet and singlet excitation
transfer in three similar systems containing methylene bridges (155). They
observed totally efficient triplet energy transfers and fluorescent emission
from intramolecular exciplexes.

Keller and Dolby (156) made use of a stiff steroid backbone to study intramolecular triplet-energy transfer from benzophenone to naphthalene and
from carbazole to naphthalene. The compounds they used are **12a** and **12b**
in which the interchromophore distances are about 15 Å center to center.
They found the transfer to be about 20% efficient in **12a** and 12% efficient in
12b, the rates being 25 sec^{-1} and 0.04 sec^{-1}, respectively. The authors suggested
that the dipole–dipole coulombic mechanism is operating; however, other
explanations are possible.

There is much literature concerning investigations of electronic energy
transfer in proteins and nucleic acids. Only a few comments about the results
of these studies will be made here.

Contrary to expectations, intramolecular excitation transfer in DNA is
relatively unimportant and certainly need not be invoked to explain the
luminescence and photochemical properties of the polymer (164). It will be
recalled that DNA is a double-stranded helical polymer consisting of a
sugar–phosphate backbone to which is attached the four kinds of nitrogen
bases, adenine (A), guanine (G), thymine (T), and cytosine (C). The bases of
one strand are hydrogen-bonded to coplanar bases on the other strand. The
hydrogen-bonding is specific; A is always bound with T, and G with C. The
coplanar bases lie in planes perpendicular to the helical axis. Spectroscopic

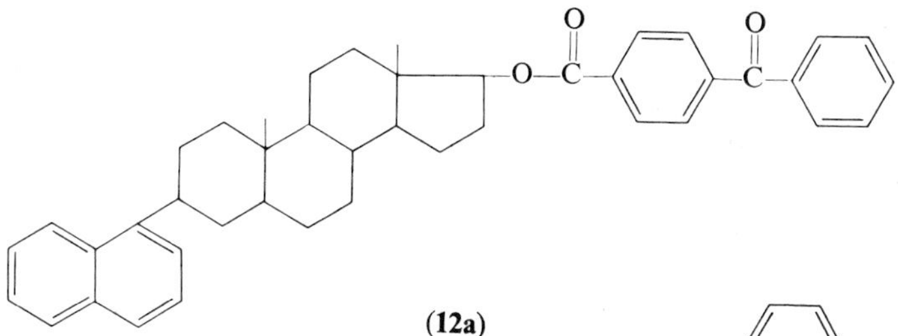

(12a)

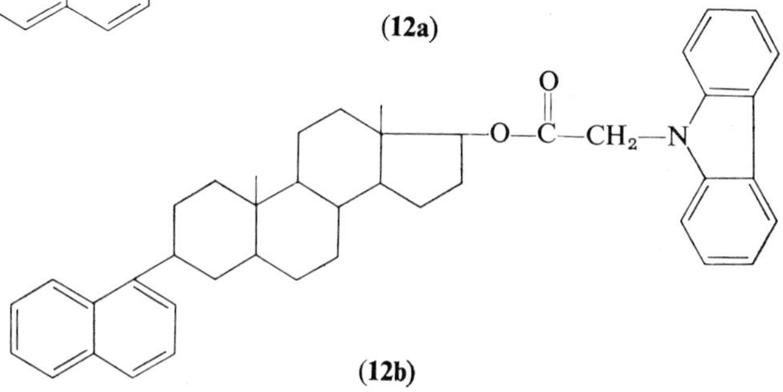

(12b)

studies on the monomers (157–163) have shown that the lowest excited singlet energies are in the order A > T > G > C, and the triplet levels C > G > A > T. The phosphorescence from DNA has been identified as that of T (160), consistent with a triplet-energy transfer model. Calculations based upon monomer spectral properties and the DNA geometry predict that singlet excitations transfer between all possible inter- and intrastrand neighbors should occur (158,163). However, in actuality both singlet and triplet excitation transfers in DNA are probably precluded. The situation seems to be the following. Poly G and poly C exhibit fluorescence and phosphorescence, but the double-stranded polynucleotide poly G:poly C shows none. The excitation in either G or C is evidently quenched at the singlet level when they are hydrogen-bonded. That the G–C pairs do not contribute to the luminescence of DNA directly or indirectly through energy transfer is demonstrated by the fact that the intensity of the phosphorescence from various DNAs can be correlated with the A–T content (160). Thus the quenching in the G–C pair occurs faster than energy transfer to A–T pairs. Transfer from A–T pairs to G–C pairs is also shown to be unimportant by the dependence of the luminescence on A–T content. The explanation for this lies in the fact that the DNA fluorescence originates from exciplexes (161), that is, excited state complexes between two neighboring bases on the same strand. The exciplex energy levels lie significantly lower than those of the isolated monomers so that excitation can become trapped in the exciplexes. Since A seems to be quenched when hydrogen bonded, for example in polyadenylic acid:polyuradylic acid (159), one can invoke the following model. Excitation of G, C, and perhaps A in DNA leads to very fast quenching of the excitation, precluding transfer. Excitation of T leads to very fast exciplex formation, precluding transfer. Intersystem crossing in the exciplex leads to the T triplet directly and since T has the lowest-lying triplet state triplet excitation transfer does not occur. There is some evidence that triplet excitation does migrate within runs of thymines in DNA (164).

One goal of luminescence studies on proteins is the interpretation of the spectroscopic data in terms of tertiary structure. The emphasis has been on fluorescence measurements and thus one is concerned with the possibility of singlet excitation transfer. The bulk of the work has come from the laboratory of Weber (165–167).

Although proteins are made up of twenty different amino acids, only three have low-lying excited states (absorb significantly above 2400 Å) and support fluorescence. These are the three aromatic amino acids, phenylalanine, tyrosine, and tryptophan. In addition, many enzymes contain other groups (prosthetic groups) which have low-lying states, such as flavins and metallo-porphyrins, or contain transition metal ions with low lying levels. Also coenzymes and inhibitors which bind to the enzyme may contain moieties with low-lying states. These may be suitable acceptors for excitation transfer from the enzyme.

The lowest excited singlet levels of the aromatic amino acids lie in the order phenylalanine > tyrosine > tryptophan. In addition to nearest neighbor transfer, the Förster equation predicts that singlet excitation transfer from tyrosine to tryptophan should occur with a R_0 value of 17 Å, about the order of average enzyme diameters (168). Unfortunately no definitive example of such a transfer has been presented. The difficulty lies in the fact that the emission properties of tyrosine are extremely sensitive to environment and pH so that it is not easy to separate environmental quenching from energy transfer. There is certainly singlet energy transfer in heme containing proteins. For example, very little fluorescence is observed from myoglobin and hemo-globin (169). The Förster R_0 values for transfer from tryptophan to hemes lie in the range 30–40 Å (168). The sensitized fluorescence of the coenzyme NADH concomitant with quenching of tryptophan fluorescence from dehydrogenases with which it binds has been observed by Velick (170).

IV. APPLICATIONS OF ELECTRONIC ENERGY TRANSFER TO THE PHOTOCHEMISTRY AND SPECTROSCOPY OF ORGANIC COMPOUNDS

Extensive use of electronic energy transfer (starting about 1960) in prepara-tive organic photochemistry and in the study of the mechanisms of photoreactions followed very soon after the elucidation of the energy transfer processes. More recently electronic energy transfer has been employed to detect and characterize molecules in excited electronic states, and in studies of radiationless processes. In these regards, the combination of electronic energy transfer plus a characteristic photoreaction of the donor or acceptor has been an especially powerful tool.

In the following sections many of the ways in which electronic energy transfer has been used in photochemistry and spectroscopy are reviewed with specific examples. Discussions of the principles involved and the pitfalls commonly encountered as well as discussions about the choice of appropriate sensitizers and quenchers are included.

A Multiplicity of Mechanisms for Sensitization and Quenching: A Warning. In the remainder of this chapter are numerous examples of sensitization and quenching of photoreactions, fluorescence, phosphorescence, etc., all of which involve electronic energy transfer from a donor (sensitizer) or to an acceptor (quencher). Before beginning discussions about these examples, it is important to note that there are, of course, mechanisms for sensitization and quenching which do not involve electronic energy transfer as defined here. Thus, an excitation transfer mechanism cannot be automatically assumed. This point cannot be overemphasized because misinterpretations can be easily made.

Some examples of sensitization or quenching not involving electronic energy transfer are mentioned below.

9,10-Dibromoanthracene was found to be an efficient photosensitizer for the isomerization of *cis*-stilbene and its derivatives in benzene solution. At first it was thought that excitation transfer from the triplet state of 9,10-dibromoanthracene to the olefin. But it was subsequently shown that the isomerization was catalyzed by bromine atoms or hydrogen bromide generated in the photolysis of the dibromoanthracene (171). Of course, this is a common sort of mechanism occurring in radical chain reactions initiated through the action of light on an initiator (sensitizer). For initiators like benzoylperoxide or azoisobutyrlnitrile photolysis leads to chain initiating radicals by fragmentation of the initiator. Benzophenone can be used as an initiator. In this case, the initiating radicals are formed when triplet benzophenone abstracts a hydrogen atom from the solvent or monomer.

Another mode of sensitization involves the formation of a ground-state complex between the substrate and the sensitizer. Excitation of the complex leads to a chemical change in the substrate. The ferrocene-sensitized photoisomerization of the 1,3-pentadienes (172) and the cuprous chloride-sensitized photoisomerization of 1,5-cyclooctadiene (173) **13** (Eq. (78)) are examples of this kind of scheme.

Schenck (174–180) has taken the viewpoint that energy transfer is rarely

$$(13)$$

$$(78)$$

involved in sensitized photoreactions. In the Schenck "relay" mechanism the excited sensitizer (the triplet state is generally considered) interacts with the substrate to form a reactive complex. The nature of the interaction has not been spelled out, but in some cases Schenck has implied covalent bond formation. When the substrate is activated in this way it may undergo isomerization, rearrangement, or may react with another reagent. The sensitizer is eventually excised unharmed and so it is a sort of photocatalytic agent. Typical representations of the Schenck mechanism are given by Eqs. (79)–(84).

$$S \xrightarrow{h\nu} \cdot S \cdot \quad \text{(excited, biradical state)} \tag{79}$$

$$\cdot S \cdot + X \longrightarrow \cdot S\text{--}X \cdot \tag{80}$$

$$\cdot S\text{--}X \cdot \longrightarrow \cdot S\text{--}Y \cdot \quad \text{(rearrangement)} \tag{81}$$

$$\cdot S\text{--}Y \cdot \longrightarrow S + Y \tag{82}$$

or

$$\cdot S\text{--}X \cdot + R \longrightarrow \cdot S\text{--}X\text{--}R \cdot \quad \text{(addition)} \tag{83}$$

$$\cdot S\text{--}X\text{--}R \cdot \longrightarrow S + X - R \tag{84}$$

$$S = \text{sensitizer}$$

$$X = \text{substrate}$$

There is no case for which this addition–elimination mechanism has been clearly demonstrated.* Sensitized oxidations of organic systems employing molecular oxygen and dyes as sensitizers first thought to involve the Schenck mechanism have been shown to involve free excited singlet oxygen produced by energy transfer from the triplet sensitizer (181,182). However, something like the Schenck mechanism may well be operating in several systems where single bond cleavages have been effected by the action of an excited sensitizer. Complex formation between the excited sensitizer and the substrate could lead to chemical change in the substrate by paths involving neither nonvertical excitation transfer nor covalent bonding of the substrate and sensitizer.

One kind of quenching of an excited substrate in solution which does not involve electronic energy transfer to the quencher is some reversible chemical

* Note added in proof: Interesting findings of relevence to this mechanism are reported in N. C. Yang, J. T. Cohen, and A. Shani, *J. Am. Chem. Soc.*, **90**, 3264 (1968); R. A. Caldwell and G. W. Sovocool, *J. Am. Chem. Soc.*, **90**, 7138 (1968); and S. M. Japar, M. Pomerantz, and E. W. Abrahamson, *Chem. Phys. Letters*, **2**, 137 (1968).

reaction with the latter. The formation of even a weak complex between the excited substrate and the potential quencher may be sufficient to effect quenching through, for example, induction of internal conversion or inter-system crossing. Bromobenzene quenches the anthracene singlet in solution even though the singlet level of bromobenzene lies much higher than that of anthracene. The quenching mechanism has been shown to be induction of intersystem crossing in the anthracene by the bromobenzene (183). The singlet states of several aromatic hydrocarbons are quenched by conjugated dienes such as 1,3-pentadiene (139) (see Section IV–2–B) without concomitant electronic excitation of the diene. It has been suggested (143a, 184) that complex formation between the excited aromatic hydrocarbon and the diene facilitates internal conversion to the ground state.

In most cases experiments involving sensitization or quenching are useful only if the mechanism of the sensitization or quenching is known. It is usually convenient (see below) if the mechanism involves electronic energy transfer, since the rate of the process can be easily estimated. An electronic energy transfer mechanism is ideally established if it can be shown that the acceptor is promoted to an excited state as a consequence of the quenching of the donor. This is not always easy to demonstrate and, furthermore, most photochemical laboratories are not equipped to do so. However, there is a simple (but not perfectly rigorous) criterion that can be applied. Any sensiti-zation or quenching process which does not involve energy transfer is bound to be sensitive to the detailed structure of the sensitizer or quencher. If electronic energy transfer is involved the process should not be particularly sensitive to the detailed structure of the sensitizer or quencher but, as has been shown, should depend on the spectral properties of the substrate and sensitizer or quencher.

1. Solution Kinetics and Energy Transfer

The rates of processes involving molecules in excited states are of prime interest. Two kinds of approaches are available for determining these rates. The more direct method, the pulsed excitation experiment, is the more difficult to carry out. It involves pulsed excitation of the sample, preferably with a light pulse of duration short compared to the lifetime of the excited state of interest. Then the dynamics of the excited state or some immediate product must be monitored, e.g., emission decay curve determined. If, on the other hand, the rate of one process involving the excited state is known and the efficiency (quantum yield) of that process monitored in the presence and absence of a competing process, the rate of the latter can, instead, be deter-mined from quantum yields obtained from experiments involving continuous excitation. Experiments of this type have been used to determine excitation transfer rates for systems in which the rate of some competing process was known. Of course the situation can be reversed if the energy transfer rate is known.

It is instructive to derive the kinetic expressions for some simple situations involving electronically excited molecules in solution. The first to be considered is the quenching experiment, probably the most common approach being used to determine rates of excited-state processes in solution. It involves the competition between the process of interest and the quenching of the excited state in most cases by energy transfer to an added quencher. The bimolecular quenching of fluorescence in solution is a simple case with which to begin.

Assume the mechanism of Eqs. (85)–(88) where the rate of production

	Rate	
$X \xrightarrow{h\nu} X^*$	fI	(85)
$X^* \longrightarrow X + h\nu'$	$k_1[X^*]$	(86)
$X^* \longrightarrow X$	$k_2[X^*]$	(87)
$X^* + Q \longrightarrow X + Q$	$k_3[X^*][Q]$	(88)

of the fluorescent state X^* of a solute X is constant and equal to the product of the light intensity I and the efficiency of light absorption f; k_2 represents the sum of the rate constants for decay of X^* by all other processes except fluorescence and quenching by quencher Q. Quenching by Q may or may not involve electronic energy transfer.

The rate of change of $[X^*]$ is given by

$$\frac{d[X^*]}{dt} = fI - k_1[X^*] - k_2[X^*] - k_3[X^*][Q] \tag{89}$$

So that applying the steady state approximation gives

$$fI = (k_1 + k_2 + k_3[Q])[X^*] \tag{90}$$

The fluorescence quantum yield in the presence of quencher is

$$\phi_Q = k_1[X^*]/fI = k_1/(k_1 + k_2 + k_3[Q]) \tag{91}$$

and in the absence of quencher is

$$\phi_0 = k_1/(k_1 + k_2) \tag{92}$$

The ratio of these yields, which is relatively easy to obtain experimentally, is

$$\phi_0/\phi_Q = 1 + [k_3/(k_1 + k_2)][Q] \tag{93}$$

or

$$\phi_0/\phi_Q = 1 + k_3[Q]\tau \tag{94}$$

where $\tau = 1/(k_1 + k_2)$ is the lifetime of X^* in the absence of quencher.

Equation (94) has come to be called the Stern-Volmer (185) expression. A plot of ϕ_0/ϕ_Q versus [Q] will give a straight line with a slope k_3 if the mechanism is correct. Since τ, the fluorescence lifetime, can be obtained in a number of ways including direct measurement of fluorescence decay in a pulsed experiment, the rate constant for quenching can be extracted. Recent applications of this method of obtaining bimolecular fluorescence quenching constants have been provided by Hammond and co-workers (139,186). Fluorescent-state lifetimes could be determined from this kind of an experiment if the quenching rate were known. However, this approach would be practical only for those cases for which it can be assumed that the quenching occurs at the diffusion-controlled rate, which can be calculated (see Section III–1–E) without reference to the fluorescence lifetime.

Before proceeding to more kinetic analyses it is worthwhile to examine in terms of numbers the relationship of the excited-state lifetime τ_{X*}, the bimolecular quenching rate constant k_q, the quencher concentration [Q], and the quenching efficiency, as expressed by Eq. (94). This can be done by studying Table 11, where $[Q]_{1/2}$ and $[Q]_{0.99}$ denote the quencher concentrations

TABLE 11

	$[Q]_{1/2}$ (moles/liter)			$[Q]_{0.99}$ (moles/liter)		
τ_X^* (sec)	$k_q=10^8$	10^{10}	10^{12} liter mole^{-1} sec^{-1}	$k_q=10^9$	10^{10}	10^{11} liter mole^{-1} sec^{-1}
10^{-11}	10	10^{-1}				
10^{-10}	1	10^{-2}		10		
10^{-9}	10	10^{-1}	10^{-3}	10	1	
10^{-8}	1	10^{-2}	10^{-4}	10	1	10^{-1}
10^{-7}	10^{-1}	10^{-3}	10^{-5}	1	10^{-1}	10^{-2}
10^{-6}	10^{-2}	10^{-4}	10^{-6}	10^{-1}	10^{-2}	10^{-3}
10^{-5}	10^{-3}	10^{-5}	10^{-7}	10^{-2}	10^{-3}	10^{-4}
10^{-4}	10^{-4}	10^{-6}	10^{-8}	10^{-3}	10^{-4}	10^{-5}
10^{-3}	10^{-5}	10^{-7}	10^{-9}	10^{-4}	10^{-5}	10^{-6}

	k_q (liter mole^{-1} sec^{-1})						
$[Q]_{1/2}$ (moles/liter)	$\tau_{X*} = 10^{-9}$	10^{-8}	10^{-7}	10^{-6}	10^{-5}	10^{-4}	10^{-3}
10	10^8	10^7	10^6	10^5	10^4	10^3	10^2
1	10^9	10^8	10^7	10^6	10^5	10^4	10^3
10^{-1}	10^{10}	10^9	10^8	10^7	10^6	10^5	10^4
10^{-2}	10^{11}	10^{10}	10^9	10^8	10^7	10^6	10^5
10^{-3}	10^{12}	10^{11}	10^{10}	10^9	10^8	10^7	10^6
10^{-4}		10^{12}	10^{11}	10^{10}	10^9	10^8	10^7
10^{-5}			10^{12}	10^{11}	10^{10}	10^9	10^8
10^{-6}				10^{12}	10^{11}	10^{10}	10^9
10^{-7}					10^{12}	10^{11}	10^{10}

required to quench, respectively, 50 and 99% of the excited molecules. Bimolecular quenching rate constants have maximum values between 10^9 and 10^{10} liter mole^{-1} sec^{-1} in ordinary solvents, the diffusion-controlled rate constant, unless the quenching mechanism involves long-range Förster-type excitation transfer for which still faster rates are possible. Taking $k_q = 10^{10}$ liter mole^{-1} sec^{-1}, a common circumstance, it can be seen from Table 11 that for [Q] $\leq 10^{-3}M$ virtually no quenching of excited species of $\tau \leq 10^{-8}$ sec will occur, and [Q] $\geq 10^{-3}M$ assures quenching of all species of $\tau \geq 10^{-5}$ sec. Most excited singlet state species have $\tau \leq 10^{-8}$ sec and many triplet state species have $\tau \geq 10^{-5}$ sec in fluid solution.

The diffusion-controlled rate can be assumed for many cases of exothermic triplet excitation transfer in solution so that the quenching experiment can very often be employed to obtain information about the dynamics of triplet states in solution (see Section IV-2-C). Unfortunately, very few compounds phosphoresce in fluid solution so that generally some other detectable characteristic of the triplet state molecule or the quencher must be monitored. Thus, the triplet quenching experiment usually involves some chemical reaction of the compound of interest or the quencher.

For example, consider the following scheme:

$$\text{Rate}$$

$$X \xrightarrow{h\nu} X^{*1} \Big\} \qquad \qquad \alpha fI \qquad \qquad (95)$$
$$X^{*1} \xrightarrow{\alpha} X^{*3} \Big\} \qquad \qquad \qquad \qquad (96)$$

$$X^{*3} \longrightarrow X' \qquad \qquad k_1[X^{*3}] \qquad \qquad (97)$$

$$X^{*3} \longrightarrow X \qquad \qquad k_2[X^{*3}] \qquad \qquad (98)$$

$$X^{*3} + Q \longrightarrow X + Q^{*3} \qquad k_3[X^{*3}][Q] \qquad (99)$$

where α is the efficiency of intersystem crossing, X' is a rearrangement (or solvent addition) product of X^{*3}, and k_1 is the specific rate constant for the primary process in the pathway to X'. The reciprocal of the quantum yield for production of X' is given by Eq. (100). Thus a plot of $1/\phi_{X'}$ versus [Q]

$$\frac{1}{\phi_{X'}} = \frac{1}{\alpha}\left(1 + \frac{k_2}{k_1}\right) + \frac{k_3[Q]}{\alpha k_1} \qquad (100)$$

has a slope equal to $k_3/\alpha k_1$ and an intercept of $(1/\alpha)(1 + k_2/k_1)$. The quenching rate constant can be calculated from the Debye expression (Eq. (37)), and α may be determined by a number of methods now available (see below). Thus both k_2 and k_1 can be determined.

The lifetime of an unreactive triplet state in solution can be determined if the quencher undergoes some detectable process. For example, consider Eqs. (101)–(106). In this scheme the quencher Q undergoes a reaction after

$$\text{Rate}$$

$$\left.\begin{array}{l} X \xrightarrow{h\nu} X^{*1} \\ X^{*1} \xrightarrow{\alpha} X^{*3} \end{array}\right\} \qquad \alpha f I \qquad \begin{array}{l} (101) \\ (102) \end{array}$$

$$X^{*3} \longrightarrow X \qquad\qquad k_1[X^{*3}] \qquad (103)$$

$$X^{*3} + Q \longrightarrow X + Q^{*3} \qquad k_2[X^{*3}][Q] \qquad (104)$$

$$Q^{*3} \longrightarrow Q' \qquad\qquad k_3[Q^{*3}] \qquad (105)$$

$$Q^{*3} \longrightarrow Q \qquad\qquad k_4[Q^{*3}] \qquad (106)$$

being excited to its triplet state by energy transfer leading to the product Q' with an efficiency $\beta = k_3/(k_3 + k_4)$. The reciprocal of the quantum yield of Q' is

$$1/\phi_{Q'} = 1/\alpha\beta + \frac{1}{\alpha\beta\tau k_2[Q]} \qquad (107)$$

where α is the intersystem crossing efficiency for X and $\tau = 1/k_1$ is the lifetime of X^{*3}. A plot of $1/\phi_{Q'}$ versus $1/[Q]$ gives a straight line with slope $1/\alpha\beta\tau k_2$ and intercept $1/\alpha\beta$. The ratio of the intercept to slope gives τk_2 and k_2 may be calculated from the Debye equation if the quenching is diffusion controlled. Liu (141) has used such a scheme to determine the $T_2 \rightarrow T_1$ internal conversion rate for some anthracene derivatives.

The situation is a little more complex when a bimolecular reaction is involved. For instance, consider the photoreduction of benzophenone (B)

$$\text{Rate}$$

$$\left.\begin{array}{l} \phi_2 CO \xrightarrow{h\nu} \phi_2 CO^{*1} \\ \phi_2 CO^{*1} \xrightarrow{\alpha} \phi_2 CO^{*3} \end{array}\right\} \qquad \alpha f I \qquad \begin{array}{l} (108) \\ (109) \end{array}$$

$$\phi_2 CO^{*3} + \phi_2 CHOH \longrightarrow 2\phi_2\dot{C}OH \qquad k_r[B^*][BH_2] \qquad (110)$$

$$\phi_2 CO^{*3} \longrightarrow \phi_2 CO \qquad\qquad k_d[B^*] \qquad (111)$$

$$\phi_2 CO^{*3} + Q \longrightarrow \phi_2 CO + Q^{*3} \qquad k_q[B^*][Q] \qquad (112)$$

$$2\phi_2\dot{C}OH \longrightarrow \phi_2 COHCOH\phi_2 \qquad k_c[BH]^2 \qquad (113)$$

with benzhydrol (BH_2) (187), Eqs. (108)–(113). The quantum yield of disappearance of benzophenone ϕ_B in the absence of quencher is given by Eq. (114) and that in the presence of quencher by Eq. (115).

$$1/\phi_B = 1/\alpha + (k_d/\alpha k_r[BH_2]) \qquad (114)$$

$$\frac{1}{\phi_B} = \frac{1}{\alpha}\left(1 + \frac{k_d}{k_r[BH_2]}\right) + \frac{k_q[Q]}{\alpha k_r[BH_2]} \qquad (115)$$

The ratio k_d/k_r was obtained from experiments in the absence of quencher, and k_q/k_r obtained from addition experiments with quencher added. If the quenching is diffusion-controlled k_q can be calculated, and k_d and k_r

determined. Values for these rate constants obtained in this way by Hammond and co-workers (187) agree perfectly with those obtained by direct observation of the benzophenone triplet in a flash photolysis (pulsed) experiment (188).

2. Applications to Organic Photochemistry

A. TRIPLET SENSITIZATION OF PHOTOCHEMICAL REACTIONS

$$S \xrightarrow{h\nu} S^{*1} \tag{116}$$

$$S^{*1} \longrightarrow S^{*3} \tag{117}$$

$$S^{*3} + A \longrightarrow S + A^{*3} \tag{118}$$

$$A^{*3} \longrightarrow \text{Products}$$

or   (119)

$$A^{*3} + B \longrightarrow \text{Products}$$

By a triplet-sensitized reaction (Eqs. (116–119)) is meant one in which the triplet state of the substrate (A) is populated by energy transfer from a sensitizer (S) in its triplet state. The sensitizer absorbs the exciting light. Some of the several reasons why one would choose to excite a substrate in this indirect manner are given below.

Avoiding the Substrate Singlet State. Suppose that a substrate undergoes chemical change from both its lowest excited singlet and lowest triplet states to give different products. One could avoid the singlet-state reaction and obtain only the triplet-state reaction by populating only the triplet state through energy transfer from a suitable sensitizer.

Increasing Efficiency through Sensitization. Suppose a substrate undergoes a reaction by way of its triplet state but that the quantum yield is low because the yield of triplets is low, either intrinsically or because of self-quenching of the singlet or other processes degrading the singlet. One can then increase the reaction quantum yield by increasing the yield of substrate triplets through the use of a sensitizer possessing high intersystem-crossing efficiency under the reaction conditions. This assumes, of course, that triplet-energy transfer from the sensitizer to the substrate is efficient.

Increasing the Range of Useful Exciting Light Wavelength. Suppose there is a large singlet–triplet splitting in a substrate which undergoes a reaction from its triplet state. It would be advantageous to use a sensitizer with a small singlet–triplet splitting in order to make use of source light not absorbed by the substrate alone.

Some Examples of Sensitized Reactions. The following examples illustrate one or more of the applications mentioned above.

Photolysis of *cis*-dibenzoylethylene, **14**, in alcohols leads to formation of the one-to-one adduct **15** (Eq. (120)). This reaction does not involve the

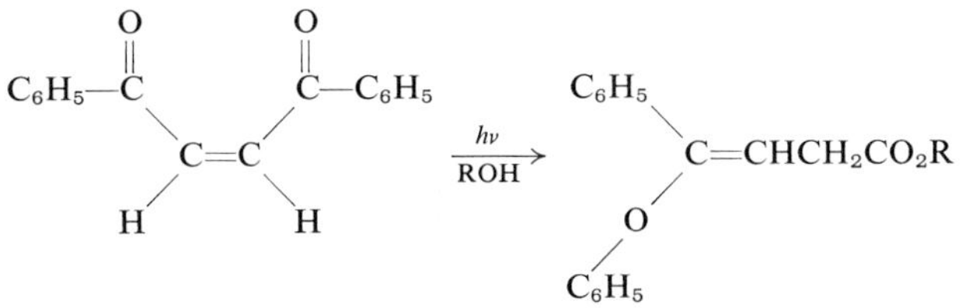

$$
\underset{\textbf{(14)}}{\overset{\displaystyle\begin{array}{cc} O & O \\ \| & \| \\ C_6H_5{-}C & C{-}C_6H_5 \end{array}}{\underset{\begin{array}{cc} H & H \end{array}}{C{=}C}}}
\xrightarrow[ROH]{h\nu}
\underset{\textbf{(15)}}{\overset{\displaystyle C_6H_5}{\underset{\underset{C_6H_5}{O}}{C{=}CHCH_2CO_2R}}}
\qquad (120)
$$

triplet state as an intermediate since excitation of *cis*-dibenzoylethylene to its triplet state by energy transfer from a triplet sensitizer (e.g., benzophenone) leads to an altogether different reaction, the reduction of the carbon–carbon bond (Eq. (121)) (189,190).

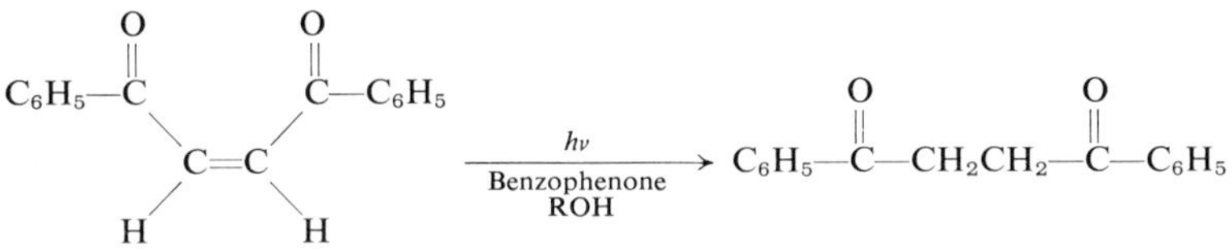

$$
\underset{\begin{array}{cc} H & H \end{array}}{\overset{\displaystyle\begin{array}{cc} O & O \\ \| & \| \\ C_6H_5{-}C & C{-}C_6H_5 \end{array}}{C{=}C}}
\xrightarrow[\substack{Benzophenone \\ ROH}]{h\nu}
C_6H_5{-}\overset{O}{\overset{\|}{C}}{-}CH_2CH_2{-}\overset{O}{\overset{\|}{C}}{-}C_6H_5
\qquad (121)
$$

Direct photolysis of myrcene, **16**, yields chiefly the tautomeric cyclobutene, **17** (191). The triplet-sensitized isomerization leads mainly to the interesting bicyclo-[2.1.1]-hexane, **18**, in high yield (192).

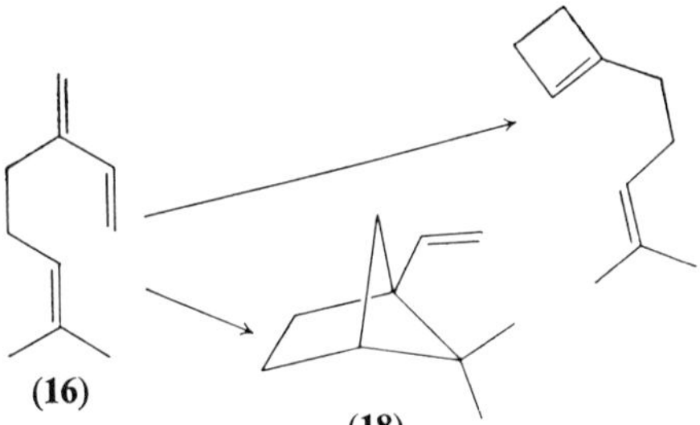

(17)   (122)

(16)

(18)

Ethylpyruvate ($E_T = 65$ kcal/mole), **19**, undergoes photolysis in inert solvents to give carbon monoxide and acetaldehyde. The reaction involves

$$
CH_3\overset{O}{\overset{\|}{C}}\underset{\underset{O}{\|}}{C}{-}O{-}CH_2CH_3
\xrightarrow[\phi H]{h\nu}
CO + 2CH_3CHO
\qquad (123)
$$

(19)

the triplet state and proceeds with a quantum yield of 0.17 (193). The measured intersystem crossing efficiency of ethylpyruvate in benzene solution is 54% (194). Thus the quantum yield of the reaction can be increased if the triplet yield can be increased. The benzophenone ($E_T = 68.5\ \text{kcal/mole}$) sensitized reaction (95% of the incident light absorbed by the benzo-phenone) has a quantum yield of 0.34 (193). This is just what is expected since benzophenone undergoes intersystem crossing with 100% efficiency, or about twice that of ethylpyruvate.

Norbornadiene, **20**, yields the tautomeric quadricyclene, **21**, when irradiated

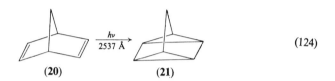

$$\tag{124}$$

$$(20) \qquad\qquad (21)$$

in solution with 2537-Å light (195). This same interconversion can be achieved with higher quantum efficiency with light of wavelengths up to 3800 Å when benzophenone is employed as sensitizer (196). Thus, in addition to the greater quantum efficiency of the sensitized reaction, the latter allows the entire output of the light source in the ultraviolet range to be useful.

Mechanistic Information. In uncovering the mechanism of a photo-chemical reaction one of the important questions to be answered, of course, is which electronic state of the molecule is involved in the primary photo-chemical event. Because of fast and usually totally efficient internal conver-sion, only two excited states of the molecule need normally be considered as precursors, the lowest excited singlet and triplet states. One may be able to decide whether or not the lowest triplet state is an intermediate through the use of a triplet sensitizer to populate the lowest triplet state specifically.

Consider the four paths shown in Figure 17. In path a the primary photo-chemical step takes place when the molecule is in the S_1 state. Path b has the chemistry occurring in the vibrationally excited ground state achieved by internal conversion from the S_1 state. In path c the primary event takes place when the molecule is in the T_1 state. Path d has the chemistry occurring in the vibrationally excited ground state achieved by intersystem crossing from the T_1 state.

Now suppose that excitation of a molecule into its singlet manifold leads to formation of a product P. A sensitization experiment can then be performed in which the T_1 state of the molecule is populated, bypassing the S_1 state. If no P is formed in the sensitized reaction then one may conclude its formation in the direct photolysis does not involve the T_1 state as a precursor, that is neither mechanism c nor d operates. Of course, there is the possibility that a higher lying triplet state is involved, but this can be tested by using higher energy triplet sensitizers.

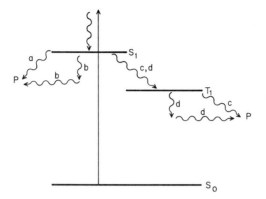

Fig. 17. Four possible pathways for formation of a photoproduct P as a result of excitation of a substrate to an excited singlet state. The primary photochemical process occurs in the S_1 state according to path a, in the T_1 state according to path c, and in the vibrationally excited ground state according to paths b and d.

The case in which P is also produced in the triplet sensitized reaction is, unfortunately, less informative. The production of P upon specifically populating the T_1 state means simply that the latter can serve as a precursor for P. It does not demand that either c or d operates in the direct photolysis, that is, this result does not preclude paths a and b.

Quantum yield measurements allow one to extract a little more from sensitization experiments. For example, if it can be shown that the sum of the quantum yields for the production of P and the $S_1 \rightarrow S_0$ fluorescence is greater than the quantum yield of P under conditions where the T_1 state can be achieved with 100% quantum efficiency (this requires that the quantum yield of sensitizer triplets is unity), then paths other than c and d must be invoked for the direct photolysis.

A strong argument for the involvement of the triplet state of the substrate in the direct photolysis can be made if it can be shown that the ratio of the quantum yield of product in the sensitized reaction to that in direct photolysis is equal to the ratio of quantum yield for intersystem crossing of the sensitizer to that of the substrate. Of course, one must insure that all sensitizer triplets are transferred to substrate triplets.

Another situation in which a sensitization experiment can be used to argue for a triplet-state intermediate in the direct photolysis is the following. Suppose that more than one product is formed in a photochemical reaction. If the same products are formed in the same ratio in the triplet sensitized reaction, the triplet state is strongly suggested as an intermediate in the direct photolysis.

It is shown later (Section IV–2–B) that triplet-quenching experiments are usually more informative than sensitization experiments in learning about the multiplicity of the state involved in the photochemistry. However, companion sensitization and quenching experiments are usually desirable. Some examples of triplet-sensitization experiments in mechanism studies follow.

2-Methoxynaphthalene undergoes photodimerization in benzene solution (197). The triplet state of benzophenone ($E_T = 68.5$ kcal/mole) lies higher than that of 2-methoxynaphthalene ($E_T = 62$ kcal/mole). When a deaerated solution of 2-methoxynaphthalene and benzophenone in benzene is irradiated with light absorbed only by the latter, no dimer could be detected after doses much larger than necessary to observe the dimer in the direct photolysis. Thus one may safely conclude that the photodimerization of 2-methoxynaphthalene does not involve the interaction of a triplet 2-methoxynaphthalene with a ground-state molecule. Since there is no association of the naphthalenes in the ground state under the reaction conditions, and since path b of Figure 17 is precluded for a bimolecular reaction in solution, the most likely mechanism involves the interaction of the 2-methoxynaphthalene excited singlet with a ground state molecule probably through the intermediacy of the excimer.

The photolysis of ethylpyruvate in benzene (see previous section) proceeds with a quantum yield of 0.17 and ϕ_{isc} is 0.54 (194). The quantum yield of benzophenone ($\phi_{isc} = 1.00$) sensitized photolysis is 0.34. This data is consistent with a mechanism involving the triplet state of ethylpyruvate as an intermediate. Quenching experiments have proven this to be the case. It is noteworthy to point out that having shown a photoreaction proceeds by way of the triplet state through quenching experiments, sensitization experiments could be used to determine ϕ_{isc} for the substrate.

An elegant early use of triplet sensitization in the study of mechanism involved the question of reactivity versus electronic state for methylene, $:CH_2$. Several experiments (198), notably those of Frey (199), strongly suggested that photolysis of diazomethane CH_2N_2 in the gas phase leads to methylene in an excited singlet state which possessed extremely high chemical reactivity. For instance, the species produced in this way undergoes nonselective insertion into the C—H bonds of added hydrocarbons. If a large amount of inert gas is present, the very reactive singlet methylene can relax, through collisions, to a less reactive and more discriminate species proposed to be the triplet ground state. If the photolysis of diazomethane is carried out in solution using a solvent with which methylene can react, e.g., a hydrocarbon, reactivity very much like that of the proposed singlet species in the gas phase is observed. The gas phase and solution results are reconciled if in the solution the very reactive ("singlet") methylene reacts chemically with solvent much faster than it is "cooled" by collisions with solvent molecules. Spectroscopic studies and molecular orbital calculations supported the idea of a ground-state triplet methylene and a closely lying excited singlet state. However, there was an alternative rationale for the chemistry which assigned the two reactive states of methylene as vibrationally excited and vibrationally relaxed states of the same (ground) electronic level. The results of Hammond and Kopecky (200) resolved the question in favor of the singlet–triplet model. They examined the triplet-sensitized photolyses of diazomethane in various reactive solvents and found product distributions different from those obtained in the direct photolyses and which were close to those associated with triplet methylene.

De Mayo and co-workers (201) have shown through sensitization experiments that the photochemical cycloaddition of cyclopentenone to cyclohexene can proceed by way of an excited triplet state of cyclopentenone but not by way of the lowest triplet state. They observed that benzophenone ($E_T = 68.5$ kcal/mole) is ineffective as a sensitizer for the reaction, even though the triplet excitation is transferred to the cyclopentenone. On the other hand, acetophenone ($E_T = 73.5$ kcal/mole) and cyclopropylphenyl ketone ($E_T = 74$ kcal/mole) are effective sensitizers.

Choosing a Sensitizer (202). Primarily, a "good" triplet sensitizer must function efficiently in the steps shown in Eqs. (116)–(118). High efficiency in the energy-transfer step (Eq. (118)) is practically assured (in fluid solution) if the triplet-excitation energy of the sensitizer is higher than that of the substrate, the sensitizer triplet is sufficiently long lived ($\tau \geq 10^{-7}$ sec), and the concentration of the substrate (acceptor) is sufficiently high ($\geq 0.01 M$). In those cases where the course of the reaction is strongly dependent on the sensitizer-triplet energy, a more careful choice of sensitizer with respect to energy content may be necessary.

Most of the time one wants the sensitizer to absorb strongly at longer wavelengths than those at which the acceptor absorbs; that is, the lowest excited-singlet state of the sensitizer should lie lower than that of the substrate.

Thus, in most cases, a combination of high triplet energy, high intersystem-crossing efficiency (Eq. (117)), and long wavelength absorption is sought in a triplet sensitizer. This combination is often fulfilled in simple aromatic carbonyl compounds in which the lowest excited states both have the $n \to \pi^*$ configuration. It is no wonder that these compounds have been extensively used as sensitizers.

A number of compounds which have been used as sensitizers are listed in Table 12 together with their triplet excitation energies. Some intersystem crossing efficiencies are also listed. All of the compounds in the list absorb strongly at 3130 Å and shorter wavelengths; many absorb at 3650 Å, and some absorb as far into the visible as 5000 Å.

Of course characteristics other than energy content and triplet yield may

TABLE 12

Triplet Excitation Energies[a] of Selected Sensitizers

	E_T (kcal/mole)		
	Hydrocarbon[b] glass	Hydroxylic[c] glass	ϕ_{Isc}[d]
Propiophenone	74.6		1.00
Xanthone	74.2		
Acetophenone	73.6	76.3	1.00
1,3,5-Triacetylbenzene	73.3		
1,3-Diphenyl-2-propanone	72.2		
Benzaldehyde	71.9		
Triphenylmethyl phenyl ketone	70.8		
3-Benzophenone sulfonic acid sodium salt		70.2	
Carbazole	70.1	70	0.36
Diphenylene oxide	70.1		
Triphenylamine	70.1	70.1	0.88
Dibenzothiophene	69.7	69.3	
o-Dibenzoylbenzene	68.7		
Benzophenone	68.5	69.2	1.00
4,4'-Dichlorobenzophenone	68.0		
p-Diacetylbenzene	67.6		
Fluorene	67.6		0.31
9-Benzoylfluorene	66.8		
Triphenylene	66.6	67.2	0.95
p-Cyanobenzophenone	66.4		
Biphenyl	65.6		
Thioxanthone	65.5		
2-Triphenylene sulfonic acid sodium salt		65.0	
Phenylglyoxal	62.5		
Anthraquinone	62.4	63.3	0.90
Phenanthrene	62.2	61.8	0.76
α-Naphthoflavone	62.2		
Flavone	62.0		

(continued)

decide whether a particular compound would be useful as a triplet sensitizer for a particular photoreaction. For example solubility may be a problem. In preparative work one would want easy separation of sensitizer and photoproducts. Or, for example, the sensitizer may have to be noninterfering in some analytical determination. Most of the time one has a choice of several possible sensitizers in a certain energy range and can find one which would be appropriate. However, it is important to point out that a sensitizer of particular energy and with other particular characteristics can often be "tailormade." For instance, if water solubility is desired one could simply introduce

TABLE 12 (*continued*)

	E_T (kcal/mole)		
	Hydrocarbon[b] glass	Hydroxylic[c] glass	ϕ_{isc}[d]
Ethyl phenylglyoxalate	61.9	63.0	
4,4'-*Bis*(dimethylamino)benzophenone	61.0	62	1.00
Naphthalene	60.9	61	0.75
2,6-Naphthalene disulfonic acid disodium salt		60.0	
β-Naphthylphenyl ketone	59.6		
β-Naphthaldehyde	59.5		
β-Acetonaphthone	59.3	59.5	0.84
α-Naphthylphenyl ketone	57.5	57.7	
Chrysene	56.6		0.67
α-Acetonaphthone	56.4	58	
α-Naphthaldehyde	56.3	56.3	
5,12-Naphthacenequinone	55.8	55.8	
Biacetyl	54.9	57.2	
Acetylpropionyl	54.7	57.2	
Benzil	53.7	57.3	0.92
Fluorenone	53.3		0.93
1,2,5,6-Dibenzanthracene		52.2	0.89
1,2,3,4-Dibenzanthracene		50.8	
Pyrene	48.7		
Acridine	45.3		
Anthracene	42.0	42.6	0.75

[a] Adapted from ref. 202. These energies generally refer to the maximum of the 0–0 band of the phosphorescence measured at 77°K.

[b] In most cases a mixture of methylcyclohexane and isopentane.

[c] In most cases EPA, ether–isopentane–ethanol, 5:5:2.

[d] See Section IV–3–C.

a sulfonate group at an innocuous position in a compound having the desired energy content, etc.

The stability of the sensitizer is, of course, an important consideration since the efficiency of the overall reaction will be decreased if the sensitizer is lost, for instance, through a photoreaction. For example, many carbonyl compounds undergo photoreduction in solvents that serve as hydrogen atom donors, and so these compounds should be used only in solvents which are poor hydrogen donors such as benzene. A more subtle problem may arise if the sensitizer is converted to a compound having a low-lying triplet state since such a compound may act as a quencher and shut off the reaction entirely. It should be noted that sensitizers need not always be absolutely photostable since energy transfer to the substrate will often reduce the photoreactivity of the sensitizer.

Triphenylene is recommended as a "good" sensitizer for orienting experiments since it exhibits a relatively high excitation energy, undergoes intersystem crossing with high efficiency, absorbs at relatively long wavelengths, and is very photostable.

Sensitizer Triplet Energies. It is important to note how the triplet-excitation energies listed in Table 12 are defined and how they were extracted from the spectroscopic data.

One is interested in how much excitation energy is available in a triplet sensitizer for transfer to an acceptor. Now, if the transfer involves a vertical transition in the sensitizer, the largest amount of energy that may be transferred corresponds to the onset (blue edge) of the $T_1 \rightarrow S_0$ (phosphorescence) spectrum. Operationally the difficulty arises in defining the onsets of the spectra. Even if there were some convention, for example defining the onset as the energy at which the spectral intensity first reaches a value which is 1% of the maximum, the value would depend upon the quality of the spectrum. On the other hand, an energy that is easy to define experimentally for structured spectra is that of the maximum of the highest energy band in the spectrum. For systems of not too high symmetry this band is usually the 0–0 band.

All the energies listed in Table 12 were extracted from the phosphorescence spectra of the compounds dissolved in rigid glasses at 77°K. Some examples are shown in Figure 18. For almost all the compounds in Table 12 the position of the 0–0 band maximum is taken for the triplet-excitation energy. Thus the values underestimate the onsets by amounts which depend on the breadth of the band. For example, the 0–0 band maximum of the phosphorescence spectrum (Fig. 18) of acetophenone in a hydrocarbon glass is at 73.9 kcal/mole whereas the "onset" is much closer to 75.2 kcal/mole. For anthraquinone, the 0–0 band maximum lies at 62.4 kcal/mole and the "onset" lies at 63.5 kcal/mole. For most applications these discrepancies are insignificant. However, there are instances where fine resolution of sensitizer energies is important. Then one must study each sensitizer rather carefully. One approach that can be taken to decide about the triplet-excitation energy is to compare the phosphorescence and $S_0 \rightarrow T_1$ absorption spectra.

Many phosphorescence spectra exhibit little or no structure, for example that of benzil (Fig. 18). The values of the triplet-excitation energies listed in Table 12 for those compounds which exhibit such spectra correspond to the energy of the first maximum in the spectrum and so many significantly underestimate the onset energies.

Finally, it must be kept in mind that the phosphorescence spectra were obtained from samples in frozen solvents so that solvent reorganization about

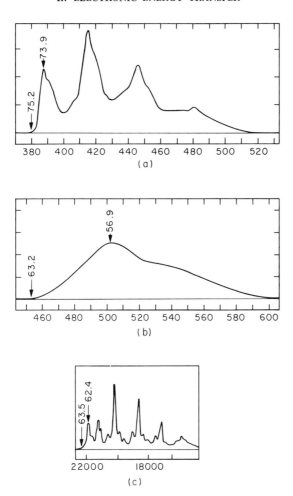

Fig. 18. Phosphorescence spectra of acetophenone (*a*), benzil (*b*), and anthraquinone (*c*) recorded from solutions of the compounds in hydrocarbon glasses at 77°K.

the excited state is prohibited. Such reorganization is not prohibited in fluid solution so that the excited triplet solute should be stabilized in fluid solution compared to the frozen glass (203). In addition, if the energy transfer process is a Franck-Condon process, the sensitizer arrives in the ground state destabilized with respect to solvation. Both of these factors reduce the amount of energy the sensitizer would be able to deliver in fluid solution compared to rigid solid solution. The magnitude of this kind of solvent effect depends in general upon the difference in charge distribution in the ground and excited state and upon the polarity of the solvent. Specific sensitizer–solvent interactions such as hydrogen bonding are, of course, very important if the interaction is strongly dependent upon the electronic state of the sensitizer. If one is particularly concerned with the energy of the sensitizer it would be best to use the phosphorescence spectrum obtained in a relatively non-interacting solvent like a saturated hydrocarbon and to use a hydrocarbon solvent for the experiments in fluid solution.

B. QUENCHING OF PHOTOCHEMICAL REACTIONS

$$A \xrightarrow{h\nu} A^{*(1)} \tag{125}$$

$$A^{*(1)} \longrightarrow A^{*(3)} \tag{126}$$

$$A^{*(1)} \longrightarrow P \tag{127}$$

$$A^{*(3)} \longrightarrow P \tag{128}$$

$$A^{*(1)} + Q \longrightarrow A + Q^{*(1)} \tag{129}$$

$$A^{*(3)} + Q' \longrightarrow A + Q^{*(3)} \tag{130}$$

In the following sections some practical applications of the quenching of excited states to solution photochemistry will be described. Specifically, the quenching process considered is electronic-energy transfer from the substrate to a quencher molecule. Either the excited singlet or the triplet state of the substrate can be quenched. Efficient quenching of the singlet state, of course, precludes intersystem crossing.

Three possible situations with regard to the relative dispositions of the substrate (A) and quencher (Q) lowest excited states are shown in Figure 19. In Figure 19a is shown the classical triplet quenching scheme, which is, of course, the classical scheme for transfer of only triplet excitation. If the situation is like that shown in Figure 19b, singlet and/or triplet excitation may be transferred from A to Q.

In Figure 19c is shown the case where only singlet excitation may be transferred from A to Q, but now triplet excitation may be transferred back to A. All three schemes will be encountered in the following brief review of the use of quenchers in organic photochemistry.

Avoiding the Triplet-State Reaction.   Suppose a substrate undergoes reactions from both its excited singlet and triplet states. It is possible to obtain only the singlet-state reaction by quenching the triplet reaction through triplet-energy transfer from the substrate to a suitable quencher. The classical triplet quenching scheme, Figure 19a, is, of course, the most straightforward. However, quenchers with excited-singlet states lying lower than the lowest excited singlet of the substrate (Fig. 19b) may be used in many cases, since

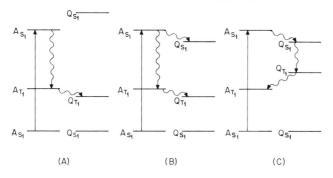

(A) (B) (C)

Fig. 19. Three different quenching schemes: (*a*) classical triplet quenching, only triplet excitation can be transferred from A to Q; (*b*) both singlet and triplet excitation transfer are energetically allowed; (*c*) Q can accept excitation from the singlet state of A but can return triplet excitation.

one may be able to employ the quencher at a concentration such that the substrate triplet is quenched with total efficiency but the substrate singlet is hardly affected (see Section IV–1).

Avoiding the Singlet-State Reaction. Quenching of the substrate excited-singlet state by energy transfer to a quencher molecule precludes intersystem crossing in the substrate. That is, any triplet-state reaction is also turned off unless the quencher can pass triplet excitation back to the substrate (Fig. 19*c*). Of course, the same result is attained by exciting only the quencher, which would be called a triplet sensitizer under these circumstances. However, these considerations are not trivial since they bring out an important point. In a triplet-sensitized reaction, one need not always insure that the substrate absorb none of the exciting light if efficient singlet excitation from the substrate to the sensitizer can be achieved.

Mechanistic Studies. The classical triplet quenching scheme shown by Figure 19*a* allows, in many cases, an easy determination of whether a particular photoproduct has a triplet-state precursor or is formed by way of a path which does not pass through a triplet state of the reactant molecule. The various possibilities are considered below. It is assumed that the only way the quencher can interact with the compound of interest is as an acceptor of its triplet excitation energy. It is also assumed that the quencher does not compete for the exciting light.

If a particular photoproduct is formed in the absence but not in the presence of the triplet quencher, then its formation must involve a triplet-state precursor. On the other hand, if the quantum yield of a photoproduct is unaffected by the presence of a triplet quencher one cannot automatically conclude that a triplet-state precursor is not involved in its formation. A triplet-state precursor may indeed be involved, but undergoes some process leading to the photoproduct at a rate which precludes quenching by energy transfer under the particular conditions which were chosen. The courses of action available to deal with this dichotomy include the following.

One can sometimes increase the quencher concentration to the point where every excited molecule would have a quencher as nearest neighbor at all times. Thus the quenching is no longer diffusion limited and can occur at the maximum rate. Under these conditions triplet-energy transfer should certainly compete favorably with any bimolecular chemical reaction of the substrate. Thus if a photoreaction involving a bimolecular primary process is not affected by addition of a quencher at very high concentration ($> 1M$), it most likely does not involve a pathway which includes the triplet state. However, if the primary process is unimolecular the same result is still interpretable in two ways, no triplet-state path or a very fast triplet reaction. The companion sensitization experiment (see Section IV–2–A) could yield definitive information. If the photoproduct is not produced upon sensitized formation of the triplet state of the substrate, then its formation cannot involve the triplet state. However, formation of the photoproduct upon triplet sensitization does not preclude paths for the direct photolysis which do not involve the triplet state. Thus, the latter result of sensitization does not resolve the ambiguous result of the quenching experiment. More complicated experiments are in order. The question has boiled down to deciding whether the substrate triplet state is quenchable at a rate faster than that of the primary process from the triplet state. If it is, then the ineffectiveness of the quencher to interfere with the direct photolysis would mean that no triplets are formed and that the formation of the photoproduct, of course, does not involve the triplet state. The experiment to do, then, is a combination of triplet sensitization and quenching. The substrate triplet is produced by transfer from a sensitizer in the absence and presence of the quencher. Of course, one is limited in the amount of quencher which can be used since it must not compete favorably with the substrate for sensitizer triplets. Now if, after accounting for quenching of sensitizer triplets by the quencher, there is quenching of the photoreaction, the ineffectiveness of the quencher in the direct photoreaction means that the pathway of the latter does not involve the triplet state.

An easy way to determine whether or not triplet-state quenching is occurring is sometimes afforded by the use of quenchers such as olefins and conjugated dienes which undergo easily detectable reactions (isomerizations and dimerizations) from their triplet states (see Sections III–7 and IV–2–B). Consider a case in which the quantum yield of a photoproduct is unaffected by a quencher but quencher chemistry characteristic of its triplet state is detected. One may then conclude that the photoproduct arises by paths which do not involve the lowest triplet state of the donor.

Finally, there are cases, of course, in which the same product arises by two or more paths, only some of which involve a triplet-state intermediate. The triplet quencher can, at most, block only the paths involving the triplet-state intermediate so that the fraction of the product arising from paths which do not involve the triplet state will survive. By assuring that all the triplet-state molecules are quenched by the added quencher one can determine the fraction of product due to other mechanisms.

Choosing a Triplet Quencher. The ideal specific-triplet quencher possesses a lowest-lying excited-singlet state which lies much higher than that of the substrate and a triplet state which lies lower than the lowest lying triplet state of the substrate. This insures nearly diffusion-controlled triplet quenching and no singlet quenching if no quenching modes other than energy transfer are important. Interaction of the quencher and excited substrate should lead to nothing other than electronic energy transfer. For simplicity in quantitative studies the quencher should not compete with the substrate for exciting light. Usually the triplet-excitation energy is unimportant as long as it is lower than that of the substrate. But there are occasions when a quencher possessing a well-defined, triplet-excitation energy is required. The excited quencher should be chemically inert and should be capable of shedding excitation energy very quickly. Other requirements, e.g., solubility, specific chemical compatibility, etc., will differ depending on the application. Of course, the quencher should not interfere with the analytical technique or workup procedure to be used.

Obviously compounds with relatively low-lying triplet states and large singlet–triplet splittings are prime candidates for useful triplet quenchers. Two kinds of compounds, olefins, conjugated dienes and higher polyenes, and aromatic hydrocarbons, generally fulfill these requirements. As expected, most of the compounds which have been used as triplet quenchers belong to one of these classes.

Conjugated Dienes and Higher Polyenes. Conjugated dienes and higher polyenes exhibit large energy gaps (~ 30 kcal/mole) between the onsets of their $S_0 \to S$ absorption spectra and their $S_0 \to T$ absorption spectra. The dienes have $S_0 \to T$ onsets at 60 kcal/mole or less (205,206) and do not absorb significantly above 2800 Å (Table 12). This characteristic makes these compounds extremely useful as triplet quenchers. However, in many other respects, they are far from ideal. But if they are used with care, most complications can be avoided. A detailed discussion of the use of conjugated dienes as triplet quenchers is given below.

Hammond, Liu, Turro, and co-workers (131,207,208) have shown that several alicyclic dienes can be excited to triplet states by energy transfer from sensitizers having triplet energies much lower than those required to excite the dienes in a vertical fashion as judged by the $S_0 \to T_1$ absorption spectra.

On the other hand, the cyclic dienes, such as cyclohexadiene, behave nor-mally. An interesting model which explains these apparent energy dis-crepancies (see Figs. 20 and 21) has come out of their investigations of the triplet-sensitized isomerization of the 1,3-pentadienes (131), and the triplet-sensitized dimerizations of isoprene (207), butadiene (207), cyclopentadiene (208), and 1,3-cyclohexadiene (209).

The first important feature of the diene model (Fig. 20) derived by Ham-mond and co-workers is the great increase in bond order between the central carbon atoms which occurs on excitation to the lowest triplet (and presumably the lowest excited singlet) state. In the ground state the central C—C bond is essentially a single bond and a fast dynamic equilibrium occurs between the s-trans- and s-cis-conformers of alicyclic dienes. Nonbonded interactions in the s-cis-conformer usually make it the less favored form. In the triplet state the central C—C bond is nearly a full double bond. This is predicted by

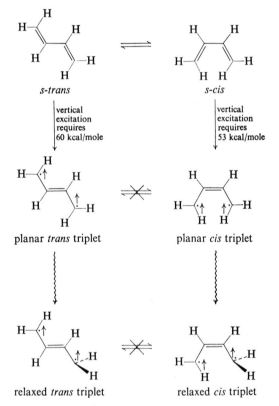

Fig. 20. The Hammond model for the lowest triplet state of an alicyclic diene (see ref. 207).

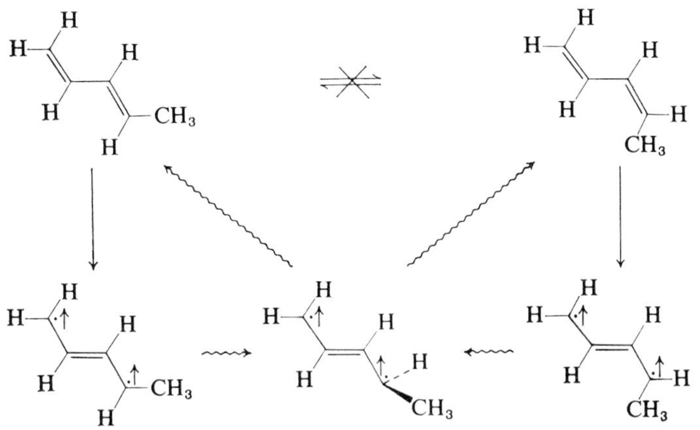

Fig. 21. The Hammond model for the triplet sensitized isomerization of 1,3-pentadiene (piperylene).

molecular orbital theory in every approximation. All the treatments show that the lowest triplet state is attained by promoting an electron from an orbital which is antibonding between the central carbons to one which is bonding between these centers. Interconversion of the cis- and trans-triplets is presumed to be a high-energy process and does not occur at room temperature. The important observation is that the planar cis-triplet is much less energetic than the planar trans-triplet probably due to some favorable 1,4-interaction in the former. This results in a much lower spectroscopic or vertical excitation energy (that required to excite the planar ground state molecule to the planar excited state) for the s-cis-diene (~ 53 kcal/mole) than for the s-trans (~ 60 kcal/mole). Excitation to the planar triplet is what is observed in the $S_0 \rightarrow T_1$ absorption spectra (see Fig. 22). The vibrational progression in the spectra is probably due to central C—C stretching vibration in the excited state (the spacing is about 1400 cm^{-1} for butadiene). The $S_0 \rightarrow T_1$ absorption spectra of alicyclic dienes exhibit onsets at about 60 kcal/mole (Table 12A). That is the s-cis spectrum is not observed. But this is simply because usually only a small fraction ($\sim 1\%$) of the diene has the s-cis conformation. Thus, the vertical excitation energies listed in Table 12A for alicyclic dienes is that for the s-trans-conformer. And the fact that, for example, butadiene is very efficient at quenching triplets with energies as low as 53 kcal/mole is due to the s-cis-conformer present.

There is some evidence that the planar triplet is not the lowest energy form (131,207). Hammond and co-workers have proposed that twisting about one of the essential single bonds in the triplet relieves electron–electron repulsion leading to a lower energy (207). Twisting only one of the terminal

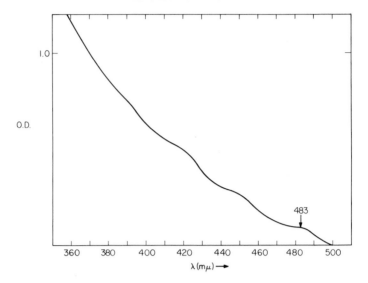

Fig. 22. The singlet–triplet absorption spectrum of 2,4-hexadien-1-ol dissolved in ethyl iodide. The maximum of the longest wavelength band is taken for the triplet excitation energy, in this case 59.5 kcal/mole.

TABLE 12A

Vertical Triplet Energies of Some Dienes and
Higher Polyenes

Compound	$\Delta E(S_0 \rightarrow T_1)$[a,b] (kcal/mole)
Isoprene	60.1
2,4-Hexadien-1-ol[c]	59.5
1,3-Butadiene	59.3
trans-1,3-Pentadiene	58.8
Chloroprene	58.6
Cyclopentadiene	58.3
1-Chlorobutadiene[c]	57.4
cis-1,3-Pentadiene	56.9
1-Methoxybutadiene[c]	56.6
1,3-Cyclohexadiene	53.5, 52.5
trans,trans-1,3,5-Hexatriene	47.5
1,3,5,7-Octatetraene (all trans)	39.0

[a] Maximum of the longest wavelength band observed in the $S_0 \rightarrow T_1$ absorption spectrum (oxygen perturbed).

[b] Data of Evans (reference 205).

[c] Data of Kellogg and Simpson (reference 206).

groups takes advantage of the resonance energy of the allyl system which is left behind. The dienes, therefore, are possible candidates for acceptors which can undergo nonvertical excitation (see Section III-7). Nonvertical-excitation transfer to dienes has been invoked to explain sensitized dimerizations of dienes using low-energy triplet sensitizers. However, alternative explanations involving higher sensitizer triplet states have some experimental support.

In summary, there is a "fuzziness" in the triplet excitation energies of alicyclic dienes. This is because of the existence of *cisoid* and *transoid* forms with different excitation energies and, less important, the possibility of non-vertical excitations. One should be cautious, then, in using dienes as triplet quenchers if the quencher triplet energy needs to be well defined. Fortunately this is usually not the case.

A more important complication in the use of dienes as triplet quenchers is that they can lead, at high concentrations, to efficient quenching of singlet states. For example, Hammond and co-workers have shown that the 1,3-pentadienes, isoprene, and 1,3-cyclohexadiene quench the fluorescence of such aromatic hydrocarbons as naphthalene, 1,2-benzanthracene, and 1,2,5,6-dibenzanthracene (139,186). The Stern-Volmer plot for the quenching of 1-methylnaphthalene fluorescence in benzene solution by 1,3-pentadiene (a mixture of isomers) is shown in Figure 23.

Efficient quenching of the singlet states of aromatic hydrocarbons by dienes requires high concentrations of the latter compared to the concentration necessary to completely quench the corresponding triplets. This is not

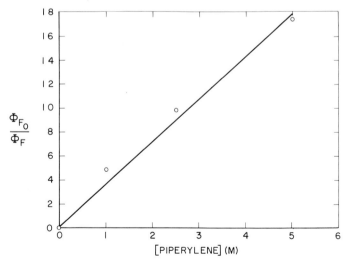

Fig. 23. The Stern-Volmer plot for the quenching of 1-methylnaphthalene fluorescence in benzene solution by 1,3-pentadiene (mixture of isomers) (see ref. 139).

because the specific rates for singlet quenching are low. On the contrary, they are surprisingly high; for example, the specific rate constant for the quenching of naphthalene singlets by 1,3-cyclohexadiene in benzene solution was found to be 2.2×10^9 liters mole^{-1} sec^{-1} (139)! The efficiencies at low diene concentration are relatively low compared to those for triplet quenching because the singlet-state lifetimes are short. This is an important point. A review of Table 11 will show that even if both singlet and triplet quenching occur at the same rate it is possible to find a quencher concentration such that the triplet is 99% quenched and the singlet only 1% quenched if the triplet lifetime is 10^4 times longer than the singlet lifetime, a common occurrence. Thus, careful control of the diene concentration will usually remove any uncertainty about singlet quenching. However, complications due to singlet quenching may well be a problem if one is forced to use high quencher concentrations in order to compete with, for example, a fast unimolecular process in the excited substrate.

The quenching of the excited singlet states of aromatic hydrocarbons by dienes is an interesting process. Note that in the examples mentioned above the excited singlet levels of the aromatic hydrocarbons lie lower in energy than the long wavelength "cutoff" of the absorption spectra of the dienes used. Thus, if the quenching involves electronic energy transfer, a nonvertical transition in the diene is necessary. However, there is no evidence that the quenching leads to electronic excitation of the diene. As a matter of fact what evidence exists points to the opposite conclusion (184). The quenching probably involves complex formation between the excited aromatic hydrocarbon and the diene—an exciplex, really. Efficient radiationless decay to ground-state species would then occur from the complex (184). Another possibility is that the exciplex can lead into adduct formation. Photoadducts of dienes with benzene, naphthalene, and some naphthalene derivatives have been found (184). The dienes quench the fluorescence from these compounds (139,184,186) and it is known that adduct formation does not involve the attack of triplet diene on the aromatic hydrocarbon.

A nontrivial characteristic of the dienes listed in Table 12A is that they are all liquids at room temperature and are very soluble in most organic solvents. Thus they are very convenient to work with and may even be used neat. It is also important to mention that the 1,3-pentadienes or isoprene mixed with ether and alcohol form very good glasses at 77°K (222). 2,4-Hexadien-1-ol is sufficiently soluble (about $10^{-3}M$) in water to be used as a triplet quencher in that solvent (214). Lamola synthesized the diene 22 for use as a quencher at high concentrations in water.

Olefins. Several olefins have been used as triplet quenchers by various investigators (Table 13). The simple aliphatic olefins have very large singlet–triplet gaps but have high triplet-excitation energies and so are of limited

$$H_3C \diagdown \overset{\overset{\displaystyle H}{|}}{C} = \overset{\overset{\displaystyle H}{|}}{C} \diagup CH_2N^+(CH_3)_3$$

(the structure shows H above and below each of the two central carbons, with Cl⁻ beneath the $CH_2N^+(CH_3)_3$ group)

(22)

TABLE 13

Olefins Useful as Triplet Quenchers

Compound	E_T (kcal/mole)
trans-Stilbene	49[a]
cis-Stilbene	57[a]
Styrene	61.5[b]
Diphenylacetylene	62.5[b]

[a] See Section III–7.
[b] Data of Evans, ref. 205.

utility. The phenyl-substituted olefins have much lower triplet excitation energies but smaller singlet–triplet splittings.

The olefins, like the dienes, suffer from poor definition of the triplet-excitation energies. For example, despite the fact that the vertical triplet-excitation energy of *cis*-stilbene is 57 kcal'mole ($S_0 \rightarrow T_1$ absorption spectrum) it is capable of quenching triplet donors with excitation energies as low as 42 kcal/mole. The quenching mechanism probably involves the promotion of the *cis*-stilbene to a twisted triplet state (nonvertical excitation, see Section III–7). In addition, the *cis–trans* isomerization of the olefin is usually the result of exciting it to the triplet state. Since the triplet-excitation energies of the isomers are usually different, this leads to a change in the quencher excitation energy during the course of the reaction. Again, these considerations are important only if it is necessary to employ a quencher with a well-defined triplet excitation energy.

Aromatic Hydrocarbons. The aromatic hydrocarbons exhibit singlet–triplet splittings of about 20 kcal/mole and, therefore, should be useful as triplet quenchers in many instances. Furthermore, the singlet and triplet energies are very well defined so that some of the complications associated with the use of dienes as quenchers are precluded. The aromatic hydrocarbons show fair photochemical stability in solution. Although some of the hydrocarbons undergo photodimerization (e.g., anthracene), this reaction is relatively inefficient if only the triplet state is excited. The aromatic hydrocarbons do possess long-lived triplet states in solution ($\sim 10^{-3}$ sec) so that electronic excitation energy is "around" for a long time after the transfer and could lead to undesirable side effects. But this should be a rare occurrence.

Pertinent data for several useful compounds is given in Table 14. 1-Methylnaphthalene is a liquid at room temperature and is miscible with benzene, for example, and can be used in high concentrations or even neat (although it

TABLE 14

Some Aromatic Hydrocarbons Useful
as Triplet Quenchers

Compound	E_T (kcal/mole)
Biphenyl	~ 70 [c]
Phenanthrene	62.2 [b]
Naphthalene	60.9 [b]
1-Methylnaphthalene	60.1 [b]
Anthracene	42.5 [a]
Naphthacene	29.3 [d]
Azulene	31–39 [d]

[a] From $S_0 \rightarrow T_1$ absorption spectra; data of Evans (205).
[b] Data of Herkstroeter, Lamola, and Hammond (202).
[c] See ref. 143.
[d] Data of Lamola, Herkstroeter, Dalton, and Hammond (225).

is difficult to highly purify). Azulene has found extensive use as a triplet quencher mostly because of its low triplet energy (31–39 kcal/mole) which, unfortunately, is not well defined. Another desirable feature of the azulene triplet is that it is very short lived and so does not act as a sensitizer. Unfortunately, azulene possesses a low-lying singlet state. Actually the reason azulene can be used as a triplet quencher at all is because it has a large "window" in its absorption spectrum (3100–4000 Å) through which one can excite the donor without exciting the azulene. However, it must be kept in mind that azulene may act as a singlet quencher at sufficiently high concentration if the donor possesses a higher lying singlet state.

Rare-Earth Ions. It has been demonstrated that lanthanide ions (nonchelated) are acceptors of triplet excitation from organic sensitizers in solution (210–212). For example, the characteristic $f \rightarrow f$ fluorescence from Sm^{3+}, Dy^{3+}, Tb^{3+}, and Eu^{3+} can be observed on exclusive excitation of aromatic carbonyl compounds in solutions of the latter and the lanthanide ion in acetic acid (211,212).

Several features of the rare-earth ions make them potentially very useful as triplet quenchers. The quenching of the photoreaction could be correlated with the sensitized fluorescence of the quencher, a very nice and easy check. Of especial importance for photobiology, the lanthanide ions can be used in water solution (213). Finally, the rare-earth ions show only weak and narrow absorption bands throughout the visible and ultraviolet so that it is very easy to avoid direct excitation of the quencher.

Unfortunately at this time not enough is known about the details of excitation transfer from organic sensitizers to rare-earth ions in solution to allow their routine use. One should, then, proceed with caution. For example, energy matching is very important (211,212) since the ions possess narrow and well-separated absorption bands. The rates of transfer are not known. Finally, the ions should be capable of inducing (upon collision) intersystem crossings; the external heavy-atom effect. Thus the ions may serve both as singlet and triplet quenchers at high concentrations. Energy transfer from excited singlets to the ions may also occur.

Some Examples of the Use of Quenchers. The following three examples demonstrate the use of quenchers in the control of photochemical reactions and in obtaining information about the multiplicity and reactivity of excited-state precursors.

The photolysis of uracil in aqueous solution leads to dimers **21** and the photohydration product **22**. Addition of 2,4-hexadienol (214) or oxygen (215)

(21)   **(22)**
(mixture of isomers)

leads to quenching of dimer production but has no effect on the photo-hydration. This demonstrates that the dimers arise by way of the uracil triplet state but that the photohydration reaction does not involve the triplet state. Companion triplet sensitization experiments led to the same conclusions. It was of interest to investigate the photohydration reaction in detail (kinetics, pH dependence, etc.). This could be done most simply if the photodimerization could be turned off. Of course, this can be easily accomplished by having sufficient triplet quencher present. The hexadienol can not be used in this regard since at concentrations high enough to completely quench the photodimerization the drive absorbs a good deal of the excitation light. Burr and co-workers (216) successfully used oxygen to quench the dimerization. They ran the photoreactions with oxygen gas bubbling through the solutions and were able to study the photohydration kinetics without interference from photodimerization. It is important to point out that oxygen is not a specific triplet quencher; that is, oxygen is capable of quenching excited-singlet states too. However, for the case of uracil in aqueous solution at room temperature, the excited-singlet lifetime is sufficiently short ($< 10^{-11}$ sec) to preclude quenching by the oxygen. The triplet state has a 10^{-5} sec lifetime.

A nice example of the control of a photochemical reaction by a compound which acts both as a singlet quencher and a triplet sensitizer is afforded by the photodimerization of coumarin in the presence of benzophenone. The photodimerization of coumarin **23** is interesting because different techniques for carrying out the reaction lead to different dimers. The direct irradiation of coumarin in ethanol yields the *cis* head-to-head dimer **24** with low quantum

yield (217). Hammond et al. (219) have proposed that this dimer is formed by addition of excited-singlet coumarin to a ground-state molecule most likely involving an excimer intermediate. The benzophenone-sensitized reaction proceeds with high efficiency to give the *trans* head-to-head dimer **25** (218). Production of this dimer must involve the triplet state of coumarin produced by triplet-energy transfer from benzophenone which is initially excited (3660 Å). However, the *trans* head-to-head dimer is produced with good quantum yield in solutions containing small amounts of benzophenone even when all the light is absorbed by the coumarin (3130 Å). Hammond and co-workers (219) have proposed that this control is achieved because benzophenone acts to quench the coumarin singlets but then after intersystem crossing transfers triplet excitation back to the coumarin. Figure 24 shows

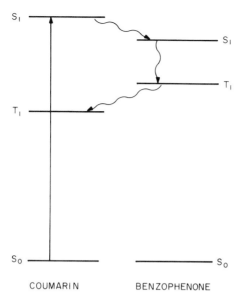

COUMARIN   BENZOPHENONE

Fig. 24. The relative dispositions of the lowest excited-singlet states and the lowest triplet states of coumarin and benzophenone. Benzophenone can act as a singlet quencher but triplet sensitizer for coumarin (see ref. 219).

that the lowest lying excited states of coumarin and benzophenone are favorably located for such a double excitation transfer.

A very elegant example of the use of triplet quenchers has been provided by Wagner and Hammond (220) who examined the effects of 1,3-pentadiene (piperylene) on the Norrish Type II photoelimination reaction (Eq. (125)) of a number of aliphatic and aromatic ketones. It is proposed that the reaction

$$
\underset{R_1 CCH_2CH_2CHR_2R_3}{\overset{O}{\overset{\|}{}}} \xrightarrow{h\nu}
\left[
R_1 - \overset{\overset{H}{|}}{\underset{\cdot}{\overset{O}{\underset{|}{C}}}} - CH_2CH_2\underset{\cdot}{CR_2R_3}
\right]
$$

$$
\underset{R_1 CCH_3}{\overset{O}{\overset{\|}{}}} \longleftarrow \underset{R_1 C = CH_2}{\overset{OH}{\overset{|}{}}} + CH_2 = CR_2R_3 \qquad (125)
$$

proceeds by way of the diradical formed by abstraction of a γ-hydrogen by the carbonyl oxygen, in an n,π^* excited state. The results of the quenching study for two compounds, 2-hexanone and butyrophenone, are shown in Figure 25 which is a plot of ϕ_0/ϕ, the ratio of the quantum yields without and with piperylene present as a function of the piperylene concentration. The compounds behave quite differently. The photoreaction involving butyrophenone is essentially completely quenched with $0.01 M$ piperylene. On the

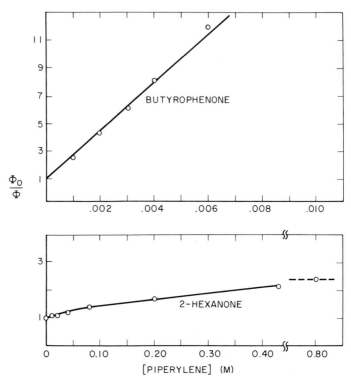

Fig. 25. Stern-Volmer plots of the piperylene quenching of the photoclevage of butyrophenone and 2-hexanone (see ref. 220).

other hand, the piperylene quenching is much less efficient for 2-hexanone
and levels off at high concentrations to the limit $\phi_0/\phi = 2.38$. This residual
reactivity at high quencher concentration is due to the singlet state. Thus for
2-hexanone (and other aliphatic ketones as well) the type II cleavage reaction
proceeds both by way of the lowest excited-singlet state and the triplet state.
In the case of the butyrophenone (and other aryl ketones as well) all the type
II cleavage proceeds by way of the triplet state. Reaction at the excited-singlet
level is evidently precluded because of the very fast intersystem crossing in
the aryl ketones. The linear portions of the quenching curves yield rate data.
The Stern-Volmer expression for the quenching of a unimolecular process
applies (see Section IV–1), that is $\phi_T^0/\phi_T = 1 + (k_q[Q]/k_r)$, where k_q is the
quenching rate constant, k_r is the rate of the primary process, and [Q] is the
quencher concentration. The quenching rate was assumed to be the diffusion-
controlled rate and so approximate reaction rates could be determined from
the slopes of the quenching plots. One can see immediately from Figure 25
that the reaction rate constant is much greater for 2-hexanone than for

butyrophenone. Wagner and Hammond found $k_r = 1 \times 10^9 \text{ sec}^{-1}$ and $3 \times 10^6 \text{ sec}^{-1}$ for 2-hexanone and butyrophenone, respectively. Thus Wagner and Hammond were able to extract from these relatively simple quenching experiments a large amount of quantitative information about the reactivities of both the lowest excited singlet and triplet states of aliphatic and aromatic ketones in the Norrish type II reaction.

C. RATES OF PRIMARY PROCESSES AND LIFETIMES OF EXCITED-STATE PRECURSORS

The use of intermolecular electronic energy transfer to determine rates of primary processes and lifetimes of excited molecules in solution has been described in Section IV-1. Very complicated schemes can be developed for a particular case. However, these would simply be combinations and variations of the simple schemes described.

As was pointed out in Section IV–1 the great utility of energy transfer experiments in fluid solution in determining rate constants is that the transfer rate is known if it is the diffusion-controlled rate. Therefore, the other rates can be determined from steady state measurements on quantum yields. The problem, then, is to ensure that the energy transfer step is, in fact, a diffusion-controlled process.

If one is interested in an "order-of-magnitude" determination it is probably always safe to take triplet-excitation transfer in fluid solution to be the diffusion-controlled when the triplet energy of the donor exceeds that of the acceptor by 3–4 kcal/mole or more (see Section III–3). The rates for such "exothermic" transfers are indeed always found to be near the diffusion-controlled rate but deviations are serious if one is interested in more accurate determinations.

The clearest discussions about the use of triplet quenchers to obtain kinetic data and the question of the rate of the energy transfer in step have been provided by Wagner (221). He points out that there are two tests one can sometimes perform to determine whether or not triplet-excitation transfer occurs at the diffusion-controlled rate for a particular donor–acceptor pair. One test, of course, is to vary the viscosity of the solvent. The diffusion-controlled transfer rate should be inversely proportional to the solvent viscosity. However, it is not always possible to change the solvent without affecting processes other than the excitation transfer, e.g., the primary photochemical process.

Wager (221) derived the modified Stern-Volmer expression given by Eq. (126) where K_q is the bimolecular rate constant for quenching, [Q] is the

$$\phi_0/\phi = (1 + K_q[\text{Q}]\tau_0)/(1 - \alpha u) \qquad (126)$$

concentration of quencher, τ_0 is the lifetime of the excited molecule being quenched, u is the fraction of the molecules which have at least one quencher molecule as a nearest neighbor at all times, and α is the probability that the energy will be transferred from the excited molecule to the quencher during the lifetime of a solution encounter. When the transfer is diffusion controlled $\alpha = 1$. Then at moderate values of u the quenching curves should curve upwards until the limiting value is obtained at $u \sim 1$. Under these conditions every excited molecule is born with a quencher as nearest neighbor and $\phi_0/\phi = 1 + k_{et}\tau_0$ where k_{et} is the rate of energy transfer (unimolecular) between the neighbors. Values for k_{et} have only been approximated but should be very high ($> 10^{10}$ sec^{-1}) for "exothermic" transfers. Thus one would observe the curvature if the decay rate $(1/\tau_0)$ of the triplet donor is comparable to k_{et}. That is to say, one must have a measurable ϕ_0/ϕ at moderate values of u. Thus this test is applicable only for donors which undergo fast unimolecular reactions. Two pretty examples have been provided by Wagner and are shown in Figure 26. Figure 26a is a Stern-Volmer plot for 2,4-hexadien-1-ol quenching of the photolysis of γ-methylvalerophenone in t-butyl alcohol. The dotted line is the extrapolated linear slope obtained at low concentrations of quencher and the curved solid line is that predicted from Eq. (126) taking $\alpha = 1$ and values of u calculated by assuming a random distribution of molecules in solution. It had been shown in other studies that the rate constants for quenching of triplet valerophenone in tertiary alcohols by conjugated dienes vary inversely with solvent viscosity indicating they are diffusion controlled. Figure 26b is a Stern-Volmer plot for the quenching of the triplet state of γ-phenylbutyrophenone by cis-1,3-pentadiene in pentane solution. The linearity of the plot persists to nearly neat quencher. This linear behavior is expected for low values of α since Eq. (126) collapses quite rapidly to Eq. (94) as α becomes less than unity. In this case α is estimated to be about 0.3.

Of course, these tests are qualitative. If one requires transfer rate data to high accuracy one must resort to direct determinations using some pulsing technique, flash photolysis in the case of triplet excitation transfer.

Finally, it is important to emphasize the complications due to static quenching at high quencher concentration so eloquently pointed out by Wagner (221). As stated above, at high quencher concentrations where the excited molecule of interest is "born" with a quencher as nearest neighbor, the quenching is not limited by diffusion. Therefore, values of rate constants determined from quenching studies at high quencher concentrations require careful interpretation.

3. Applications in Spectroscopy

A. DETECTION AND IDENTIFICATION OF EXCITED SPECIES

Low Temperature Emission Spectroscopy. An easy way to distinguish between fluorescence and abnormally short-lived phosphorescence without

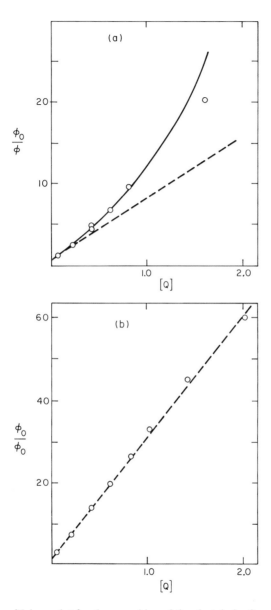

Fig. 26(a) Stern-Volmer plot for the quenching of the photolysis of γ-methylvalerophenone in t-butyl alcohol by 2,4-hexadien-1-ol. The dotted line is the extrapolated slope found at low quencher concentrations; the curved solid line is that calculated from equation 126 (see text).

(b) Stern-Volmer plot for the quenching of the photolysis of γ-phenylbutyrophenone by cis-1,3-pentadiene in pentane solution. (From reference 221.)

resorting to lifetime measurements is to introduce a triplet quencher into the system. The lowest triplet state of the quencher must lie below the short wavelength cutoff of the emission in question, while the lowest excited singlet state of the quencher should lie well above this energy and, for easiest interpretation, the quencher should not absorb the exciting light. If the emission is attenuated in the presence of the quencher it can be assigned as a phosphorescence; if it is unaffected it is a fluorescence.

Significant attenuation of donor phosphorescence in rigid media requires a rather large concentration of acceptor and complete quenching would require every donor molecule to possess at least one acceptor molecule as a nearest neighbor. In this regard acyclic dienes ($E_T \sim 60$ kcal/mole) and trienes ($E_T \sim 50$ kcal/mole) are excellent candidates. For example, mixtures containing up to 33% 1,3-pentadiene or isoprene with 3-methylpentane or with ether and ethanol form clear glasses when frozen at 77°K. These glasses are transparent (1 cm path) to nearly 3000 Å. It has been demonstrated (222) that the phosphorescence of benzophenone ($E_T = 69$ kcal/mole) is completely quenched in a glass containing 1:1:1 isoprene–ether–ethanol.

An example of the application of this technique concerns the blue emission (~ 80 kcal/mole) observed from cis-stilbenes in rigid media at 77°K (222). The emission had been assigned as both fluorescence and phosphorescence. It was found, however, that the intensity of the emission is unattenuated on going to glasses containing up to 33% 1,3-pentadiene (222). Therefore the emitting state must be a singlet.

This technique also provides for easy separation of overlapping fluorescence and phosphorescence spectra. Totally efficient triplet quenching as described above would leave only the fluorescence. Alternatively, one could obtain just the phosphorescence through sensitization with a suitable triplet donor. The emission spectra of biacetyl, anisil and benzil were originally analyzed using these techniques (223).

Flash Photolysis. The effect of added triplet quencher on the lifetime of a transient observed by the flash photolytic technique provides an easy method for deciding whether the transient is a triplet-state species or some chemical intermediate (radical, ion, or short-lived isomer). For example, the transient spectrum observed by flashing benzophenone in benzene solution was assigned to the ketyl radical rather than triplet benzophenone ($E_T = 69$ kcal/mole) because the lifetime of the species was found to be unaffected by the presence of naphthalene ($E_T = 61$ kcal/mole).

Since one measures lifetimes and not intensities using this technique, competition by the quencher for exciting light is usually of no concern. However, one must be sure that the quencher is specific for triplets; that is, it must be unreactive towards possible chemical intermediates.

Chemical Detection of Excited Triplet Molecules. With few exceptions, organic compounds do not exhibit phosphorescence in fluid solution. The triplet states of these compounds can often be detected in absorption by the flash photolytic technique. The application of lasers in this technique makes possible the detection of transients of lifetimes as short as 1 nsec. There is an often simpler method of detecting excited triplet molecules in solution which can yield nearly as much information. The compound of interest is simply tested as a sensitizer for a system which undergoes detectable photo-chemistry from its triplet state. The existence of excited triplet molecules of interest is indicated if the photochemical reaction occurs. Quantitative determinations can lead to such information as the intersystem crossing efficiency of the compound of interest (see Section IV-3-C), the lifetime of its triplet state (see Sections IV–1 and IV–2-C), and even its triplet excitation energy (see next section).

B. TRIPLET EXCITATION ENERGIES

The determination of the triplet-excitation energy of a compound that does not phosphoresce can be determined with fairly good accuracy by using triplet–triplet energy transfer. A number of examples have been reported in which triplet energy transfer was the only method available since observation of the $S_0 \rightarrow T_1$ absorption spectrum even in perturbing environments did not give results or gave equivocal results. In some instances the energy transfer approach was used to clear up equivocal or erroneous phosphorescence data. The various approaches in the use of triplet energy transfer to determine triplet excitation energies are all relatively simple.

The basic idea common to the examples which are given below is that the compound of interest is used as the donor or acceptor of triplet excitation energy and the relative rates of energy transfer to or from a series of com-pounds of known triplet energies which bracket that of the compound of interest are determined usually in fluid solution. The various methods of determining the transfer rates differentiate the various approaches which have been taken.

Figure 6 (Section III–3) can serve to illustrate the most direct approach. The rate of quenching of the biacetyl triplet in benzene solution is constant and nearly diffusion controlled for quenchers whose triplet energies are less than about 50 kcal/mole, and drops off very quickly to less than four orders of magnitude smaller for quenchers whose triplet energies are greater than about 61 kcal/mole. These values bracket the triplet energy of biacetyl (55 kcal/mole) and one would be close to the correct energy by taking the mid-point between the brackets. This particular case is not a perfect example since the quenching rates were determined by monitoring the biacetyl phos-phorescence intensity. The triplet energy could, of course, be determined directly from the phosphorescence spectrum. Were biacetyl not phosphorescent in fluid solution, as is the case with almost all organic compounds, the quenching rates could be determined by monitoring its triplet–triplet absorption using the flash-photolytic technique. Alternatively, one could use biacetyl as the quencher and examine the rate of quenching of a series of donors whose triplet–triplet absorption could be monitored. The latter approach was used by Lamola, Herkstroeter, Dalton, and Hammond (225) to bracket the triplet energy of azulene. The azulene triplet has not been detected by any direct spectroscopic method and so it was used as a quencher for the triplets of anthracene and naphthacene in benzene at room temperature. The decay of the anthracene and naphthacene triplets with and without added azulene at various concentrations was determined by the flash-photolytic technique. The rate constant for the quenching of the anthracene triplet ($E_T = 42$ kcal/mole) by azulene was found to be 7.2×10^9 liters mole^{-1} sec^{-1} and that for the quenching of triplet naphthacene ($E_T = 29$ kcal/mole) $\sim 10^7$ liters mole^{-1} sec^{-1}. Consequently the investigators inferred that the excitation energy of the azulene triplet lies between 31 and 39 kcal/mole. It is interesting to note that Pariser (226) calculated the value to be 33.7 kcal/mole.

The shape of the quenching rate constant versus donor triplet energy plot (the quencher is constant) gives, in addition to information about the spectroscopic triplet energy of the quencher, information about the geometry of the relaxed triplet (see Section III–7).

If the compound of interest undergoes a chemical reaction from the triplet state, the transfer of triplet energy from a series of donors can be examined by monitoring the chemistry. A very pretty example of this approach to the determination of the triplet excitation energy of a species was provided by Hardham and Hammond (227). It had been determined that formation of the triplet state of the benzene–maleic anhydride charge-transfer complex **26** leads to the benzene–maleic anhydride adduct **27** (Eq. (127)). The triplet state of the complex can be reached by interaction of triplet maleic anhydride with benzene, intersystem crossing from the excited singlet state of the complex, or excitation of the ground state complex to the triplet state by energy transfer from a triplet donor. Attempts to observe the triplet complex in emission and absorption failed. However, its vertical triplet energy could be estimated from the relative quantum yields for adduct formation induced by triplet sensitizers of various energies. The experimental results are listed in Table 15. A lower limit of 66.5 kcal/mole can be placed on the E_T of the complex from these data. It was also shown that maleic anhydride quenches the photo-reduction (with benzhydrol) of benzophenone ($E_T = 68.5$ kcal/mole) in benzene solution but not in cyclohexane–acetone, or carbon tetrachloride. From the rate of quenching an E_T value of about 68 kcal/mole could be extracted for the maleic anhydride–benzene complex. Uncomplexed

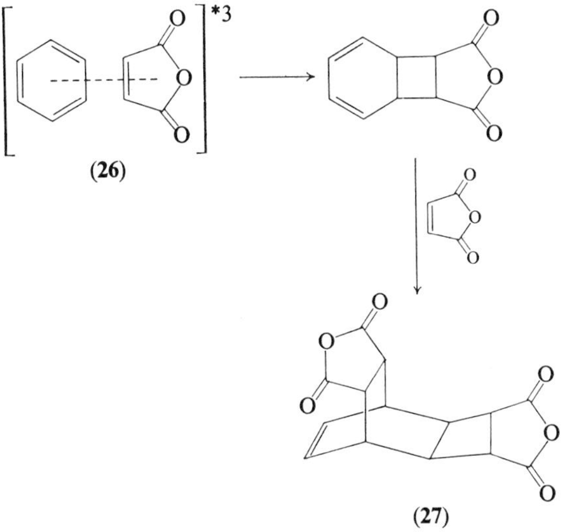

(26)

(127)

(27)

TABLE 15

Yields of Addition Product Obtained by Irradiating Solutions of
Maleic Anhydride (1.0M) in Benzene in the Presence of Various
Additives

Additive	E_T (kcal/mole)	Relative adduct yield
Sensitizers[a]		
Propiophenone	74.7	26
Xanthone	74.2	14
Acetophenone	73.6	41
Benzaldehyde	71.9	36
Benzophenone	68.5	46
4,4′-Dichlorobenzophenone	68.0	59
p-Diacetylbenzene	67.7	35
p-Cyanobenzophenone	66.4	40
Inhibitors[b]		
Triphenylene	66.6	0
Thioxanthone	65.5	0
Anthraquinone	62.4	0
2-Acetylfluorene	62.6	0
Naphthalene	60.9	0
Crysene	56.6	0

[a] Exciting light absorbed only by additive.
[b] Nonsensitizers and also quenchers, that is, these compounds
inhibited reaction even when the exciting light was absorbed by
the maleic anhydride–benzene complex.

maleic anhydride has a triplet excitation energy of 72 kcal/mole (as judged by its phosphorescence spectrum, $S_0 \rightarrow T_1$ absorption spectrum, and quenching of acetophenone photoreduction), which is consistent with the results in cyclohexane–acetone and carbon tetrachloride. Thus, by using energy transfer techniques it could be shown that binding energy of the maleic anhydride–benzene complex is greater by 4 kcal/mole in the triplet state than in the ground state.

An estimate of the triplet-excitation energy of 1,2-diazanorbornene **28** was obtained by monitoring the ability of a number of compounds with various triplet excitation energies to sensitize its decomposition (228).

(28)

The simplest "chemical" method for determining the triplet-excitation energy of a compound is to use it as a triplet sensitizer in one of the systems whose photochemistry is very sensitive to the triplet energy of the sensitizer. Most of these systems contain two acceptors of different triplet-excitation energies so that the relative efficiencies at which the two acceptors are excited by energy transfer would depend on the energy of the donor. These systems include the stilbenes and α-methyl stilbenes (Section III–7), β-methyl styrenes, and 1,3-pentadienes, all of which undergo *cis–trans* photoisomerizations, and the butadiene and isoprene which undergo photodimerization (Section IV–2–B). The photostationary isomer ratios for the systems which undergo *cis–trans* photoisomerization depend on the triplet energy of the sensitizer because the isomers have different triplet-excitation energies (Section III–7). Plots of the photostationary content versus the triplet energy have been determined with very good accuracy for these systems especially in the case of the stilbenes. These data, which have been published (131), were obtained using sensitizers with well-defined triplet-excitation energies. The curves for the stilbenes and α-methyl stilbenes are shown in Figures 9 and 10, respectively. The procedure to be followed in determining the triplet energy of a compound is simply to use it to sensitize the isomerization of an appropriate isomer pair, determine the isomer ratio at the photostationary state, and calculate the triplet energy from the appropriate plot. The procedures for analyzing the isomer mixtures have been described in detail. They involve vapor phase chromatography and are fast and relatively simple. All of the *cis–trans* systems were studied using benzene as solvent. Despite the fact that the small amount of data available indicates that the solvent has little effect on these systems (131) it is recommended that benzene be used as solvent if at all possible.

The triplet-sensitized photodimerization of open chain conjugated dienes such as butadiene yields a mixture of dimeric products whose composition is dependent upon the triplet-state energy of the sensitizer. This is a consequence of the fact that the ground-state diene is a mixture of conformers (s-cis, s-trans) whose triplet-excitation energies differ and whose triplet states lead to very different product ratios. The product composition as a function of sensitizer triplet energy has been carefully determined for two dienes, buta- diene and isoprene (207). So that the procedure to follow in determining the triplet energy of a compound of interest is to use it to sensitize the photo- dimerization of butadiene or isoprene, determine the product composition, and read off the triplet energy from the appropriate plot. The product com- position is easily and accurately determined by vapor phase chromatography. One advantage of the diene dimerization method over the photoisomerization method is that, in the former, doses must be sufficient to give only detectable amounts of dimeric products, while in the latter one must irradiate until the photostationary isomer ratio is achieved. This advantage is especially im- portant when one is dealing with a sensitizer which undergoes photochemistry of its own.

C. RADIATIONLESS TRANSITIONS

Sensitized Phosphorescence.   In one of the first applications of energy transfer to the study of radiationless transitions, Ermolaev (229) compared the phosphorescence yields of various acceptors with the yields obtained by exciting the acceptor triplet by energy transfer from a suitable triplet donor (rigid media at 77°K) Ermolaev determined γ values (Eq. (128)) from energy

$$\gamma = \frac{\phi_{sp}^A}{\phi_p^D - \phi_p^{DA}} \tag{128}$$

transfer experiments in which ϕ_{sp}^A, the quantum yield of acceptor phospho- rescence, and ϕ_p^{DA} the quantum yield of donor phosphorescence were measured (the exciting light was absorbed only by the donor). In Eq. (128) ϕ_p^D is the phosphorescence yield of the donor in the absence of the acceptor. That is γ is a sort of coefficient of utilization of the excitation energy transferred to the acceptor, and is characterized by the ratio of sensitized phosphorescence of the acceptor to the loss of donor phosphorescence due to energy transfer. Now if all of the triplet acceptor molecules emit, γ should be ϕ_{isc}^D/ϕ_p^D. That is, if in both the donor and acceptor there is no radiationless decay from the triplet state, γ should be unity. Examination of Table 16 shows that this is not the case for the donor–acceptor pairs listed. If, on the other hand, there

TABLE 16

Quantum Yields for Sensitized Phosphorescence in
Rigid Media at 77°K[a]

Donor	Acceptor	$\dfrac{\phi_p{}^A(1 - \phi_f{}^D)}{(1 - \phi_f{}^A)\phi_p{}^D}$[b]	γ[c]
Benzophenone	Naphthalene	0.06	0.07
Benzophenone	1-Chloronaphthalene	0.22	0.12
Benzophenone	1-Bromonaphthalene	0.19	0.20
Benzophenone	1-Iodonaphthalene	0.29	0.35
Acetophenone	Naphthalene	0.08	0.10
Phenanthrene	Naphthalene	0.30	0.30
Phenanthrene	1-Chloronaphthalene	1.0	0.73
Phenanthrene	1-Bromonaphthalene	0.94	0.99

[a] Data of Ermolaev (229).
[b] Calculated from the emission quantum yields for the isolated
donor and acceptor; the yields used were those determined by
Ermolaev.
[c] $\gamma = \phi_{sp}{}^A/(\phi_p{}^D - \phi_p{}^{DA})$ is calculated from the data of the energy-
transfer experiment.

is no radiationless decay from the excited-singlet state to the ground state, γ
would be related to the emission yields of the isolated donor and acceptor as
shown by Eq. (129). As shown in Table 16, there is good agreement between

$$\gamma = \frac{\phi_p{}^A(1 - \phi_f{}^D)}{(1 - \phi_f{}^A)\phi_p{}^D} \qquad (129)$$

the γ values calculated using Eq. (128) and those using Eq. (129). Thus
Ermolaev concluded that for the donors and acceptors listed radiationless
deactivation of the triplet state is an important process at 77°K, whereas the
radiationless $S_1 \rightarrow S_0$ process is relatively unimportant.

The sensitized phosphorescence experiment is most clearly applied to the
extreme case, that is the case of a compound which exhibits no phosphorescence in glasses at low temperatures. The lack of phosphorescence may be
due to a lack of intersystem crossing in the compound or may mean that the
triplet state is produced but subsequently decays by radiationless paths entirely.
The efficiency of radiationless deactivation of the triplet state of the compound can be easily assessed, of course, by populating the triplet state by
energy transfer from a suitable sensitizer. The efficiency of the transfer can be
determined by monitoring, for example, the phosphorescence of the sensitizer.
Two examples of this application follow.

Frozen dilute solutions (77°K) of thymine in 50% ethylene glycol–water
do not exhibit phosphorescence or a triplet ESR signal when excited with

ultraviolet light. Upon addition of acetone or acetophenone to the solution phosphorescence and ESR signals associated with the thymine can be easily detected. Therefore, it is concluded that under the conditions of the experiment thymine does not undergo intersystem crossing.

No phosphorescence can be detected from samples of *trans*-stilbene dissolved in hydrocarbon glasses at low temperature. This is not surprising because the quantum yield of fluorescence is near unity under these conditions so that there is no intersystem crossing (230). Addition of suitable triplet sensitizers such as benzophenone have no effect on this observation despite the fact that most of the sensitizer phosphorescence is quenched in the presence of the stilbene (230). Thus it can be concluded that even at 77°K in a rigid environment the triplet state of stilbene decays entirely by radiationless paths.

Intersystem Crossing. Almost simultaneously Ermolaev and Sveshnikova (68,231) and Kellogg and Bennett (70,232) reported on long-range Förster-type transfer from the triplet state of aromatic hydrocarbons to the singlet states of fluorescent dyes (see Section III–2–D). The latter investigators used this phenomenon to measure the efficiencies of intersystem crossing (ϕ_{isc}) and phosphorescence (ϕ_p) of the donors in plastic films at 77°K (232). The method involves two experimentally determined quantities, the phosphorescence to fluorescence ratio of the donor in the absence of an acceptor (ϕ_p^D/ϕ_f^D) and the efficiency of donor phosphorescence $k_p/(k_p + k_{T_1 \to S_0})$ (see Fig. 27). The first quantity can be measured directly. The efficiency of donor phosphorescence is determined from the change in the donor phosphorescence to fluorescence ratio upon addition of the acceptor as follows. The difference in the ratio is assumed to be due to triplet–singlet transfer from the donor to the acceptor. Then it follows that the efficiency of donor phosphorescence is

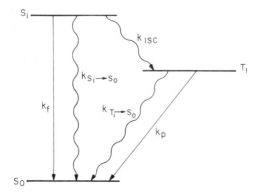

Fig. 27. Definition of rate constants used in the Kellogg–Bennett scheme for determining phosphorescence efficiencies.

given by equation where $\Delta\phi_p$ is the change in donor phosphorescence yield

$$\frac{k_p}{k_p + k_{T_1 \to S_0}} = -\frac{\Delta\phi_p\phi_f{}^A}{\phi_{df}{}^A} \tag{130}$$

(relative to donor fluorescence) upon adding the acceptor, $\phi_f{}^A$ is the fluorescence quantum yield of the acceptor (determined in a separate experiment) and $\phi_{df}{}^A$ is the yield of acceptor delayed fluorescence (relative to the donor fluorescence) which is a consequence of the energy transfer from the donor triplet state. If the radiationless $S_1 \to S_0$ process is assumed to be negligible, ϕ_f, ϕ_{isc}, and ϕ_p can be calculated from Eqs. (131), (132), and (133).

$$\phi_f = [1 + (\phi_p/\phi_f)(k_p + k_{T_1 \to S_0}/k_p]^{-1} \tag{131}$$

$$\phi_{isc} = 1 - \phi_f \tag{132}$$

$$\phi_p = \frac{\phi_{isc}k_p}{k_p + k_{T_1 \to S_0}} \tag{133}$$

The fluorescence to phosphorescence ratio can be easily determined with fair accuracy. The absolute fluorescence yields for the acceptors are more difficult to determine accurately. Thus the phosphorescence efficiencies are probably as accurate as the acceptor fluorescence yield data. In addition, the accuracy of the ϕ_{isc} and ϕ_p values obtained depend on the validity of the assumption that radiationless $S_1 \to S_0$ deactivation is negligible. Some of the ϕ_{isc} values obtained by Kellogg and Bennett are listed in Table 17.

An easy and direct method for the determination of intersystem crossing yields of donors in fluid solution has been developed by Lamola and Hammond (233). The same approach was used by Cundall and co-workers (234, 235) for the gas phase. The method is outlined schematically in Figure 28. The compound to be studied is used as a photosensitizer for an induced photochemical reaction known to involve the triplet state of the acceptor (quencher). The quantum yield of the induced process is then measured under conditions chosen to make the transfer step completely efficient. Under these conditions the simple relationship of Eq. (134) applies. In Eq. (134) ϕ_{isc} is the inter-

$$\phi(\text{product}) = \alpha\phi_{isc} \tag{134}$$

system crossing efficiency of the sensitizer, ϕ (product) is the quantum yield of the induced quencher photochemistry, and α is the efficiency at which the quencher triplet is converted to the product. The latter can be determined by using a sensitizer having $\phi_{isc} = 1.0$. In principle any well-characterized reaction known to involve the triplet state of the quencher can be used. Lamola and Hammond used the triplet photosensitized cis–trans isomerizations of some selected olefins and dienes as the monitoring reactions. These

TABLE 17

Some Experimental Intersystem Crossing Yields

Compound	Lamola and Hammond[a] ϕ_{isc}	Kellogg and Bennett[b] ϕ_{isc}	Parker and Joyce[c] ϕ_{isc}	Wilkinson[d] ϕ_{isc}
Naphthalene	0.67[e]	—	0.65	0.75
Naphthalene-d_8	(0.67)[e]	0.53	—	—
Triphenylene	0.95	0.85	—	—
Phenanthrene	0.76	0.88	—	—
Acenaphthene	0.47	—	0.45	—
Chrysene	0.67	—	—	—
Chrysene-d_{12}	—	0.60	—	—
Benzophenone	1.00	—	—	—
Acetophenone	1.00	—	—	—
Triphenylamine	0.88	—	—	—
Anthracene	—	—	—	0.70
9-Phenylanthracene	—	—	[0.70]	0.51

[a] In benzene solution at room temperature (233).
[b] In polar plastics at 77°K (232).
[c] In ethanol at room temperature (237) based on 0.70 for anthracene.
[d] In ethanol at room temperature (238).
[e] Corrected value of Stephenson (236).

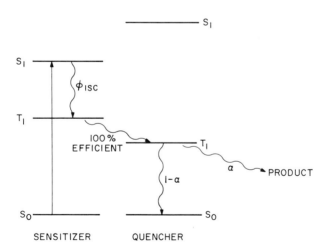

Fig. 28. The Lamola-Hammond scheme for determining intersystem crossing efficiencies of sensitizers in solution (see text).

reactions had been carefully studied (α is known very accurately) and the requisite analytical measurements could be made very accurately using vapor-phase chromatography.

Most of the original determinations of Lamola and Hammond were performed with cis-piperylene as the quencher. The discovery shortly thereafter that conjugated dienes can interact with the excited singlet states of aromatic hydrocarbons warranted reinvestigation of the ϕ_{isc} values for these compounds. It has been shown that the dienes quench the excited-singlet states of aromatic hydrocarbons without chemical consequences. Thus, the effect of quenching at the excited singlet level of the compound of interest by the quencher is to decrease the measured ϕ_{isc}. Fortunately, at concentrations of piperylene ($\sim 0.05M$) convenient for measurements only rather long-lived singlets are quenched with significant efficiency. One can easily correct for quenching at the singlet level by performing measurements over a sufficiently large range of quencher concentration and extrapolating to zero quencher concentration. Alternatively one can correct the ϕ_{isc} value measured at any single quencher concentration by employing the fluorescence-quenching efficiency of the quencher measured under the same conditions. Thus quenching at the singlet level by cis-piperylene, for example, only mildly reduces its usefulness as a quencher in the triplet counting scheme since it can be easily corrected for when it occurs. Some values of ϕ_{isc}, measured by Lamola and Hammond have been corrected for singlet quenching by Stephenson (236), are listed in Table 17.

In an interesting variation on the Hammond and Lamola approach, Parker and Joyce (237) measured ϕ_{isc} values for donors in fluid solution by monitoring the delayed fluorescence from an appropriate acceptor (Eqs. (135–139)).

$$D \xrightarrow{h\nu} D^{*1} \tag{135}$$

$$D^{*1} \xrightarrow{\phi_{\mathrm{isc}}} D^{*3} \tag{136}$$

$$D^{*3} + A \xrightarrow{p_e} D + A^{*3} \tag{137}$$

$$A^{*3} + A^{*3} \xrightarrow{p} A^{*1} + A \tag{138}$$

$$A^{*1} \longrightarrow A + h\nu' \tag{139}$$

If the light is absorbed only by the donor and the donor triplets are completely quenched, the quantum efficiency (steady state) of the resulting sensitized, delayed fluorescence of the acceptor $\phi_{\mathrm{DF}}^{\mathrm{A}}$ is given by Eq. (140),

$$\phi_{\mathrm{DF}}^{\mathrm{A}} = \tfrac{1}{2}\phi_{\mathrm{F}}^{\mathrm{A}} p k_r I (p_e \phi_{\mathrm{isc}}^{\mathrm{D}} \tau^{\mathrm{A}})^2 \tag{140}$$

where k_r is the bimolecular diffusion-controlled rate constant, p is the probability that an encounter between two acceptor triplets gives rise to an excited singlet acceptor, $\phi_{\mathrm{F}}^{\mathrm{A}}$ is the fluorescence efficiency of the acceptor, I is the rate of light absorption by the donor, p_e is the probability that a quenching encounter between a donor triplet and acceptor yields a triplet acceptor, and τ^A is the acceptor triplet lifetime. The ratios of the intensities of sensitized delayed fluorescence (I_{DF}^A) from two solutions containing the same acceptor but different donors in the same solvent and measured with equal exciting light intensities is given by Eq. (141).

$$\frac{(I_{DF}^A)_1}{(I_{DF}^A)_2} = \left[\frac{(p_e \phi_{isc}^D)_1}{(p_e \phi_{isc}^D)_2}\right]^2 \tag{141}$$

If p_e is the same for all donors (that p_e is unity for all donor–acceptor pairs where the donor energy is higher than that of the acceptor is generally accepted), then relative ϕ_{isc} values for various donors can be obtained by comparing the sensitized, delayed fluorescence intensities of an appropriate acceptor.

According to Parker and Joyce (237) the ideal acceptor for their scheme should have a low-lying triplet so that it can accept triplet excitation from a large range of donors and should not compete for existing light. The effect of absorption of exciting light by the acceptor can be minimized if the latter has a low ϕ_{isc}. The acceptor chosen for some preliminary experiments was perylene.

Included in Table 17 are ϕ_{isc} values determined by Wilkinson and co-workers (238) using a very clever and accurate scheme which does not involve intermolecular excitation transfer. The scheme involves measuring the relative decrease in the fluorescence yield and the relative increase in the triplet yield (monitored by the triplet–triplet absorption in a flash photolysis experiment) due to the introduction of a "heavy-atom" species (e.g., bromobenzene, ethyl iodide, xenon) to a solution of the compound of interest. Wilkinson and co-workers showed that the heavy-atom species quenches the fluorescence of the compound being examined by inducing intersystem crossing. Consequently the fluorescence quenching and the triplet induction are related by Eq. (142), where F and F^0 are the fluorescence intensities in the presence and absence of quencher, respectively and D_T and $D_T{}^0$ are the initial optical densities of the triplet state following flash excitation in the presence and absence of quencher.

$$\frac{F^0}{F} = \left(\frac{D_T}{D_T{}^0}\frac{F^0}{F} - 1\right)\phi_{isc} + 1 \tag{142}$$

D. LIFETIMES OF EXCITED MOLECULES IN SOLUTION

The use of intermolecular excitation transfer to determine the lifetimes of excited molecules in solution has been described in Sections IV–1 and IV–2–B. One simply adds a known amount of quencher compound specific for the state of interest and monitors its effect on some observable parameter which is proportional to the concentration of the excited molecule. One may monitor the steady-state fluorescence or phosphorescence from the excited species of interest, some photochemistry connected with the latter, or the resultant emission or photochemistry of the quencher. If the rate of transfer of excitation from the donor to the quencher is known, then the lifetime of the donor can be determined (see Section IV–1).

A recent spectacular application of this approach has been made by Liu and Edman (141). They have provided good evidence that the 9,10-dibromo-anthracene-sensitized photorearrangement of 2,3-bis(perfluoromethyl)bicyclo-[2.2.2]octa-2,5,7-triene involves energy transfer to the latter from the second triplet state (but not the lowest triplet state) of the anthracene. By measuring the dependence of the quantum yield for the reaction on the concentration of the quencher and assuming that the energy transfer proceeds at the diffusion-controlled rate, Liu and Edman calculated the rate constant for the $T_2 \rightarrow T_1$ interval conversion process to be 5×10^{10} sec^{-1}. This is perhaps the first determination of the rate of an internal conversion involving two excited states.

References

1. D. L. Dexter, *J. Chem. Phys.*, **21**, 836 (1953).
2. Th. Förster, *Discussions Faraday Soc.*, **27**, 7 (1959).
3. P. Livingston, *J. Phys. Chem.*, **61**, 860 (1957).
4. G. Porter and F. Wilkinson, *Proc. Roy. Soc. (London)*, Ser. A, **264**, 1 (1961).
5. V. L. Ermolaev, *Usp. Fiz. Nauk.*, **80**, 3 (1963).
6. G. W. Robinson and R. P. Frosch, *J. Chem. Phys.*, **38**, 1187 (1963).
7. F. Wilkinson, in *Advances in Photochemistry*, Vol. 3, W. A. Noyes, G. S. Hammond, and J. N. Pitts, Jr., Eds., Interscience, New York, 1964, pp. 241–268.
8. N. J. Turro, *Molecular Photochemistry*, Benjamin, New York, 1965.
9. R. G. Bennett and R. E. Kellogg, "Mechanisms and Rates of Radiationless Energy Transfer," in *Progress in Reaction Kinetics*, Vol. 4, G. Porter, Ed., Pergamon Press, London, 1966.
10. J. G. Calvert and J. N. Pitts, Jr., *Photochemistry*, Wiley, New York, 1966.
11. J. N. Pitts, Jr., F. Wilkinson, and G. S. Hammond, in *Advances in Photochemistry*, Vol. 1, W. A. Noyes, G. S. Hammond, and J. N. Pitts, Eds., Interscience, New York, 1963, ch. 1.
12. M. W. Windsor, "Luminescence and Energy Transfer," in *Physics and Chemistry of the Organic Solid State*, Vol. 2, Interscience, New York, 1965, ch. 4.
13. Th. Förster, in *Comprehensive Biochemistry*, Vol, 22, M. Florkin and E. H. Stotz, Eds., Elsevier, Amsterdam, 1967.
14. P. Pringsheim, *Fluorescence and Phosphorescence*, Interscience, New York, 1949, pp. 61–62.
15. E. Gaviola and P. Pringsheim, *Z. Physik.*, **24**, 24 (1924).

16. C. A. Parker and W. T. Rees, *Analyst*, **87**, 83 (1962).
17. G. S. Hammond, C. A. Stout, and A. A. Lamola, *J. Am. Chem. Soc.*, **86**, 3103 (1964).
    Kogyo (*Tokyo*), **18**, 1464 (1965).
19. For a discussion see J. D. Jackson, *Classical Electrodynamics*, Wiley, New York, 1962, ch. 4.
21. Th. Förster, *Z. Naturforsch.*, **4a**, 321 (1949); *Z. Elektrochem. Soc.*, **53**, 93 (1949), **56**, 716 (1952).
22. G. Porter and M. R. Wright, *Discussions Faraday Soc.*, **27**, 18 (1959).
23. E. Wigner, *Nachr. Akad. Wiss. Goettingen, IIa. Math. Physik. Chem. Abt.*, **1927**, see G. Herzberg, *Spectra of Diatomic Molecules*, Van Nostrand, New York, 1950, pp. 315 ff.
24. R. F. Vassil'ev, *Nature*, **196**, 668 (1962); **200**, 773 (1963).
25. A. S. Davydov, *Theory of Molecular Excitons*, trans. by M. Kasha and M. Oppenheimer, Jr., McGraw-Hill, New York, 1962; A. S. Davydov, *Zh. Eksptl. Theoret. Fiz.*, **18**, 210 (1948).
26. W. T. Simpson and D. L. Peterson, *J. Chem. Phys.*, **26**, 588 (1957).
27. Th. Förster, "Excitation Transfer," in *Comparative Effects of Radiation*, M. Burton, J. S. Kirby-Smith, and J. L. Magee, Eds., Wiley, New York, 1960.
28. Th. Förster, "Delocalized Excitation and Excitation Transfer," in *Modern Quantum Chemistry*, Vol. 3, O. Sinanoğlu, Ed., Academic, New York, 1965.
29. J. Franck and E. Teller, *J. Chem. Phys.*, **6**, 861 (1938).
30. M. Kasha, *Radiation Res.*, **20**, 55 (1963).
32. J. Frenkel, *Phys. Rev.*, **37**, 17 (1931).
33. D. Fox and O. Schnepp, *J. Chem. Phys.*, **23**, 767 (1955).
34. R. S. Knox, *Theory of Excitons*, Academic, New York, 1959.
35. D. S. McClure, in *Solid State Physics*, Vol. 8, D. Turnbull and F. Seitz, Eds., Academic, New York, 1959, p. 1.
36. D. P. Craig and S. H. Walmsley, in *Physics and Chemistry of the Organic Solid State*, Vol. 1, M. M. Labs, D. Fox, and A. Weissberger, Eds., Wiley, New York, 1963, p. 585.
37. J. Jortner, S. A. Rice, and R. Selbey, "Excitons and Energy Transfer in Molecular Crystals," in *Modern Quantum Chemistry, Part III*, O. Sinanoğlu, Ed., Academic, New York, 1959, p. 139.
38. L. D. Landau and E. M. Lifshitz, *Quantum Mechanics Nonrelativistic Theory*, Pergamon Press, London, 1958, ch. 6.
39. K. Katsuura, *J. Chem. Phys.*, **43**, 4149 (1965).
40. See L. I. Schiff, *Quantum Mechanics*, McGraw-Hill, New York, 1949, p. 189.
41. G. W. Robinson and R. P. Frosch, *J. Chem. Phys.*, **37**, 1962 (1962).
42. H. Sternlicht, G. C. Nieman, and G. W. Robinson, *J. Chem. Phys.*, **38**, 1326 (1963).
43. G. C. Nieman and G. W. Robinson, *J. Chem. Phys.*, **39**, 1298 (1963).
45. S. W. Benson, *The Foundation of Chemical Kinetics*, McGraw-Hill, New York, 1960.
46. R. M. Noyes, in *Progress in Reaction Kinetics*, G. Porter, Ed., Pergamon Press, London, 1961.
47. P. J. Debye, *Trans. Electrochem. Soc.*, **82**, 265 (1942).
49. A. Beckett, A. Osborne, and G. Porter, *Trans. Faraday Soc.*, **60**, 873 (1964).
50. J. T. Dubois and R. L. Van Hemert, *J. Chem. Phys.*, **40**, 923 (1964).
52. S. Siegel and H. Judeikis, *J. Chem. Phys.*, **41**, 648 (1964).
53. N. Hirota and C. A. Hutchison, Jr., *J. Chem. Phys.*, **42**, 2869 (1965).

55. J. Perrin, 2me *Conseil de Chimie Solvay*, Gauthier-Villar, Paris, 1925.
56. Th. Förster, *Z. Naturforsch.*, **42**, 321 (1949).
57. E. J. Bowen and B. Brocklehurst, *Trans. Faraday Soc.*, **51**, 774 (1955).
58. E. J. Bowen and R. Livingston, *J. Am. Chem. Soc.*, **76**, 6300 (1954).
59. W. Ware, *J. Chem. Phys.*, **66**, 455 (1962).
60. R. Hardwick, *J. Chem. Phys.*, **26**, 323 (1957).
61. A. Weinreb, *J. Chem. Phys.*, **35**, 91 (1961).
62. W. H. Melhuish, *J. Phys. Chem.*, **67**, 1681 (1963).
63. R. Povinelli, Ph.D. thesis, University of Notre Dame, Notre Dame, Indiana, 1966.
64. R. G. Bennett, *J. Chem. Phys.*, **41**, 3037 (1964).
65. M. M. Zwick and H. Kuhn, *Z. Naturforsch*, **17A**, 411 (1962).
66. K. H. Drexhage, M. M. Zwick, and H. Kuhn, *Ber. Bunsen. Physik. Chem.*, **67**, 62 (1963).
67. R. G. Bennett, *J. Chem. Phys.*, **41**, 3048 (1964).
68. V. L. Ermolaev and E. B. Sveshnikova, *Akad. Nauk. USSR, Academy of Sciences Bull. Phys.*, **26**, 29 (1962).
69. V. L. Ermolaev and E. B. Sveshnikova, *Sov. Phys. Dokl.*, **8**, 373 (1963).
70. R. G. Bennett, R. P. Schwenker, and R. E. Kellogg, *J. Chem. Phys.*, **41**, 3040 (1964).
71. D. Spence, P. Ludwig, and M. Burton, unpublished results.
72. R. E. Kellogg, *J. Chem. Phys.*, **41**, 3046 (1964).
73. A. N. Terenin and V. L. Ermolaev, *Dokl. AN SSSR*, **85**, 547 (1952).
74. A. N. Terenin and V. L. Ermolaev, *Trans. Faraday Soc.*, **52**, 1042 (1956).
75. V. L. Ermolaev, *Sov. Phys. Dokl. (Dokl. AN SSSR)*, **139**, 348 (1961).
76. F. Perrin, *Compt. Rend.*, **178**, 1978 (1924).
77. S. I. Vavilov, *Zh. Eksperim. Teor. Fiz.*, **13**, 13 (1943).
78. K. B. Eisenthal and R.Murashige, *J. Chem. Phys.*, **39**, 2108 (1963).
79. S. P. McGlynn, J. D. Boggus, and E. Elder, *J. Chem. Phys.*, **32**, 357 (1960).
80. B. Smaller, E. C. Avery, and J. R. Remko, *J. Chem. Phys.*, **43**, 922 (1965).
81. H. L. J. Bäckström and K. Sandros, *Acta Chem. Scand.*, **12**, 823 (1958).
82. H. L. J. Bäckström and K. Sandros, *Acta Chem. Scand.*, **14**, 48 (1960).
83. G. Porter and F. Wilkinson, *Proc. Roy. Soc.*, **A264**, 1 (1961).
84. K. Sandros, *Acta Chem. Scand.*, **18**, 2355 (1964).
85. W. G. Herkstroeter and G. S. Hammond, *J. Am. Chem. Soc.*, **88**, 4769 (1966).
86. J. Bell and H. Linschitz, *J. Am. Chem. Soc.*, **85**, 528 (1963).
87. P. Wagner, Abstracts, 153rd Meeting, American Chemical Society, Miami Beach, Florida, April 1967, R118.
88. J. K. Roy and M. A. El-Sayed, *J. Chem. Phys.*, **40**, 3462 (1964).
89. G. S. Hammond and R. P. Foss, *J. Phys. Chem.*, **68**, 3739 (1964).
90. G. S. Hammond and R. S. Cole, *J. Am. Chem. Soc.*, **87**, 3256 (1965).
91. W. G. Herkstroeter, L. B. Jones, and G. S. Hammond, *J. Am. Chem. Soc.*, **88**, 4777 (1966).
92. J. T. Dubois and M. Cox, *J. Chem. Phys.*, **38**, 2536 (1963).
93. F. Wilkinson and J. T. Dubois, *J. Chem. Phys.*, **39**, 377 (1963).
94. T. V. Ivanova, P. I. Kudriashov, and B. Ya Sveshnikov, *Dokl. Adak. Nauk. SSSR*, **138**, 572 (1961).
95. I. B. Berlman, *Handbook of Fluorescence Spectra of Aromatic Molecules*, Academic, New York, 1965.
96. M. Furst and H. P. Kallman, *Phys. Rev.*, **89**, 416 (1956).
97. M. Furst, H. Kallman, and B. Kramer, *Phys. Rev.*, **89**, 416 (1956).
98. F. H. Brown, M. Furst, and H. Kallman, *Discussions Faraday Soc.*, **27**, 43 (1959).

99. S. G. Cohen and A. Weinreb, *Proc. Phys. Soc. (London)*, **72**, 53 (1958).
100. J. B. Birks and A. J. W. Cameron, *Proc. Phys. Soc. (London)*, **72**, 253 (1958).
101. H. Kallman, "Energy Transfer Processes," in *Comparative Effects of Radiation*, M. Burton, J. S. Kirby-Smith, and J. L. Magee, Eds., Wiley, New York, 1960, p. 342.
102. S. Lipsky and M. Burton, *J. Chem. Phys.*, **31**, 1221 (1959).
103. S. Lipsky, W. P. Helman, and J. F. Merkin, "Quenching of Electronic Energy Transfer in Organic Liquids," in *Luminescence of Organic and Inorganic Molecules*, H. P. Kallman and G. N. Spruch, Eds., Wiley, New York, 1960, p. 83.
104. S. Lipsky, "Scintillation Properties of Liquids," in *Physical Processes in Radiation Biology*, L. Augenstein, R. Mason, and B. Rosenberg, Eds., Academic, New York, 1964, p. 215.
105. M. A. Dillon and M. Burton, "Excitation Transfer and Decay Processes in Multi-Component Systems," in *Pulse Radiolysis*, M. Ebert, J. P. Keene, A. J. Swallow, and J. H. Baxendale, Eds., Academic, New York, 1965, p. 259.
106. M. Burton and H. Dreeskamp, *Z. Elektrochem.*, **64**, 165 (1960).
107. M. Burton, A. Ghosh, and Y. Yguerabide, *Radiation Res. Suppl.*, **2**, 462 (1960).
108. C. D. Amata and P. K. Ludwig, *J. Chem. Phys.*, **47**, 3540 (1967) and unpublished results.
109. R. F. Borkman and D. R. Kearns, *J. Am. Chem. Soc.*, **88**, 3467 (1966).
111. P. Wagner, *J. Am. Chem. Soc.*, **88**, 5672 (1966).
113. G. W. Robinson, *Proc. Natl. Acad. Sci. (U.S.)*, **49**, 521 (1963).
114. J. B. Birks, *Phys. Rev. Letters*, **24a**, 479 (1967).
115. G. N. Lewis, D. Lipkin, and T. Magel, *J. Am. Chem. Soc.*, **63**, 3005 (1941).
116. C. A. Parker, in *Advances in Photochemistry*, Vol. 2, W. A. Noyes, Jr., G. S. Hammond, and J. N. Pitts, Jr., Eds., Interscience, New York, 1964.
117. C. A. Parker and C. G. Hatchard, *Trans. Faraday Soc.*, **57**, 1894 (1961).
118. G. Porter and M. R. Wright, *Discussions Faraday Soc.*, **17**, 178 (1954).
119. B. Stevens and E. Hutton, *Nature*, **186**, 1045 (1960).
120. C. A. Parker and C. G. Hatchard, *Proc. Roy. Soc. (London)*, **A269**, 574 (1962).
121. C. A. Parker and C. G. Hatchard, *Trans. Faraday Soc.*, **59**, 284 (1963).
122. J. B. Birks, *Nature*, **214**, 1187 (1967).
123. N. Mataga, Y. Torihasha, and Y. Ota, *Chem. Phys. Letters*, **1**, 381 (1967).
124. T. Förster and K. Kasper, *Z. Electrochem.*, **59**, 977 (1955).
125. C. A. Parker and C. G. Hatchard, *Trans. Faraday Soc.*, **59**, 284 (1963).
126. J. P. Colpa, paper presented at 5th Meeting, European Congress on Molecular Spectroscopy, Amsterdam, 1961.
127. For example, J. B. Birks and L. G. Christophorou, *Nature*, **196**, 33 (1962).
128. C. A. Parker, *Proc. Roy. Soc. (London)*, *Ser. A*, **276**, 125 (1963).
129. G. S. Hammond and J. Saltiel, *J. Am. Chem. Soc.*, **85**, 2516 (1963).
130. J. Saltiel and G. S. Hammond, *J. Am. Chem. Soc.*, **85**, 2515 (1963).
131. G. S. Hammond, J. Saltiel, A. A. Lamola, N. J. Turro, J. S. Bradshaw, D. O Cowan, R. C. Counsell, V. Vogt, and C. Dalton, *J. Am. Chem. Soc.*, **86**, 3197 (1964).
132. A. A. Lamola, *J. Am. Chem. Soc.*, **88**, 813 (1966).
133. (a) J. R. Fox and G. S. Hammond, *J. Am. Chem. Soc.*, **86**, 4031 (1964); (b) C. Walling and M. J. Gibian, *J. Am. Chem. Soc.*, **87**, 3413 (1965).
134. G. S. Hammond and R. S. Cole, *J. Am. Chem. Soc.*, **87**, 3256 (1965).
135. G. S. Hammond, P. Wyatt, C. D. De Boer, and N. J. Turro, *J. Am. Chem. Soc.*, **86**, 2532 (1964).

136. (a) W. L. Dilling, *J. Am. Chem. Soc.*, **89**, 2742 (1967); (b) E. F. Ullman and W. A. Henderson, Jr., *J. Am. Chem. Soc.*, **89**, 4390 (1967).
137. A. Cox, P. de Mayo, and R. W. Yip, *J. Am. Chem. Soc.*, **88**, 4789 (1966).
138. W. G. Herkstroeter and G. S. Hammond, *J. Am. Chem. Soc.*, **88**, 4769 (1966).
139. L. Stephenson, D. G. Whitten, G. F. Vesley, and G. S. Hammond, *J. Am. Chem. Soc.*, **88**, 3665, 3893 (1966).
140. D. Valentine, Ph.D. thesis, California Institute of Technology, Pasadena, California, 1965.
141. R. S. H. Liu, *J. Am. Chem. Soc.*, **90**, 1899 (1967); R. S. H. Liu and J. Edman, *J. Am. Chem. Soc.*, **90**, 213 (1968).
142. R. S. H. Liu, unpublished work.
143. P. Wagner, *J. Am. Chem. Soc.*, **89**, 2980 (1967).
143a. G. S. Hammond, R. Cole, and S. Murov, unpublished results; G. S. Hammond and S. L. Murov, *J. Am. Chem. Soc.*, **90**, 2957 (1968).
144. V. L. Ermolaev and A. Terinen, *J. Chim. Phys.*, **55**, 698 (1958).
145. A. A. Lamola and G. S. Hammond, *J. Chem. Phys.*, **43**, 2129 (1965).
146. G. A. Crosby, R. E. Whan, and R. M. Alire, *J. Chem. Phys.*, **34**, 743 (1961).
147. M. Bhaumik and M. A. El-Sayed, *J. Chem. Phys.*, **42**, 787 (1965).
148. A. Terenin, in *Recent Progress in Photobiology*, E. J. Bowen, Ed., Academic, New York, 1965, p. 3.
149. G. Weber and F. W. J. Teale, *Trans. Faraday Soc.*, **54**, 640 (1958).
150. G. Weber, *Nature*, **180**, 1409 (1957).
151. G. Weber, *Trans. Faraday Soc.*, **44**, 185 (1950).
152. O. Schnepp and M. Levy, *J. Am. Chem. Soc.*, **84**, 172 (1962).
153. S. A. Latt, H. T. Cheung, and E. R. Blout, *J. Am. Chem. Soc.*, **87**, 995 (1965).
154. A. A. Lamola, P. A. Leermakers, G. W. Byers, and G. S. Hammond, *J. Am. Chem. Soc.*, **87**, 2322 (1965).
155. D. Breen and R. A. Keller, *J. Am. Chem. Soc.*, **90**, 1935 (1968).
156. R. A. Keller and L. J. Dolby, *J. Am. Chem. Soc.*, **89**, 2768 (1967).
157. J. W. Longworth, R. O. Rahn, and R. G. Shulman, *J. Chem. Phys.*, **45**, 2930 (1966).
158. M. Guéron, J. Eisinger, and R. G. Shulman, *J. Chem. Phys.*, **47**, 4077 (1967).
159. R. O. Rahn, R. G. Shulman, and J. W. Longworth, *J. Chem. Phys.*, **45**, 2955 (1966).
160. A. A. Lamola, M. Guéron, J. Eisinger, T. Yamane, and R. G. Shulman, *J. Chem. Phys.*, **47**, 2210 (1967).
161. J. Eisinger, M. Guéron, R. G. Shulman, and T. Yamane, *Proc. Natl. Acad. Sci. (U.S.)*, **55**, 1015 (1966).
162. R. O. Rahn, T. Yamane, J. Eisinger, J. W. Longworth, and R. G. Shulman, *J. Chem. Phys.*, **45**, 2947 (1966).
163. M. Guéron and R. G. Shulman, *Ann. Rev. Biochem.*, **37**, 571 (1968).
164. I. Isenberg, R. Rosenblutt, and S. L. Baird, Jr., *Biophys. J.*, **7**, 365 (1967).
165. G. Weber, *Advan. Protein Chem.*, **8**, 415 (1953).
166. G. Weber, in *Light and Life*, W. D. McElroy and B. Glass, Eds., Johns Hopkins Press, Baltimore, Maryland, 1961, p. 82.
167. G. Weber and F. J. W. Teale, in *The Proteins*, Vol. 3, H. Neurath, Ed., Academic. 1965.
168. L. Stryer, *Radiation Res.*, *Suppl. 2*, 432 (1960).
169. G. Weber and F. W. J. Teale, *Discussions Faraday Soc.*, **27**, 134 (1959).
170. S. F. Velick, *J. Biol. Chem.*, **233**, 1455 (1958).
171. D. H. Valentine, J. Saltiel, and G. S. Hammond, unpublished results.
172. J. J. Dannenberg and J. H. Richards, *J. Am. Chem. Soc.*, **87**, 1626 (1965).
173. R. Srinivasan, *J. Am. Chem. Soc.*, **86**, 3318 (1963).

174. G. O. Schenck, *Naturwiss.*, **35**, 28 (1948).
175. G. O. Schenck, H. Eggert, and W. Denk, *Ann. Chem.*, **584**, 176 (1953).
176. G. O. Schenck, I. von Welucki, and C. H. Krauch, *Ber.*, **95**, 1409 (1962).
177. G. O. Schenck, *Z. Elektrochem. Soc.*, **64**, 997 (1960).
178. G. O. Schenck and R. Steinmetz, *Tetrahedron Letters, No. 21*, 1 (1960).
179. G. O. Schenck and H. D. Becker, *Angew. Chem.*, **70**, 504 (1958).
180. G. O. Schenck and R. Steinmetz, *Bull. Soc. Chim. Belges*, **71**, 781 (1962).
181. C. S. Foote and S. Wexler, *J. Am. Chem. Soc.*, **86**, 3879, 3880 (1964).
182. D. R. Kearns, R. A. Hollins, A. U. Khan, R. W. Chambers and P. Radlick, *J. Am. Chem. Soc.*, **89**, 5455 (1967).
183. T. Medinger and F. Wilkinson, *Trans. Faraday Soc.*, **61**, 620 (1965).
184. S. Murov and G. S. Hammond, *J. Phys. Chem.*, **72**, 3797 (1968).
185. O. Stern and M. Volmer, *Phyzik Z.*, **20**, 183 (1919).
186. L. M. Stephenson, D. G. Whitten, and G. S. Hammond, "The Chemistry of Ionization and Excitation," Taylor and Francis Ltd., London, 1967, p. 35 and references therein.
187. (a) W. M. Moore, G. S. Hammond, and R. P. Fass, *J. Am. Chem. Soc.*, **83**, 2789 (1961); (b) G. S. Hammond, W. P. Baker, and W. M. Moore, *J. Am. Chem. Soc.*, **83**, 2795 (1961).
188. J. A. Bell and H. Linschitz, *J. Am. Chem. Soc.*, **85**, 528 (1963).
189. H. E. Zimmerman, H. G. C. Durr, R. G. Lewis, and S. Bram, *J. Am. Chem. Soc.*, **84**, 4149 (1962).
190. G. W. Griffin and E. J. O'Connell, *J. Am. Chem. Soc.*, **84**, 4148 (1962).
191. R. J. Crowley, *Proc. Chem. Soc.*, **245**, 334 (1962).
192. R. S. H. Liu and G. S. Hammond, *J. Am. Chem. Soc.*, **86**, 1892 (1964).
193. G. S. Hammond, P. A. Leermakers, and N. J. Turro, *J. Am. Chem. Soc.*, **83**, 2395 (1961).
194. A. A. Lamola, unpublished results.
195. W. G. Dauben and R. L. Cargill, *Tetrahedron*, **12**, 186 (1961).
196. G. S. Hammond, N. J. Turro, and A. Fischer, *J. Am. Chem. Soc.*, **83**, 4674 (1961).
197. J. Bradshaw and G. S. Hammond, *J. Am. Chem. Soc.*, **85**, 3953 (1963).
198. W. B. de More and S. W. Benson, in *Advances in Photochemistry*, Vol. 2, W. A. Noyes, Jr., G. S. Hammond, and J. N. Pitts, Jr., Eds., Interscience, New York, 1964, p. 219; P. Gaspar and G. S. Hammond, in *Carbene Chemistry*, W. Kumse, Ed., Academic, New York, 1964.
199. H. M. Frey, in *Progress in Reaction Kinetics*, Vol. 2, G. Porter, Ed., Pergamon Press, Oxford, 1964, p. 131.
200. K. R. Kopecky, G. S. Hammond, and P. A. Leermakers, *J. Am. Chem. Soc.*, **84**, 1015 (1962).
201. P. de Mayo, J-P. Pete, and M. Tchir, *J. Am. Chem. Soc.*, **89** (1967).
202. W. G. Herkstroeter, A. A. Lamola and G. S. Hammond, *J. Am. Chem. Soc.*, **86**, 4537 (1964).
203. For a discussion of environmental effects on excited states, see E. L. Wehry, in *Fluorescence*, G. G. Guilbault, Ed., M. Dekker, New York, 1967.
205. D. F. Evans, *J. Chem. Soc.*, **1957**, 1351; **1957**, 3885; **1959**, 2753; **1960**, 1735; **1961**, 1987.
206. R. E. Kellogg and W. T. Simpson, *J. Am. Chem. Soc.*, **87**, 4230 (1965).
207. R. S. H. Liu, N. J. Turro, Jr., and G. S. Hammond, *J. Am. Chem. Soc.*, **87**, 3406 (1965).
208. G. S. Hammond, N. J. Turro, and R. S. H. Liu, *J. Org. Chem.*, **28**, 3297 (1963).

209. D. Valentine, N. J. Turro, and G. S. Hammond, *J. Am. Chem. Soc.*, **86**, 5202 (1964).
210. W. J. McCarthy and J. D. Winefordner, *Anal. Chem.*, **38**, 848 (1966).
211. A. Heller and E. Wasserman, *J. Chem. Phys.*, **42**, 949 (1965).
212. P. K. Gallagher, A. Heller, and E. Wasserman, *J. Chem. Phys.*, **41**, 3921 (1964).
213. A. A. Lamola and J. Eisinger, unpublished results.
214. A. A. Lamola and J. P. Mittal, *Science*, **154**, 1560 (1966), and unpublished results.
215. C. L. Greenstock, I. H. Brown, J. W. Hunt, and H. E. Johns, *Biochem. Biophys. Res. Commun.*, **27**, 431 (1967).
216. J. Burr and E. H. Park, *Photochem. Photobiol.*, **8**, 73 (1968).
217. F. A. L. Anet, *Can. J. Chem.*, **40**, 1249 (1962).
218. G. O. Schenck, I. von Wilucki, and C. H. Krauch, *Ber.*, **95**, 1409 (1962).
219. G. S. Hammond, C. A. Stout, and A. A. Lamola, *J. Am. Chem. Soc.*, **86**, 3103 (1964).
220. P. J. Wagner and G. S. Hammond, *J. Am. Chem. Soc.*, **88**, 1245 (1966).
221. P. J. Wagner, *J. Am. Chem. Soc.*, **89**, 5715 (1967), and references therein.
222. A. A. Lamola, G. S. Hammond, and F. B. Mallory, *Photochem. Photobiol.*, **4**, 259 (1965).
223. H. L. J. Bäckström and K. Sandros, *Acta Chem. Scand.*, **18**, 48 (1960).
224. G. Porter and F. Wilkinson, *Trans. Faraday Soc.*, **57**, 1686 (1961).
225. A. A. Lamola, W. G. Herkstroeter, J. C. Dalton, and G. S. Hammond, *J. Chem. Phys.*, **42**, 1715 (1965).
226. R. Pariser, *J. Chem. Phys.*, **25**, 1112 (1956).
227. W. M. Hardham and G. S. Hammond, *J. Am. Chem. Soc.*, **89**, 3200 (1967).
228. P. S. Engel, *J. Am. Chem. Soc.*, **89**, 5731 (1967).
229. V. L. Ermolaev, *Opt. Spectr.* (*English Transl.*), **13**, 49 (1962).
230. A. A. Lamola and J. Saltiel, unpublished results.
231. V. L. Ermolaev and E. B. Sveshnikova, *Opt. Spectry.* (*English Transl.*), **14**, 320 (1964).
232. R. E. Kellogg and R. G. Bennett, *J. Chem. Phys.*, **41**, 3042 (1964).
233. A. A. Lamola and G. S. Hammond, *J. Chem. Phys.*, **43**, 2129 (1965).
234. R. B. Cundall and D. G. Milne, *J. Am. Chem. Soc.*, **83**, 3902 (1961).
235. R. B. Cundall, F. J. Fletcher, and D. G. Milne, *J. Chem. Phys.*, **39**, 3536 (1963); *Trans. Faraday Soc.*, **60**, 1146 (1964).
236. L. M. Stephenson, Ph.D. thesis, California Institute of Technology, Pasadena, California, 1967.
237. C. A. Parker and T. A. Joyce, *Chem. Commun.*, **1966**, 234.
238. (a) T. Medinger and F. Wilkinson, *Trans. Faraday Soc.*, **61**, 620 (1965); (b) A. R. Horrocks, T. Medinger, and F. Wilkinson, *Photochem. Photobiol.*, **6**, 21 (1967); (c) A. R. Horrocks, T. Medinger, and F. Wilkinson, *Chem. Commun.*, **1965**, 452; F. Wilkinson, unpublished results.

CHAPTER III

PHOTOCHEMICAL REACTIONS OF ORGANIC MOLECULES

NICHOLAS J. TURRO

Department of Chemistry, Columbia University,
New York, New York

I. ETHYLENES AND NONAROMATIC POLYENES

1. General Considerations

A. EXCITED ELECTRONIC STATES OF ALKENES

(1) A Model for the Excited States of Alkenes

Simple molecular orbital (MO) theory indicates that the lowest excited states of ethylenes result from excitation of a π-electron into a π^* (antibonding) orbital (1,2). The π^* electron essentially cancels the bonding effect of the remaining π-electron. As a result, the C=C bond becomes an essential single bond in the π,π^* states (S_1 or T_1) of simple alkenes (3).†

Indeed, detailed calculations indicate that, for ethylene, the original planar configuration produced by Franck-Condon excitation is an energy maximum in the π,π^* states (4–8). An energy minimum exists for the configuration in which the planes of the methylene groups are perpendicular to each other, since the latter configuration minimizes the electron–electron repulsion of the p-electrons in the excited state. Indeed, calculations reveal a tendency for the carbon atoms of ethylene to rehybridize to sp^3 in its lowest excited electronic state (7).

As a first approximation then, we shall employ a 1,2-biradical as a model for the π,π^* states of *alkenes* (Fig. 1). Let us now ask, what is the chemical behavior to be expected of such species?

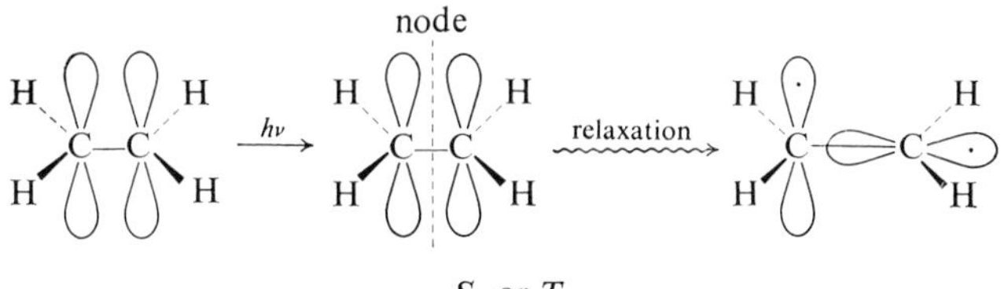

Fig. 1. Franck-Condon π–π^* excitation and relaxation of ethylene.

(2) Primary Processes of Alkenes

On the basis of the model selected to represent the π,π^* states of alkenes we can make a number of qualitative predictions concerning the photochemistry of such species and what *primary photochemical processes* (i.e., chemistry which occurs when the molecule is in an electronically excited state) are expected from the π,π^* states of alkenes.

The simplest primary process (pp-1) which we might envision is *cis–trans isomerization*, which should occur because of the essential single-bond

† Some uncertainty exists over the nature of the lowest energy *spectroscopic* states of ethylene.

nature of the carbon–carbon bond in the π,π^* state. Excitation of **1**, for example, should lead to **2**. The latter should tend to equilibrate with **3**, the biradical produced from excitation of **4**. It can be seen that if both **1** and **4** are continuously excited, a "photoequilibrium" between **1** and **4** will be set up. This equilibrium is *unrelated* to the *thermodynamic equilibrium* between **1** and

(1)   (2)

(3)   (4)

4. The photostationary or photoequilibrium composition of **1** and **4** will depend upon (among other things) the extinction coefficients of **1** and **4** in the region of lamp emission, the degree to which an equilibrium is set up between **2** and **3**, and the magnitude of the decay constants k_t and k_c.

It is expected, and found, that *cis–trans* isomerization is one of the most general and facile primary processes of alkenes.

A second primary process (pp-2) anticipated for a biradical π,π^* state is the addition to unsaturated linkages. Thus, cycloadditions of alkene π,π^* states to afford dimers or cross adducts are expected. If the alkene π,π^* state is severely twisted, as is expected for ethylene, then cycloaddition should occur in two steps, i.e., it *could* be nonstereospecific if closure to adduct is slow compared to bond rotations in an intermediate such as **7**.

(5)   (6)   (7)   (8) *trans*   (8) *cis*

If the π,π^* alkene state is a triplet, one must imagine a two-step addition irrespective of the excited-state geometry since a spin flip is required before a stable product is formed. If the π,π^* singlet state should be planar (9,10,11) the reaction *may* be concerted, since both new bonds can form simultaneously. Since ethylenes may have twisted excited states (4–8) one must be cautious in application of the Woodward-Hoffmann rules to photochemistry of alkenes.

A third primary process (pp-3) expected of a carbon biradical is the abstraction of hydrogen atoms (and presumably other atoms such as chlorine, etc.).

The fate of the expected intermediate **10** will depend on the reaction conditions and either reduction (**11**) (a second hydrogen abstraction) or coupling (**12**) may occur.

Finally, cleavages of bonds α (pp-4) or β (pp-5) to the biradical centers are anticipated.

(3) Energy Diagrams for Ethylenes

A dearth of spectroscopic evidence, especially emission data, makes it difficult to construct an accurate energy diagram for simple ethylenes (12–14). In fact, the nature of the lowest energy transition responsible for the weak absorption of monoolefins at wavelengths greater than 2000 Å is a matter of controversy (4,13,14). We shall describe the S_1 and T_1 states as π,π^* since this suffices for a discussion of their photochemistry. Such a classification may be revised as a result of further experimental and theoretical study. The justification for such an approach will rest on its success in rationalizing olefin photochemistry and on the possibility that the spectroscopic states (Franck-Condon) and photochemically active (twisted, relaxed) states of ethylenes may be relatively unrelated.

A possible energy diagram for ethylene is shown in Figure 2a. The large singlet–triplet splitting ($\Delta E \sim 60$ kcal) implies that the $S_1 \to T_1$ process is slow relative to k_s (which may involve rotation as a method of deactivation).

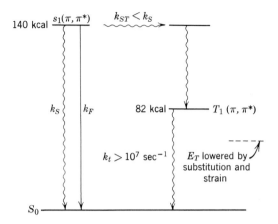

Fig. 2a. Energy diagram for ethylene (tentative).

It should be emphasized that the shape of a relaxed π,π^* state of an acyclic alkene may be a severely twisted one. Figure 2b shows the potential energy of an ethylene in S_0, S_1, and T_1 as a function of the angle twist of the CH_2 groups (4). Note that $E(T_1 - S_0)$ for the *relaxed* T_1 state and its Franck-Condon S_0 counterpart may be exceedingly small and even negative!

Substitution at the double bond is expected to decrease the energy of both the singlet† and triplet states, but it is not known by how much. When the C=C bond is located in a small ring the energy difference between S_0 and S_1 and S_0 and T_1 may be less than it is for unstrained systems (as a result of the

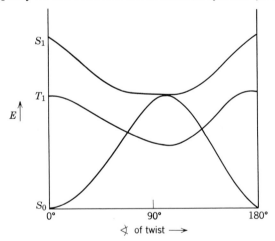

Fig. 2b. Potential energy curve for twisting of ethylene.

† Compare Woodward's rules for absorption maxima of polyenes, ref. 1, p. 196.

raising of the ground-state energy to a greater extent than that of the excited states). From energy transfer experiments, the triplet-excitation energy of norbornene and cyclopentene appears to be ~ 72–75 kcal, a considerable drop from that of ethylene.

B. EXCITED ELECTRONIC STATES OF CONJUGATED POLYENES

(1) Models for the Excited States of Conjugated Polyenes

According to simple MO theory, the π,π^* states of polyenes may be considered as vinylogs of the π,π^* state of ethylene. Thus, butadiene should behave as a 1,4-biradical in its π,π^* state. Moreover, two slowly interconvertible stereoisomeric forms of butadiene π,π^* states should exist, since the C_2—C_3 bond is an essential double bond in the excited state. The excited-state isomers **18** and **20** are related to the ground state rotamers (**17** and **19**) which

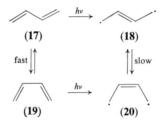

are in rapid equilibrium. It may be that the diene triplet is not planar, but twisted at one end, i.e., effectively an allyl radical fused to a free carbon radical. In this manner the unpaired electrons interact little and the energy of the state may be greatly lowered as in the analogous case for ethylene (4).

The π,π^* states of trienes and tetraenes may be likewise considered as 1,6- and 1,8-biradicals, in the first approximation.

(2) Primary Processes of Conjugated Polyenes

The primary processes expected of conjugated polyenes should be related to those of excited ethylenes if the vinylogous model suffices. However, the occurrence of intramolecular processes not available to alkenes must also be considered.

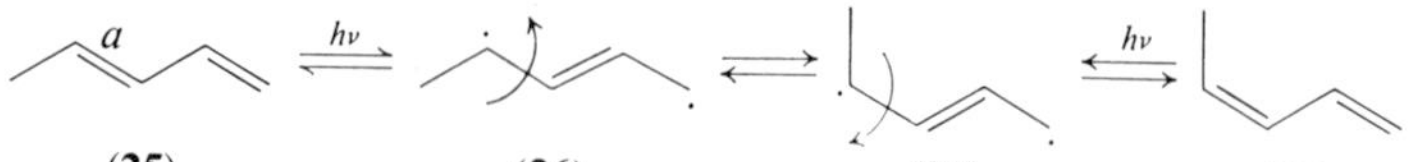

(25)   (26)   (27)   (28)

(29)   (30)

For example, *cis–trans isomerization* (pp-1) is a well-known primary photochemical process of substituted 1,3-dienes. The mechanism invisioned is rotation about bond *a* in the excited state **26**.

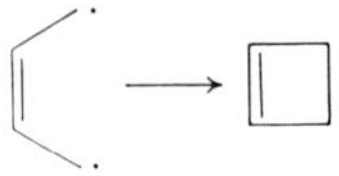

(31)   (32)

The primary process of addition to unsaturated linkages should also occur for conjugated polyenes; in addition, various intramolecular cyclizations may

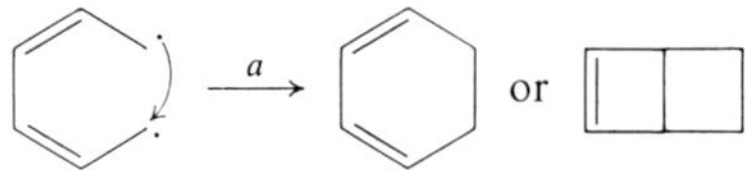

(33)   (34)   (35)

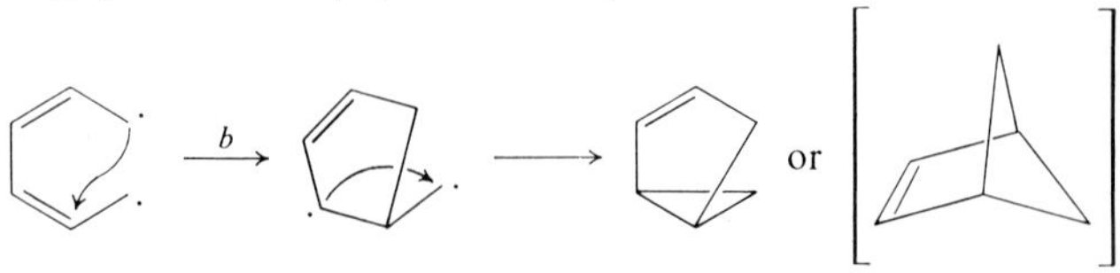

(33)   (36)   (37)   (38)

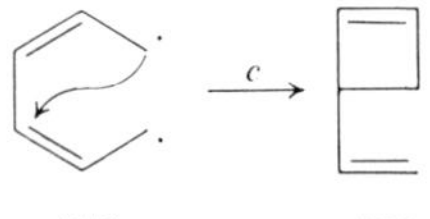

(33)   (39)

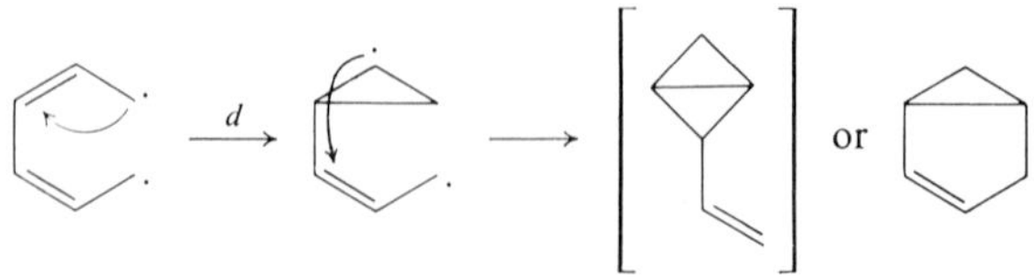

(33)   (40)   (41)   (37)

also occur. For example, butadiene can close photochemically to either cyclobutene or bicyclobutane. (See p. 158.)

For 1,3,5-hexatriene the situation is more complex and some of the possibilities for intramolecular closure are listed above (products not yet observed are in brackets).

In addition, the primary processes of α- and β-cleavage (pp-2), and abstraction (pp-3) described above should be observed for conjugated polyenes.

(42)   (43)

(44)   (45)

(46)   (47)

(3) Energy Diagrams for Conjugated Polyenes

Conjugated polyenes do not generally emit light even under favorable conditions (compare monoolefins). The triplet states of a number of dienes have been located by perturbation methods (high pressures of oxygen or ethyl iodide solutions) on their absorption spectra. Some typical data are given in Table 1. The energetic position of the S_1 (π,π^*) state of dienes is not well defined because of the broadness of the absorption spectra of these compounds. For example, estimates of the 0–0 band for $S_0 \rightarrow S_1$ absorption of butadiene range from 125 to 100 kcal. At any rate, a large singlet–triplet splitting occurs in most dienes. The energies of both the S_1 and T_1 states of cyclohexadienes appear to be lower than the corresponding energies of alicyclic dienes. Emission data (15) have been reported for a substituted cyclohexadiene—an ergosterol derivative—which shows a 0–0 fluorescence band at ~ 95 kcal.

Figure 3 indicates a tentative energy diagram for 1,3-butadiene and 1,3-cyclohexadiene.

Photochemical data indicate that dienes undergo intersystem crossing to the triplet inefficiently. This result may be due to the large S_1–T_1 energy gap (i.e., causing a low k_{st}) or to a rapid deactivation of S_1 which competes favorably with crossing to T_1 or upper triplet levels. There is some indirect evidence that cyclic diene triplets possess longer lives than alicyclic diene

TABLE 1

Singlet–Triplet Transition Energies of Some
Conjugated Dienes

Compound (16,17)	$E_3{}^{a}$
Ethylene	82
Butadiene	60
Isoprene	60
2,3-Dimethylbutadiene	60
trans-1,3-Pentadiene	59
trans-2,4-Hexadiene	59
2-Chlorobutadiene	59
1-Chlorobutadiene	57
2-Methoxybutadiene	59
Cyclopentadiene	58
1,3-Cyclohexadiene	54
cis-1,3-Pentadiene	57
1,3,5-Hexatriene	48
1,3-Pentadiyne	80
1,3-Butadiyne	76

[a] Measured by oxygen perturbation; energies
in kcal/mole. These values (presumably) refer to
spectroscopic 0–0 bands.

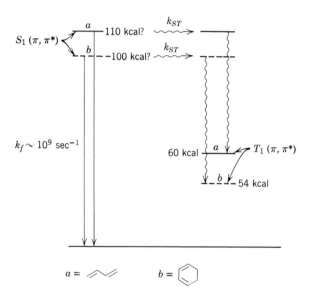

Fig. 3. Energy diagram for butadiene and 1,3-cyclohexadiene. The relaxed triplet of butadiene may be lower in energy than the "spectroscopic" triplet whose energy is indicated in the diagram.

triplets. This result may derive from the constraints placed on the system by the cyclic structure which inhibits tortional motions that cause rapid deactivation of alicyclic dienes.

C. ORBITAL SYMMETRY AND THE PHOTOCHEMISTRY OF ALKENES AND POLYENES

Consideration of the nature of our models for π,π^* states for polyenes in greater detail leads us to the recognition that the π and π^* MO's are probably going to significantly influence the photochemistry of these compounds. Indeed, Woodward and Hoffmann (9) have listed rules for the "allowedness" or "forbiddenness" of various photochemical (and thermal) processes. These rules, which may be derived from the symmetry of the π^* orbital of the polyene in question, are discussed briefly in relevant sections.

D. SUMMARY

The photochemistry of ethylenes and conjugated dienes should involve π,π^* states nearly exclusively. Features which are common to these systems are: (a) a large singlet–triplet splitting which may result in inefficient $S_1 \rightarrow T_1$ crossing, thus giving rise to a different photochemistry from direct and sensitized reactions; (b) a biradical character; (c) relatively short lifetimes because of tortional motions of the excited states which result from electron–electron repulsions (it is expected that small cyclic systems will be longer lived because of restriction of these motions); (d) the stereochemistry of closures, allowedness of cycloaddition reactions, and direction of sigmatropic reactions may be predicted in terms of the Woodward-Hoffmann hypotheses (9).

2. Photochemistry of Alkenes

A. ACYCLIC ALKENES

(1) Ethylene

The photochemistry of simple alkenes in solution (18) has not been studied extensively, probably because of the practical problems associated with keeping such compounds condensed. In addition, these compounds do not appreciably absorb light of wavelength greater than 2000 Å.

Triplet–triplet transfer offers an attractive potential means of indirect excitation of simple alkenes (19). Benzene and its alkyl derivatives, which strongly absorb the 2537-Å line of low-pressure mercury arcs are excellent candidates for sensitizers†, since their triplet-state energies (84–80 kcal/mole)

---

† However, as will be seen in examples given below, the excited states of aromatic compounds sometimes react with alkenes.

lie close to or above the value required to excite ethylene or simple alkenes (82–74 kcal/mole).

Results obtained from the vapor-phase irradiation of ethylene in the presence of mercury atoms as sensitizer (20) indicate that ethylene dimerizes, in addition to undergoing other reactions derived from its cleavage into radicals.*

$$CH_2\!\!=\!\!CH_2 \xrightarrow[\text{Hg, vapor}]{h\nu} \square \;+\; \text{other products}$$

Ethylene may serve as a substrate for addition by other excited molecules (20); for example, 3-methyl-2-cyclohexenone triplets add to ethylene to form a bicyclic ketone (Section IV–2–B).

Benzene photosensitization may be employed to effect *cis–trans* isomerization of the 1,2-dideuteroethylenes in the vapor phase (21). In addition, both fragmentation and internal hydrogen scrambling occur (21,22) to produce 1,1-dideuteroethylene.

(2) Alkenes

The photochemistry of *cis-* and *trans-*2-butene has been extensively studied in the vapor phase. Geometric isomerization is the major reaction and may be accomplished by energy transfer by use of a number of triplet sensitizers (23–30). Sensitized isomerization also occurs in solution.

1-Butene undergoes a mercury-photosensitized rearrangement to methylcyclopropane. This reaction may involve hydrogen abstraction by the triplet ethylene followed by ring closure (31).

(1)   (2)

Mercury-photosensitized rearrangement of 1,5-hexadiene vapor yields the two isomers allylcyclopropane and bicyclo[2.1.1]hexane in addition to products from free radicals produced by simple bond cleavages (32–34).

---

* In the examples given below, the main emphasis is on the reactions of the excited states of the unsaturated group in question. Often, mechanistic work to establish the excited states involved has not been done, and analogies must be employed to deduce mechanisms.

The yield of **5** may be made as high as 20% on a preparative scale by refluxing the 1,5-hexadiene through a quartz reactor surrounded by a bank of low-pressure (2537 Å) mercury lamps (33,79). Although the rearrangement to **4** looks formally similar to the rearrangement of **1** to **2**, compound **4** cannot be formed by a simple hydrogen abstraction. A mechanism involving allylic abstraction (by Hg?) followed by isomerization and closure is possible.

     (3)   (4)   (5)

Numerous reactions are known in which a reductive addition across an alkene linkage occurs. For example, irradiation of solutions of 1-alkenes and γ-butyrolactone results in the formation of addition products (35). The mechanism of such reactions has not been studied in detail, but may, in some cases, involve hydrogen abstraction by the excited alkene (produced by energy transfer?) followed by coupling.

Tetramethylethylene undergoes photodimerization to octamethylcyclo-butane. Since the reaction cannot be sensitized by molecules whose phosphorescence is quenched by tetramethylethylene, it has been proposed that this reaction proceeds via the π,π^* state (36). Both *cis*- and *trans*-2-butene undergo stereospecific dimerization to cyclobutanes (36a).

B. ALICYCLIC ALKENES

(1) Small Ring Alkenes

                (6)

Small ring alkenes (**6**, $n = 1$, 2, or 3), like their open-chain counterparts, do not exhibit appreciable absorption above 2000 Å. As the double bond becomes more heavily substituted, however, tail absorption may extend significantly toward 3000 Å.

The reported photochemistry of simple alkenes is sparse, indeed. Of the primary processes predicted and found (see below) to be significant for the C=C bond, only *cis–trans* isomerization has been looked at in any detail.

From a preparative standpoint, sensitization of the triplet state of alkenes by mercury atoms in the vapor phase (and perhaps in solution) or by benzene and its alkyl derivatives in the vapor phase or solution, seems to have been underexploited.*

It may be that a severe limit to the efficiency of photoreactions of cyclic alkenes in solution is imposed by the rapid *cis–trans* isomerization of the excited states of alkenes; i.e., an effective mechanism for decay of the excited alkene is available and all other reactions from these states must compete with rapid geometrical isomerization.†

Reactions in which an alkene is employed as a substrate for attack by another excited molecule will not be discussed in this section, but in the section describing the photochemistry of the excited molecule.

It appears that energy transfer is a suitable means of exciting small ring alkenes. The strain energy of these systems either lowers the effective energy required to excite triplets, or the reactivity and/or lifetimes of the excited states derived from these cyclic structures is greater than that of the corresponding open-chain analogs. These comments derive from qualitative observations of the rather scant knowledge we have of the photochemistry of the alkene linkage.‡

The dimerization of 1,3,3-trimethylcyclopropene is sensitized by acetone. Some selectivity is observed in this dimerization, the less sterically hindered product predominating (37,38).

$$\qquad (7) \qquad\qquad\qquad (8),\ 80\% \qquad (9),\ 20\%$$

Disubstitution of the double bond results in addition of acetone across the C=C bond, possibly initiated by hydrogen abstraction. The dimerization is

---

* Mercury photosensitization can be employed to effect 20–50 g conversion of products in favorable cases by refluxing the reactant into the irradiation zone. See refs. 33 and 79.

† The failure to observe emission or triplet–triplet absorption from simple acyclic alkenes under the most favorable conditions available attests to the short lifetimes of triplet states of olefins.

‡ Ref. 19, p. 219–220.

apparently blocked by steric hindrance. (For other examples of cyclopropene photochemistry, see Section II–3–A–(2)).

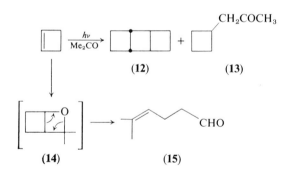

Reactions analogous to those of the cyclopropenes discussed above occur when acetone solutions of cyclobutene are irradiated (39). In addition, a product probably resulting from ring opening of an intermediate oxetane is formed. These reactions imply that energy transfer to cyclobutene occurs and that the cyclobutene triplet may add to ground-state cyclobutene, abstract a hydrogen atom from acetone, or add to ground-state acetone. The formation

of product **15**, however, may be derived from the competition between addition of acetone triplet to ground-state cyclobutene to form **14** and energy transfer.

It is interesting to note that the cyclobutene triplet does not open to the lower lying butadiene triplet. This result is pertinent to results observed in photosensitized reactions of dienes (Section I–3–A–(1)).

Irradiation of benzene solutions of cyclobutene (40) yields a 1:1 adduct proposed to be **17**. Adduct **18** is more likely in view of more recent work (see Section II–2–A–(1)).

The cyclobutene **19** undergoes ring opening to **20** upon direct irradiation (41), but the reaction is rapidly "quenched" by the product diene, which serves as a powerful internal filter even at low conversions. (See Section I–3–A–(1,2).)

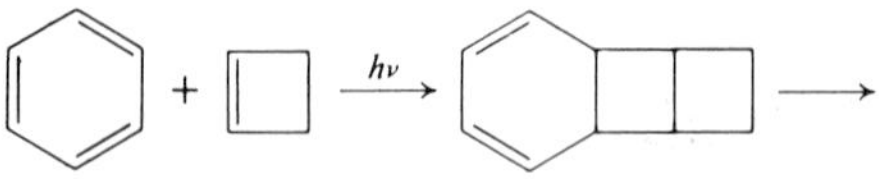

$$\text{+} \quad \xrightarrow{h\nu} \quad \longrightarrow \quad (17)$$

(16)

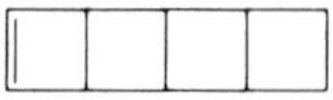

(17) 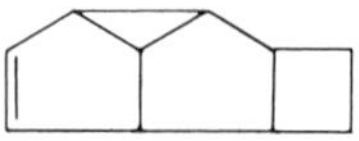   **(18)**

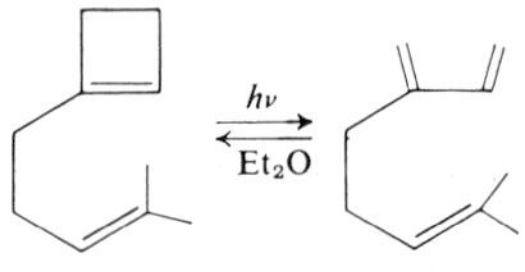

$$\underset{\text{Et}_2\text{O}}{\overset{h\nu}{\rightleftharpoons}}$$

(19)   **(20)**

Intramolecular ring closures have been employed to synthesize cage compounds in modest to good yields (61). The simplicity of these closures makes them the preparative method of choice in many cases. A dramatic example of the power of these photoclosures is provided by the syntheses of "prismanes" (42–45) from "Dewar" benzenes (which themselves are sometimes generated photochemically from benzenes (see Section II–2–A–(1)):

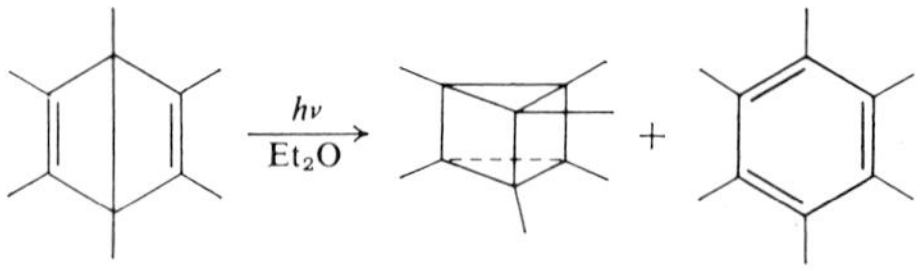

$$\xrightarrow[\text{Et}_2\text{O}]{h\nu} \quad + $$

(21)   **(22)**, 25%   **(23)**, 60%

$$\overset{h\nu}{\rightleftharpoons} \quad + $$

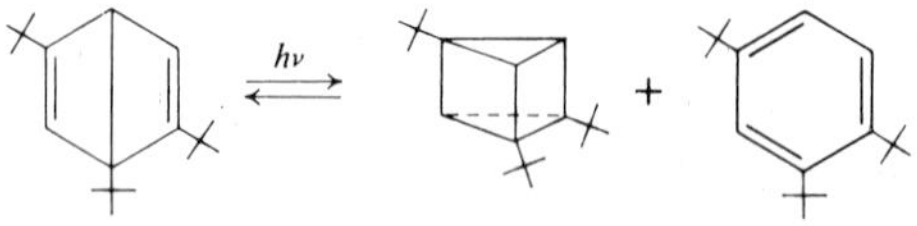

(24)   **(25)**, ~65%   **(26)**, ~25%

In less strained systems than "Dewar" benzenes (47,48) sensitization by acetone is required to effect closure.*

* See ref. 61 for a review of intramolecular ring closures.

Irradiation of acetone solutions of cyclopentene results in a complex mixture of products, consisting mainly of dimers (49). It appears that here

(27)   (28)

(29)   (30), 35%

both energy transfer from acetone to cyclopentene and reaction of acetone triplets (Section II–2–A–(2)) are occurring.

Irradiation of the epoxide of " Dewar" benzene yields an isomeric mixture of oxepin-benzene oxide (48).

Irradiation of benzene or alkyl benzenes (which absorbs all of the light) solutions of 1-methyl-cyclopentene in the presence of alcohols results in both reduction and migration of the C=C bond (50). The reaction presumably involves hydrogen abstraction to form a tertiary carbon radical which can collapse (perhaps by disproportionation?) to products.

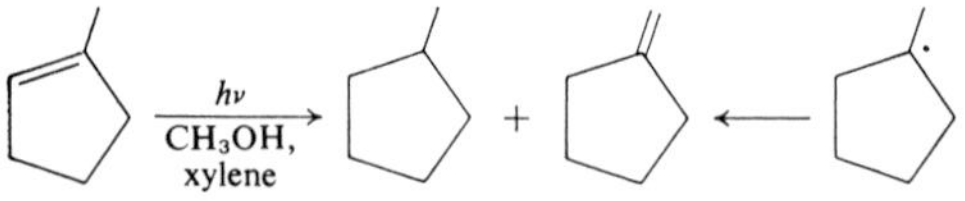

(35)   (36), 46% (37), 24%   (38)

Reactions such as the photosensitized reduction of the cyclopentene C=C bond may represent a very selective method of reduction.

The formal addition of a double bond to a single bond occurs when the norbornenes **39** or **41** are irradiated (51,52). Norbornene is known to undergo a number of acetone-photosensitized reactions. In some cases the reaction

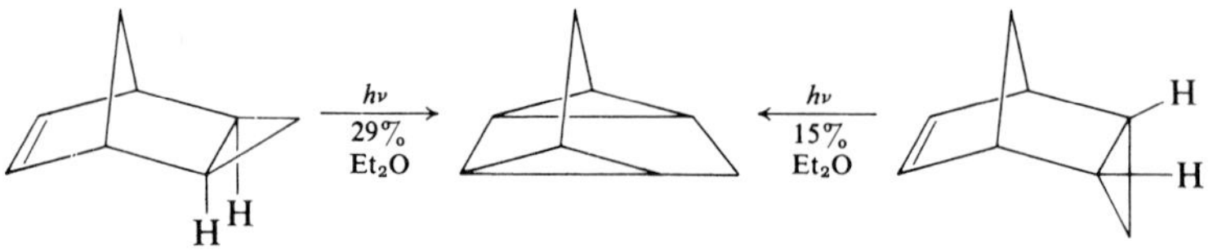

(39)   (40)   (41)

products are highly sensitive to conditions. For example, irradiation of norbornene solutions in acetone at room temperature results in photo-sensitized dimerization and reduction (54). Under reflux, the addition of acetone across the C=C bond occurs (55).

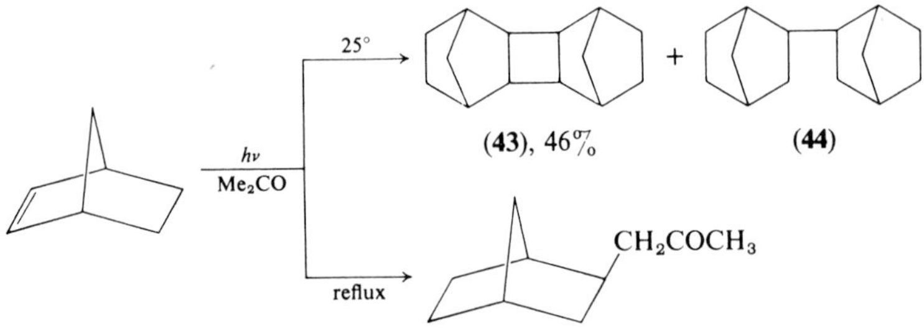

(43), 46%   (44)

CH$_2$COCH$_3$

(45), 45%

Norbornene and some of its derivatives undergo selective "photosensitized" dimerization in the presence of CuCl$_2$ or CuBr$_2$. The mechanism of this sensitization is obscure (55–57).

Norbornene also undergoes addition to methyl maleate and methyl acetylene dicarboxylate. Dimers of norbornene are not formed so the olefin may be a substrate for excited maleate or acetylene dicarboxylate (58–60).

Closure of polycyclic compounds containing cyclopentene rings to yield "cage" products are well known (61). The reactions are usually photosensitized, but may proceed under direct excitation when one or both double bonds are highly substituted. For example, *endo*-dicyclopentadiene **46** undergoes photosensitized closure to **47** while the chlorinated compound **48** closes to **49** upon direct excitation (62,63).

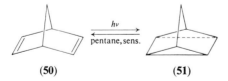

The intramolecular ring closure of norbornadienes (69a) appears to be a very general reaction and is the method of choice for preparing quadricyclenes such as tetracyclo[2.2.1.0.0]heptanes (64–68). These reactions may be effected by direct excitation or, usually more efficiently, by use of a photosensitizer. In the latter case, the choice of sensitizer is critical because the reaction is reversible and the position of the photostationary state depends upon the sensitizer (65). Generally, benzophenone or Michler's ketone is satisfactory as sensitizer.

The images in this region show structures labeled (46), (47), 62%, (48), (49), (50), and (51).

A reaction formally analogous to the photoisomerization of norbornadienes to quadricyclenes is the photorearrangement of benzonorbornadiene **52** to **53**. A possible mechanism is shown below. Since the reaction is sensitized by triplet-energy transferring agents, the sequence is probably two step. The absence of the product related to **53** (i.e., **53a**) from norbornadiene may be a

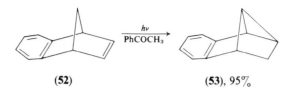

(52)

(53), 95%

(53a)

52 →

→ ≡ → 53

hν / Et₂O

(54b), 30%

(54a)

hν / Me₂CO dimers + + (54b)

—CH₂COCH₃

(55)

result of less driving force for the bond-breaking step, in the case of the parent olefin.

Irradiation of **54a** follows different paths under direct and sensitized excitation (70–72, 73).

(2) Medium- and Large-Ring Alkenes

Cyclohexene has been employed as a substrate for photoreaction and in some cases it forms photoreactive charge complexes (Section IV–6–D). Acetone, which is generally a splendid sensitizer for 3-, 4-, and 5-membered ring olefins, reacts with cyclohexene (74,75). Benzene and its alkyl derivatives seem to be better photosensitizers for reactions of cyclohexene and its simple derivatives. Energetics provide one of the simplest explanations for the difference in sensitization efficiency of acetone toward small- and medium-

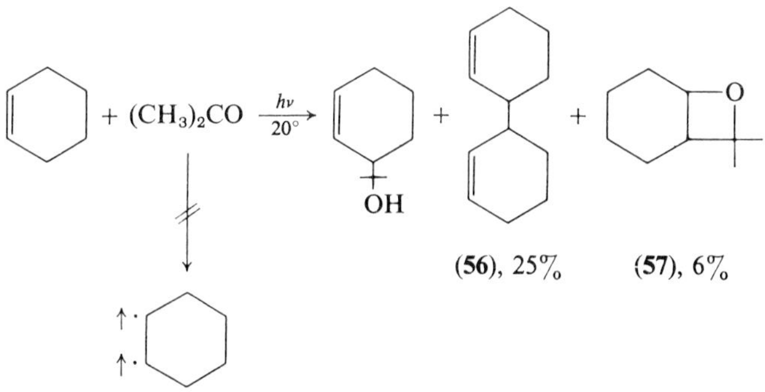

(56), 25%   (57), 6%

ring alkenes (19). If one assumes that the strain energy of small ring systems reduces the S_0–T_1 excitation energy, then acetone can provide this energy to the small ring alkenes, but not to cyclohexene. As a result, slower chemical

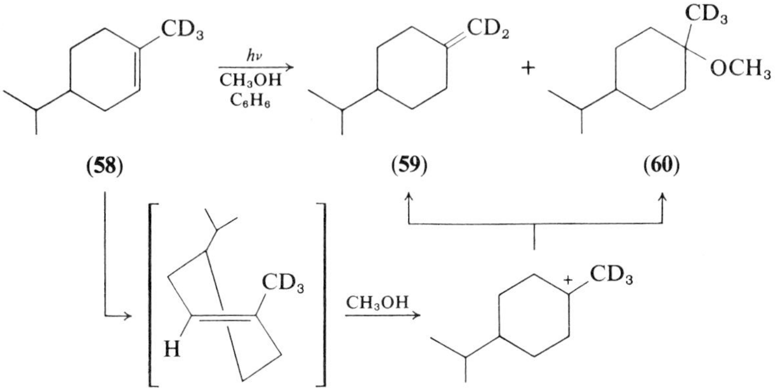

(58)   (59)   (60)

(61)   (62)

processes such as hydrogen abstraction and cycloaddition can compete with energy transfer (74).

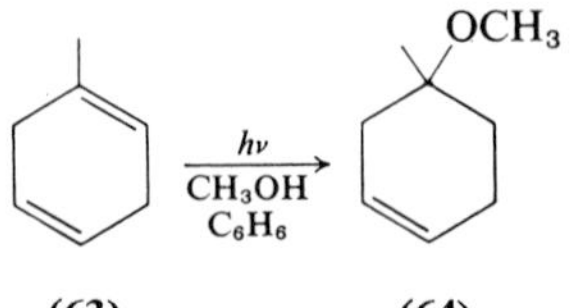

(63)   (64)

Irradiation of methanolic solutions of substituted cyclohexenes in the presence of benzene as photosensitizer yields products which are best rationalized as resulting from *ionic* intermediates (76,77). These results contrast with the photochemistry of small-ring alkenes which are nearly entirely explicable in terms of radical intermediates. The cause for this change in behavior may derive from the greater flexibility of the cyclohexene system. It may be that a *trans*-cyclohexene (77) capable of being protonated by the weak acid, CH_3OH, is formed and trapped.

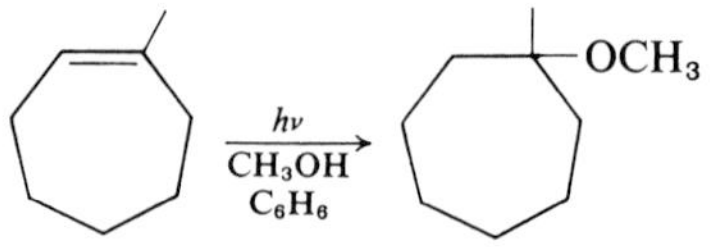

(65)   (66), 62%

1-Methylcycloheptene yields mainly the adduct **66** when irradiated under comparable conditions (76).

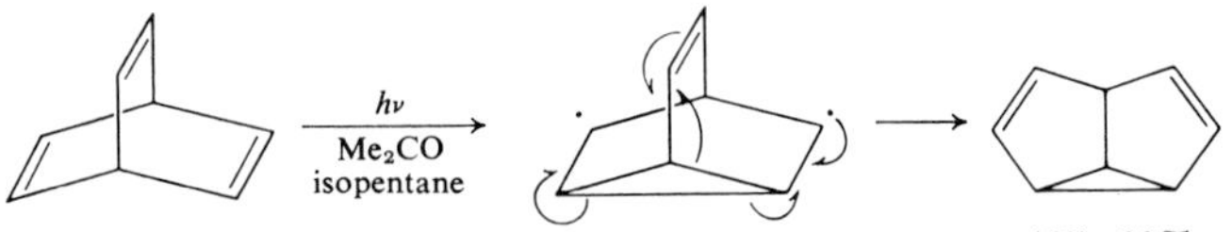

(67)   (68), 30%

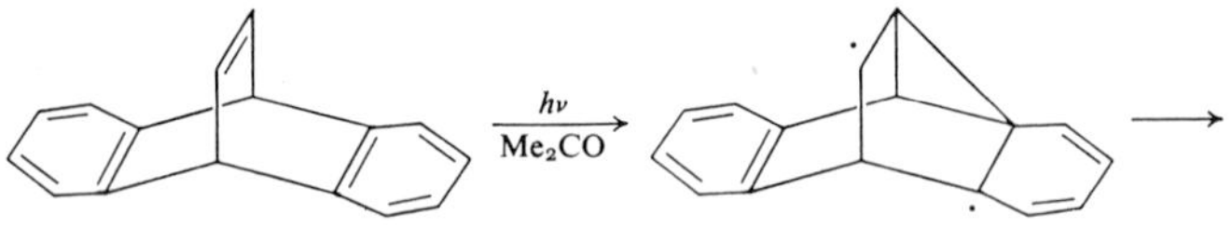

(69)

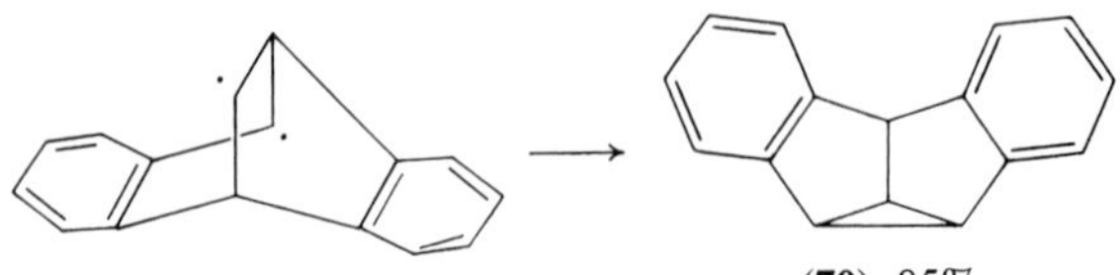

(70), 85% .

The addition reaction is selective, as shown by the above examples in which the product derived from the most stable carbonium ion intermediate is formed (76).

Intramolecular rearrangements of bicyclo[2.2.2]octadiene and its derivatives occur via a mechanism related to the norbornadiene–quadricyclene interconversion. For example, barrelene (67) yields 68 (78) and the dibenzbarrelenes (e.g., 69) undergo photosensitized rearrangement (79) to tricyclo-[3.3.0.0]octadiene derivatives (e.g., 70). Triptycene also undergoes an analogous reaction (79a).

Irradiation of ether solutions of 1,5-cyclooctadiene in the presence of $CuCl_2$ as "photosensitizer" serves as an excellent method for preparation of the tricyclic compound 72.

(71)   (72), 50%

Very little has been published concerning the photochemistry of large-ring alkenes. The photosensitized isomerization of 1,5,9-cyclododecatrienes appears to be unexceptional (83,84).

(73)   (74)   (75)

C. HETEROATOM-SUBSTITUTED ALKENES

Like alkenes, simple heteroatom-substituted alkenes have not been extensively studied. Halogen-substituted alkenes undergo cis–trans isomerization, as expected (85). However, when cis- or trans-1-iodopropene is irradiated in cyclohexane, α-cleavage occurs, followed by either elimination of a hydrogen atom (HI may be lost in one step) or hydrogen abstraction (86).

$$CH_3CH{=}CH{-}I \xrightarrow[C_6H_{12}]{hv} CH_3C{\equiv}CH + CH_3CH{=}CH_2$$
(76)   (77)   (78)

Irradiation of fumaronitrile (79) in the solid phase results in exclusive formation of 80 (87,88).*

* Photosensitized cis–trans isomerization of the 1,2-dicyanoethylenes has been reported.

(79)   (80)

Irradiation of a solution of tetracyanoethylene (TCE) and tetrahydrofuran yields **84**, presumably by hydrogen abstraction by the excited TCE to form the radicals **82** and **83** which then couple (89).

(81)   (82)   (83)   (84)

cis-Geranonitrile (**85**) is rearranged to the isomers **86, 89, 90**, and **91** by light (90,91). The *cis–trans* isomerization is presumably a primary process, in competition with a β-cleavage, leading to a pair of relatively stable allylic radicals which then couple to yield the observed rearrangement products. It has been pointed out that a new type of electronic transition may be involved here (91). Acetone sensitization yields **87** and **89** (90).

(85)   (86)   (87), 81%   (88), 19%

(89)   (90)   (91)

Irradiation of vinyl ethers usually results in β-cleavage of the O—C bond (92–96). For example, direct irradiation of the dihydrofuran **92** yields a number of rearrangement products (92). Whether the cleavage is radical or ionic in nature is not clear.

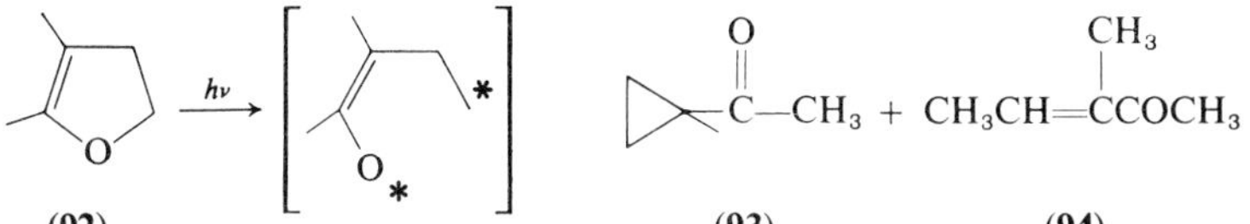

(92)   (93)   (94)

Benzene-sensitized photolysis of the sulfones **95** and **99** results in extrusion of SO_2 (**97**). The olefin mixture formed indicates that some stereospecificity is obtained. These results are of theoretical interest because they relate to symmetry selection rules which correctly predict the stereochemistry of the major isomer formed by (exited state) disrotary opening.

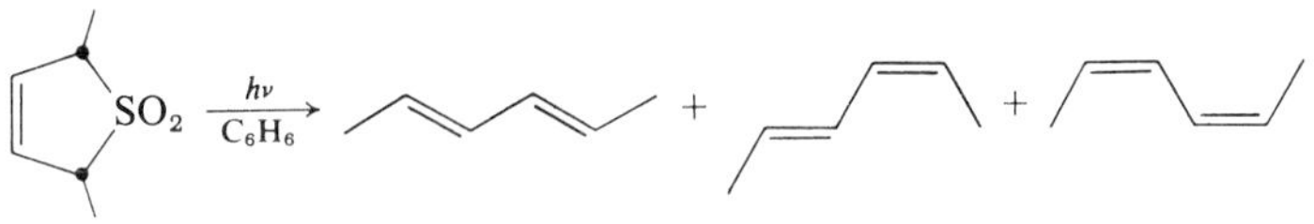

(95)   (96), 75%   (97), ~15%   (98), ~10%

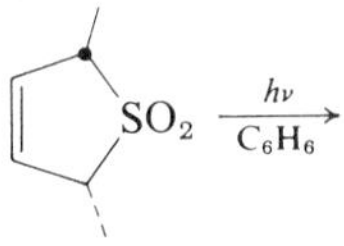

(99)

3. Photochemistry of Conjugated Polyenes

A. ACYCLIC CONJUGATED DIENES

(1) Butadiene

The primary processes discussed above for alkenes are formally the same ones required to rationalize the photochemistry of dienes. Since the conjugated 1,3-diene chromophore shows a high-intensity absorption maximum near 2200 Å and possesses "tail" absorption out to near 3000 Å, it is possible to employ 2537-Å light (low-pressure mercury lamps) to excite the singlet states of butadiene and its derivatives. Moreover, the triplet-excitation energy of dienes is usually 60 kcal/mole or lower. This relatively low triplet energy means that sensitized triplet excitation of dienes is possible with a wide range of sensitizers.†

Irradiation of dilute ether solutions of butadiene yields bicyclobutane and cyclobutene as the major products. Since butadiene consists of a pair of rapidly interconverting rotamers, it may be that excitation of the *trans*

† For reviews of conjugated diene photochemistry, see refs. 98–101.

rotamer (predominant form at 25°C) results in formation of bicyclobutane, while excitation of the *cis* rotamer results in formation of cyclobutene (102–106).

However, evidence exists that the formation of **4** may be two step (106,107). It seems strange that the small amount of *cis* rotamer should be able to capture a significant portion of the light and then to efficiently collapse to **3**.

$$\text{(1)} \xrightleftharpoons{h\nu} \text{(2)} \longrightarrow \text{(3)} + \text{(4)}$$

      (1)   **(2)**   **(3)**, 30% **(4)**, 5%

These reactions represent intramolecular cycloadditions and, if concerted, are subject to orbital symmetry considerations (107).

Irradiation of neat butadiene results in low yields of dimers and polymer in addition to **3** and **4**. The dimerization is nonselective and appears to be of little preparative value (108).

However, irradiation of butadiene in the presence of triplet sensitizers ($E_t > 60$) results in formation of dimers **5**, **6**, and **7** in high yield (109,110). Sensitizers possessing triplet-excitation energies below 60 but above 54 kcal/mole, lead to high yields of dimers, but the relative yield of **7** in the dimer mixture increases as the sensitizer energy approaches 54 kcal/mole (110,111).

$$\text{(1)} \xrightleftharpoons{} \text{(2)} \xrightarrow[\text{sens.}]{h\nu} \text{(5)} + \text{(6)} + \text{(7)}$$

      (1)   **(2)**   **(5)**, ~78%   **(6)**, ~19%   **(7)**, ~3%

This result is most easily explained by assuming that two stereoisomeric butadiene triplets are possible: a *trans* triplet (108) formed by sensitized excitation of **1**, and *cis* triplet (109) formed by sensitized excitation of **2**. If **1T** and **2T** are interconverted at a rate slower than that for formation of dimers, the variation in the ratio of dimers is explained since the *cis* rotamer, **2**, should require less excitation energy than the *trans* rotamer **1** on the basis of cyclohexadiene ($E_t = 54$) as a model for a *cis*-fused diene. Sensitizers of energy less than 60 but greater than 54 kcal/mole produce selectively larger amounts of *cis* triplet. The latter then adds to **1** to form proportionately greater amounts of **7**.

So far, attempts to photosensitize the closure of butadiene have failed (112). It should be noted that direct closure of a butadiene triplet to a cyclobutene triplet is energetically unfavorable (113).

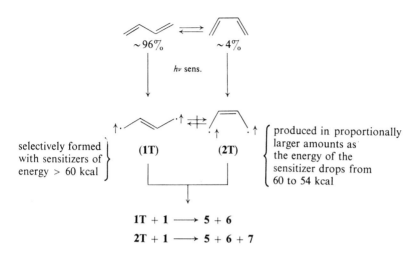

selectively formed with sensitizers of energy > 60 kcal ⎱ (1T) (2T) ⎰ produced in proportionally larger amounts as the energy of the sensitizer drops from 60 to 54 kcal

1T + 1 ⟶ 5 + 6

2T + 1 ⟶ 5 + 6 + 7

The difference between the sensitized and direct photochemistry of butadiene is paralleled by the photochemistry of substituted dienes. These results are of mechanistic and synthetic importance. On the one hand, it implies that the $S_1 \to T_1$ conversion of dienes is inefficient, and on the other hand, it allows selective formation of a wider range of products by appropriate choice of reaction conditions (114–116).

The photosensitized dimerization of butadiene represents a special case of trapping of diene triplets. One might expect that diene triplets can be trapped by other species, i.e., the usual bimolecular primary processes of diene excited states should be observed under favorable conditions. Indeed, butadiene triplets are relatively selective in their addition reactions. While other conjugated dienes may serve as substrates (or butadiene may serve as substrates for their triplets), intermolecular addition of diene triplets to nonconjugated C=C bonds does not compete with diene dimerization except in special conditions (114).

However, butadiene triplets may be added to haloolefins (117) and other substituted ethylenes (118). In these cases it is relatively easy to form the diene triplets selectively in the presence of substrates requiring higher energy for triplet excitation.

Direct excitation of a methanolic solution of butadiene (119) results in formation of the adduct **11**. It is not clear whether the reaction occurs

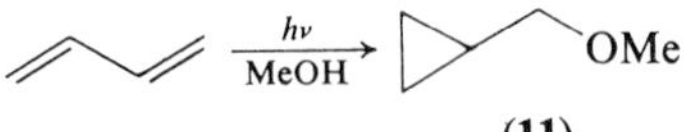

(11)

from an excited state of butadiene or is a secondary reaction of bicyclobutane with solvent (see part (3) below).

(2) Substituted Butadienes

The direct photochemical ring closure* (120–123) and photosensitized dimerization of butadienes is paralleled by substituted butadienes (120). The dimerization of isoprene shows a response to sensitizer E_T variation analogous to that shown by butadiene (109,124).

1-Alkyl butadienes undergo photosensitized and direct *cis–trans* isomerization. The photosensitized *cis–trans* isomerization of 1,3-butadienes has been used to count triplets (128) and to estimate the triplet energies of various sensitizers (126,127). Irradiation of alkyl 1,3-butadienes in alcohols yields a number of alcohol-diene adducts, some of which require the assumption of ionic intermediates (119a).

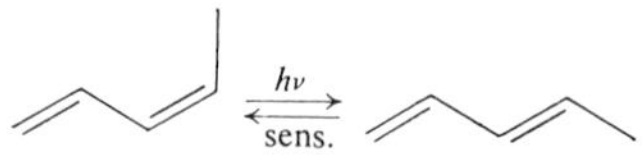

Intramolecular hydrogen transfer (120) occurs when 2-methyl-2,4-pentadiene, **13**, is irradiated directly. The product **13** undergoes isomerization to **14** which, in turn, closes to the cyclobutene **15**. Since the last reaction is essentially irreversible under the reaction conditions, a reasonable yield of cyclobutene results (121–123).*

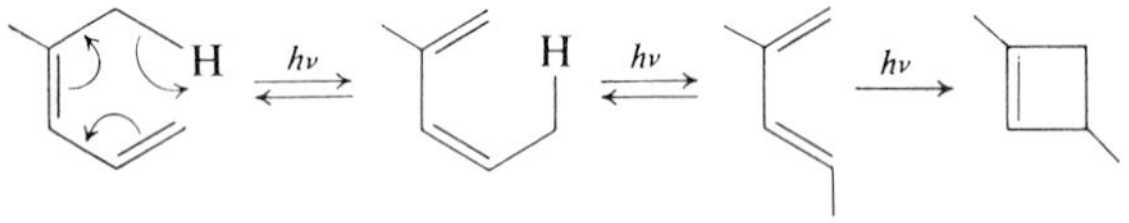

(12)   (13)   (14)   (15), 20%

Examples of intermolecular hydrogen abstraction by dienes are rare. However, this may be because such reactions have not been specifically

---

* See also refs. 98–101.

looked for. In a related system, the diyne **16**, photosensitized reduction of the triple bond occurs (129).

$$CH_3(CH_2)_3—C\equiv C—C\equiv C—(CH_2)_3CH_3 \xrightarrow[\text{pentane sens.}]{h\nu\ =\ 2537\ \text{Å}}$$
$$\text{(16)}$$

$$CH_3(CH_2)_3—CH\!=\!CH—C\equiv C—(CH_2)_3CH_3$$
$$\text{(17), } \sim 25\% \ (cis\ +\ trans)$$

Butadienes containing alkene side chains undergo direct photochemical closure to cyclobutenes as major products. Photosensitized intramolecular cycloaddition of the diene triplet on to the alkene linkage (130–133) occurs to a lesser extent. For example, myrcene, **18**, rearranges to **19** and **20** when irradiated (120,121) and a small amount of **21** is also produced. Under photosensitized conditions **18** forms **21** as the exclusive intramolecular adduct (130–132).

(**18**)   (**19**), 68%   (**20**), 10%

(**21**), 80%

These photosensitized reactions have been shown to require a long-lived biradical intermediate (131,132).

Conjugated dienes have been shown to quench the excited-singlet states of aromatic hydrocarbons. These results have practical importance in that, at high concentrations of dienes, an aromatic hydrocarbon may not be an effective triplet sensitizer because of singlet quenching (134).

B. ALICYCLIC CONJUGATED DIENES

(1) Small Ring Dienes

The photochemistry of the simplest small ring diene, 1,3-cyclobutadiene and its derivatives, must await their unambiguous syntheses and isolation. However, irradiation of tricarbonyl-cyclobutadieneiron has been shown to possibly release free cyclobutadiene (135).

It would seem that the cross-bonding reactions to form bicyclobutanes may not be favored relative to cyclobutene formation in small and medium rings because of the strain involved in such closures. Irradiation of cyclopentadiene results in formation of bicyclopentene, in low yield (136).

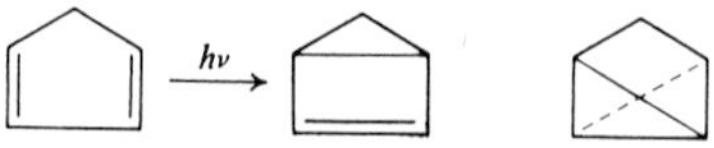

(22)   not formed

Cyclopentadiene triplets may be generated by photosensitization and are found to add to dienes (114,137) haloolefins (117), and α,β-unsaturated carbonyl compounds (139).

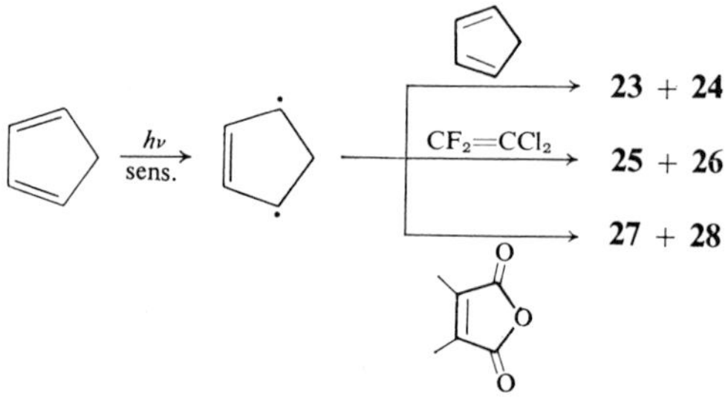

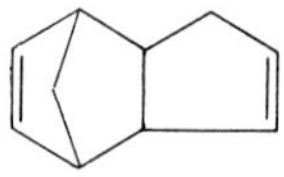

(23), 67% 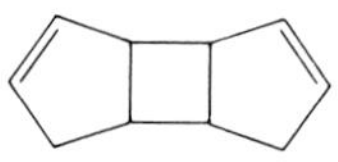   (24), 33%

(25), 30% 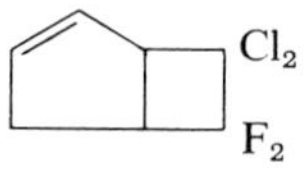   (26), 60%

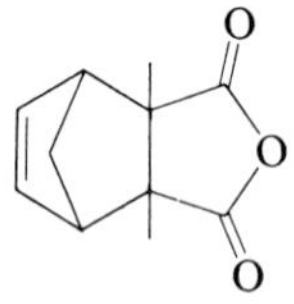

(27), 20% 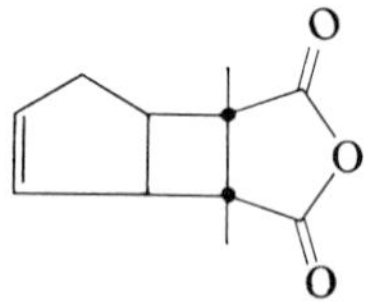   (28), 9%

Since cyclopentadiene is a *cis*-fused diene, stereoisomeric triplets are not possible and the ratio of adducts formed by attack of cyclopentadiene triplets on substrates is not dependent on sensitizer (119,138).

(2) 1,3-Cyclohexadiene and Related Compounds

The photochemistry of 1,3-cyclohexadiene and its derivatives is complicated by the fact that hexatrienes, which are often primary photoproducts, undergo further photochemical reactions. Thus, one must attempt to seperate the primary photochemistry of the cyclohexadiene system from the primary photochemistry of the hexatriene system.*†

Irradiation of neat 1,3-cyclohexadiene results in two types of β-cleavages. The first is simply the ring opening cleavage to yield 1,3,5-hexatriene **31** and the second is loss of atoms of hydrogen (by disproportionation?) to yield benzene (139,140).

(29)

(30), 86%   (31), 11%

Under photosensitized conditions, the cyclohexadiene triplets formed do not undergo cleavage reactions, but tend to add to unsaturated subtrates (117,139,141–143).

(32), 25%   (33), 75% (cis + trans)

(34), 70%   (35), 3%

An interesting intramolecular 1,4-1,4-photocycloaddition occurs when **35a** is irradiated (143). The parent hydrocarbon related to **35a** also undergoes an analogous ring closure (143a).

* Reviews: See refs. 98–101.
† For example, see ref. 164.

(35a)   (35b)

Photo-β-cleavage of **36** provides a route to bullvalene (**37**) from the cyclo-octatetraene dimer **36** (144–146).*

(36)   (37), 75%

The ring cleavage reaction of cyclohexadienes has been put to synthetic use for the syntheses of medium-sized rings (147–149). It should be noted that these cleavages are stereoselective and found to be conrotatory in accord with orbital symmetry considerations (107).

(38)   (39), 55%

An interesting, but rather special case of β-cleavage leading to aromaticization is provided by the photolysis of 7,7-dicyanonorcaradiene to form benzene and dicyanocarbene (149).

(40)

Although cyclohexadiene apparently does not close to a cyclobutene, a number of its derivatives do. At the present time it is difficult to predict whether bridging or ring opening will occur. Apparently the predominant ground-state conformation (which is related to the instantaneous excited-state conformation by the Franck-Condon principle) may determine whether ring opening or closure occurs (150).

* See also ref. 150.

When ring opening is somewhat inhibited (as in the anhydride **41**) closure occurs (150,151). The anhydride **42** has been used as a precursor for Dewar

benzene. In some systems ring opening and ring closure are competitive (151).

(3) Cyclic *trans*-Fused Dienes

Except for butadiene itself, acyclic conjugated dienes have not been reported to undergo isomerization to bicyclobutanes. Why butadiene should be peculiar is not clear. Other examples will almost certainly appear. Irradiation of cyclic *trans*-fused conjugated dienes yields bicyclobutanes or products rationally derived therefrom (152).*

For example, the diene **43** yields the bicyclobutane **44** (152).

Irradiation of the diene **44a** yields the bicyclobutane **44b** (155).

(4) Other Medium-Ring Dienes†

For cyclic C_7 and C_8 conjugated dienes, *disrotary* closures to *cis*-fused cyclobutenes are quite general. For 1,3-cycloheptadiene (156,157) and 1,3-cyclooctadiene (158,159) the closure products are the major ones, but the nature of the side reactions have not been elucidated. They probably involve hydrogen abstraction or dimerization of the diene.

The "photosensitizated" ring closure (160) of *cis,cis*-1,3-cyclooctadiene (162) has been shown to proceed in two steps: (*a*) photosensitized

* For other examples see refs. 153 and 154.
† Reviews: refs. 98–101.

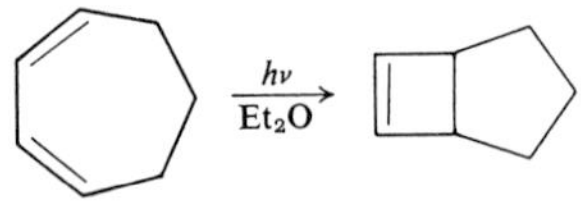

(45)   **(46), 60%**

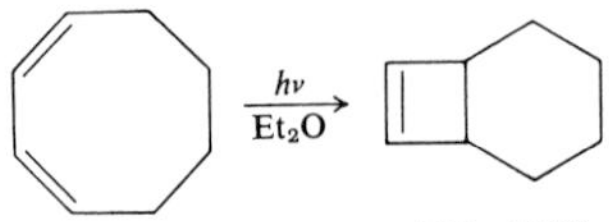

(47)   **(48), 40%**

isomerization to *cis,trans*-1,3-cyclooctadiene **49** and (*b*) thermal *conrotary* closure to the cyclobutene **50** (163).*†

This result indicates that one should consider the possibility that 1,3-cyclohexadiene-bicyclo[2.2.0]hexene conversions may proceed via a *trans,cis*-

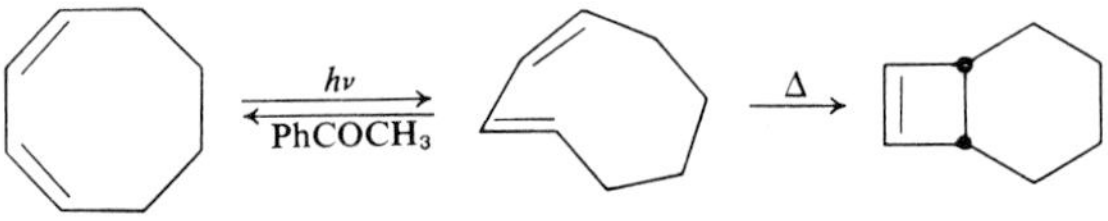

(47)   **(49), 62%**   **(50)**

1,3-cyclohexadiene intermediate, which undergoes conrotary thermal closure. ,

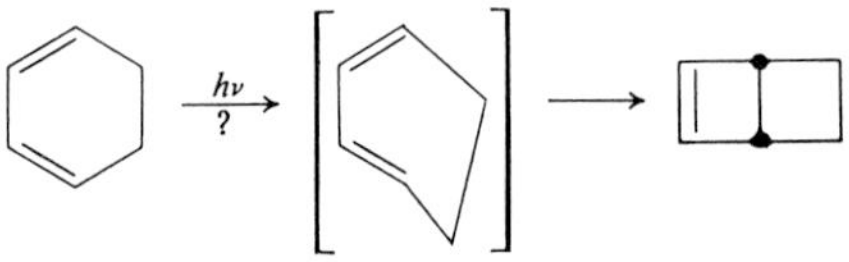

(51)

Irradiation of benzene epoxide **52** yields benzene and phenol as main products. Since phenol is the exclusive product of acetone sensitization,

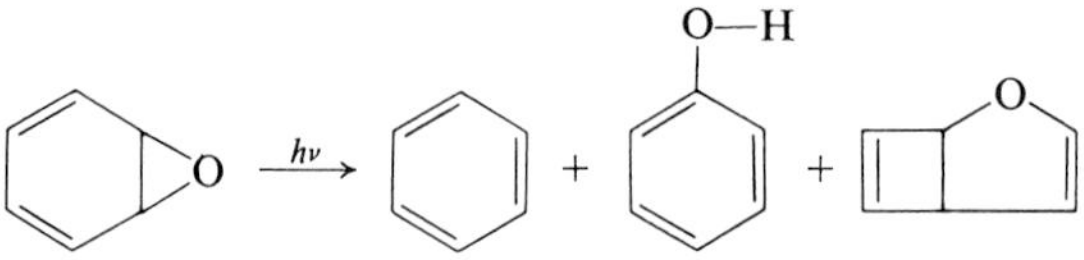

(52)   15%   75%   11%

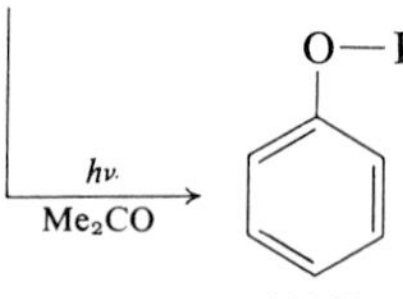

100%

* One example of a "photosensitized" closure remains, but may be rationalized as above for 1,3-cyclooctadiene (163).

† Thus it appears that triplets do not undergo valence isomerization efficiently.

there appears to be a difference in reactivity of the singlet and triplet states of **52** (191).

C. ACYCLIC CONJUGATED TRIENES

(1) 1,3,5-Hexatriene

As mentioned earlier, the photochemistry of 1,3,5-hexatrienes and the corresponding 1,3-cyclohexadienes are sometimes difficult to differentiate because these valence isomers are often in photochemical (and sometimes thermal) equilibrium.

Irradiation of *cis,cis*-1,3,5-hexatriene (produced from irradiation of 1,3-cyclohexadiene) results in formation of the valence isomers **54a**, **54b** and some polymer (164,165).

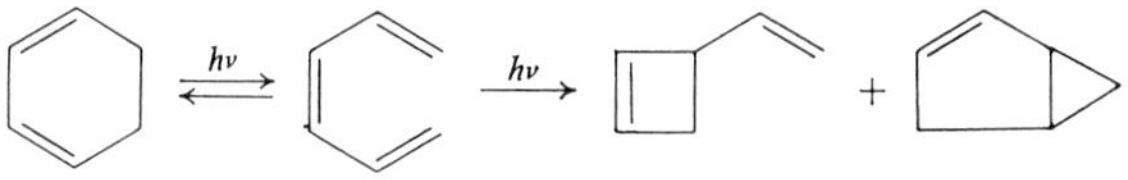

| **(54)** | **(54a)**, 12% | **(54b)**, 12% |

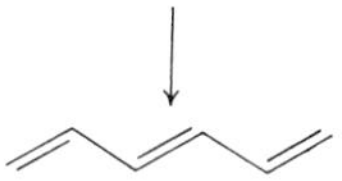

(54c)

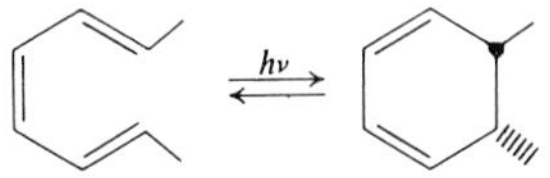

(55), 90%   **(56)**, 10%

Substituted 1,3,5-Hexatrienes. Irradiation of *trans,cis,trans*-2,4,6-octa-triene yields *trans*-5,6-dimethyl-1,3-cyclohexadiene by *conrotary* closure, leading to a photoequilibrium (166).*

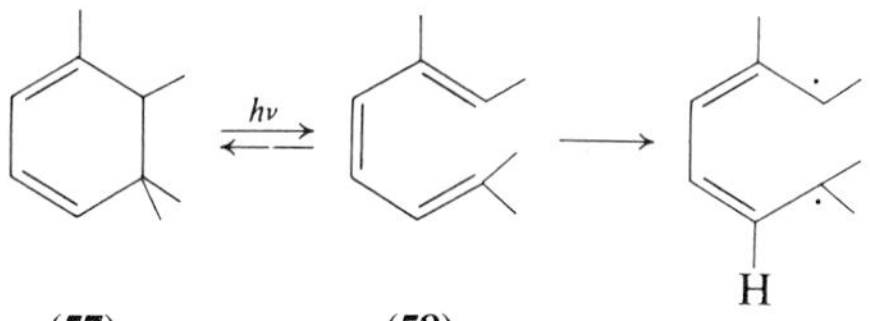

(57)   **(58)**

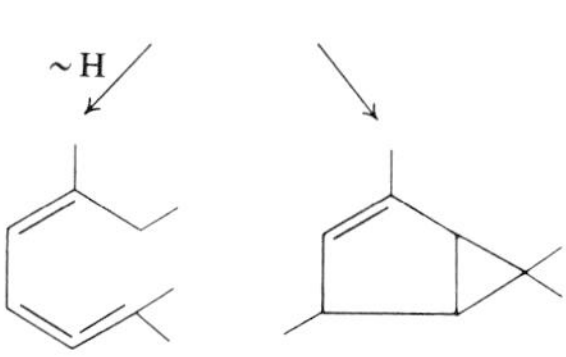

(59), 37%   **(60)**, 14%

* Thermal (disrotary) closure of **55** leads to *cis*-5,6-dimethyl-1,3-cyclohexadiene (167).

The triene **58**, produced from the cyclohexadiene **57** yields both the valence isomer **60** and the hydrogen migration product **59** (168–171).

Other important examples of 1,3,5-hexatriene photochemistry may be found in the photoreactions of compounds in the vitamin D series (172–174).

D. ALICYCLIC CONJUGATED TRIENES AND TETRAENES

(1) 1,3,5-Cycloheptatriene and Derivatives

Irradiation of 1,3,5-cycloheptatriene **61** and its simple derivatives leads to formation of the valence isomer **62** (157,175,176).

$$\text{(61)} \qquad \text{(62), 34\%} \qquad \text{(63)} \qquad \text{(64)} \qquad \text{(65)}$$

In addition to valence isomerization, photochemical 1,2-hydrogen shifts also occur. The rate of the 1,2-shift is usually comparable and sometimes greater than that for valence isomerization (177,178).

(2) Cyclooctatrienes

1,3,5-Cyclooctatriene **66** undergoes photochemical valence isomerization to **67** and **68** (179). The photoreduction product **69** is also produced as the major product.

It is interesting to note that these hydrogen shifts are predicted correctly as 1,7-shifts by the Woodward-Hoffmann rules. Furthermore, the hydrogen shift apparently occurs in the triene *singlet* state (178).

$$\text{(66)} \qquad \text{(67), 15\%} \qquad \text{(68), 6\%} \qquad \text{(69), 28\%}$$

It should be noted that **68** is structurally related to the bicyclic isomers **53b** and **60** formed from 1,3,5-hexatriene and **58** (164,179,180,184). Irradiation of **66** in methanol results mainly in formation of **67** and **68** with a minor amount of **70** (181). The cyclooctatetraene dimer **71**, when irradiated, yields the [16]-annulene **72** (182).*

---

* An intermediate has been detected in the photolysis of **66** and assigned the 1,3,5,7-octatetraene structure (183).

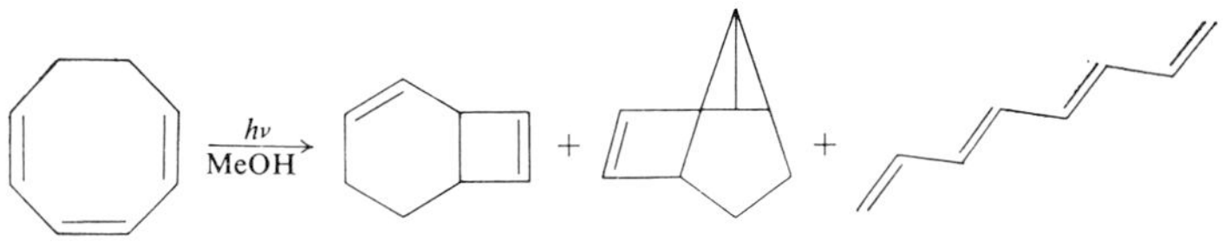

(66)   (67), 68%   (68), 32%   (70)

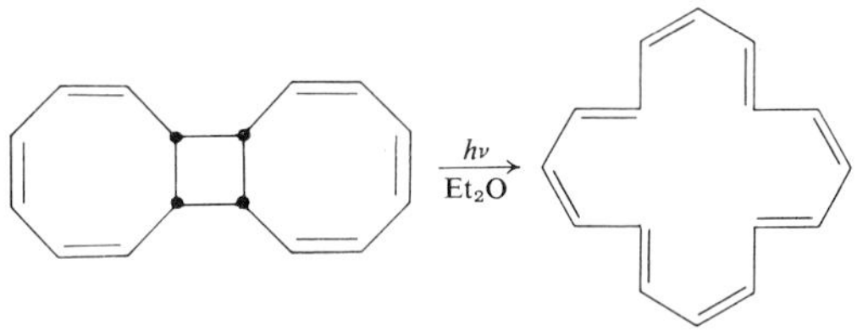

(71)   (72), 10%

(3) Cyclooctatetraene

Irradiation of cyclooctatetraene **73** apparently leads to valence isomerization, followed by cleavage to benzene and acetylene (185). At $-78°$, **73** photorearranges to semibullvalene **76** (185a).

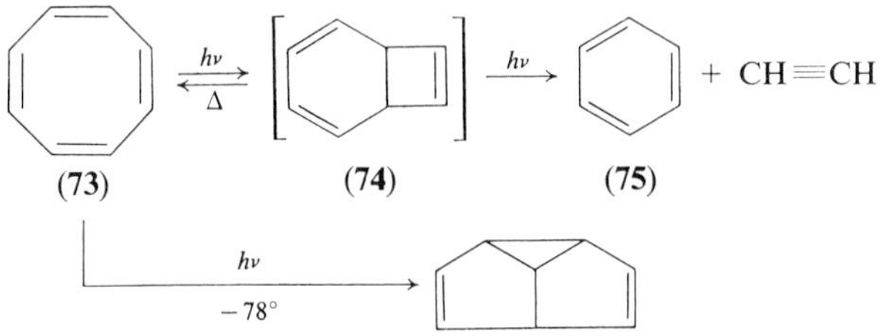

(73)   (74)   (75)

(76)

Substituted cyclooctatetraenes undergo *cis-trans* and valence isomerization (183a) and cleavage (184), but the dibenzo derivative **77** rearranges to the isomer **79**, perhaps via the valence isomer **78** (186).

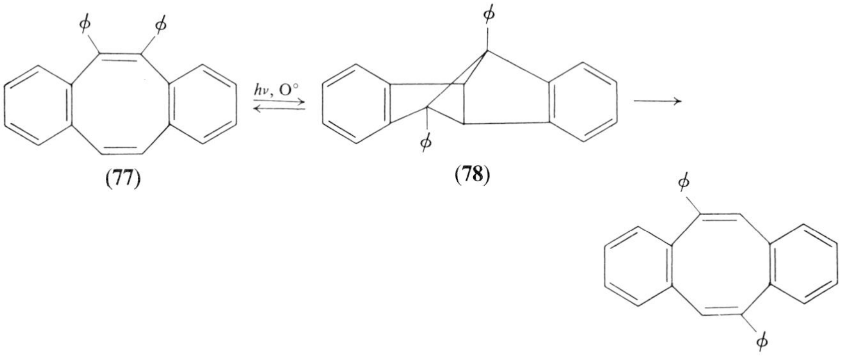

(77)   (78)

(79), 34%

E. HETEROCYCLIC DIENES AND TRIENES

(1) Furan, Pyrrole, and Thiophene

Furan, pyrrole, and thiophene have been used as substrates for solution photochemical additions but have not been reported to undergo photochemical transformations when irradiated in solution. Substituted furans and thiophenes (Section II–3–A–(1)) undergo photoreactions (187).

Irradiation of N-benzylpyrrole results in migration of the benzyl group into the ring (188).

(80)   (81), 13%

(2) Miscellaneous

The dieneamine 82 (189) and the diene ether 84 (190) undergo photocyclization to form the valence isomers 83 and 85, respectively.

(82)   (83), 81%

(84)   (85), 65%

Irradiation of the oxepine 86 yields 87 as the main product, while naphthalene sensitization yields phenol as the main product (191).

(86)   (87)

II. AROMATIC HYDROCARBONS AND SIMPLE DERIVATIVES

1. General Considerations and Theory

A. EXCITED STATES OF BENZENE AND CATACONDENSED HYDROCARBONS

(1) A Model for the Excited States of Alkenes

Simple molecular orbital theory is inadequate for a description of the electronically excited π,π^* states of benzenes. This obtains from the fact that simple theory predicts the lowest, unfilled π^* orbitals of benzene are degenerate as are the two highest filled π-orbitals (192). Thus, the problem of describing the lowest excited π,π^* states of benzene, i.e., those expected to determine its photochemistry, can only be solved with sophisticated calculations (193–195).

However, back rationalizing from experimental data, the excited π,π^* states of benzene seem to behave as if important contributors from valence forms **1a**, **1b**, and **1c** are involved. Note the relationship of some of these

(1a)	(1b)	(1c)

forms to those involved in diene and especially 1,3,5-hexatriene chemistry. In higher catacondensed aromatic compounds, in contrast to benzene, the excitation appears to be localized on certain atoms, e.g., the 9,10-positions of anthracene or phenanthrene. These biradical forms serve as primitive

(2)	(3)

models for predicting and rationalizing the known photochemistry of aromatic hydrocarbons.

(2) Primary Processes of Aromatic Hydrocarbons

Benzene and its alkyl derivatives are known to undergo valence-isomerization reactions. These have analogy in hexatriene chemistry. Thus, a number of benzene–benzvalene (195) and benzene–Dewar benzene (196) interconversions are known.

Interestingly, the Woodward-Hoffman rules (196) predict that the conversion **1b** to **5** should be allowed (i.e., treating benzene as a modified diene) to occur in disrotary manner, thus resulting in the required *cis* stereochemistry for **5**.

(1c)   **(4)**

(1b)   **(5)**

Other primary processes to be expected are (*a*) α- and β-cleavage reactions;

(*b*) addition to unsaturated systems;

(*c*) hydrogen abstraction reactions;

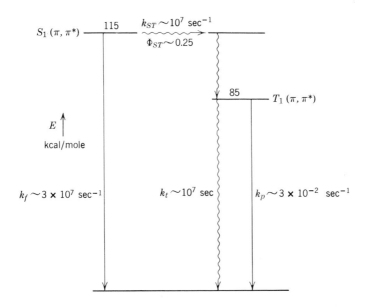

(3) Energy-Level Diagrams for Benzene and Catacondensed Aromatic Compounds

Since benzene and many of its derivatives give moderately high yields of luminescence at 77° in rigid glasses (197), information on the energy levels of these compounds has been available for some time (198). More recently, intersystem crossing yields and the lifetimes of these compounds have become available (199–201).

Figures 4, 5, and 6 depict the energy diagrams of benzene, naphthalene, and anthracene, respectively. As can be seen, the energy of the lowest triplet level drops rapidly as linear condensation of rings occurs. Interestingly T_2 for anthracene lies close to, and slightly below, S_1 (202). Thus, substitution on the anthracene nucleus may push the T_2 state above S_1, thereby greatly modifying the triplet yield (202,203).

Fig. 4. Energy diagram for benzene at 25° (tentative).

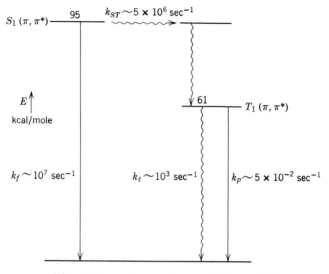

Fig. 5. Energy diagram for naphthalene at 25°.

The singlet energies E_1, triplet energies E_3, triplet decay constants, k_t, and intersystem crossing yields Φ_{st} for some aromatic hydrocarbons and their simple derivatives are given in Table 2.

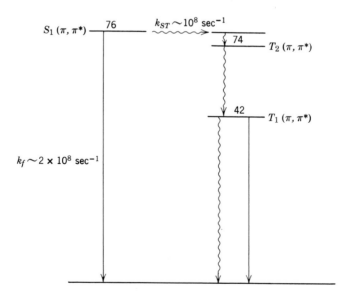

Fig. 6. Energy diagram for anthracene at 25°.

TABLE 2

Energies, Decay Constants, and Triplet Yields of Some Benzenes and
Condensed Aromatic Hydrocarbons

Compound	$E_1{}^a$	k_t	Φ_{st}	$E_3{}^a$	Ref.
Benzene	115	3	0.85	85	204–207, 209
Fluorene	95	10	0.31	68	204, 207
Triphenylene	83	2	0.95	67	207
Naphthalene	91	1	0.75	61	204, 207, 209
Pyrene	86	48	0.10	48	204, 206, 210
Anthracene	76	20	0.70	42	204, 208

^{a} Energies in kcal/mole, rate constants in sec^{-1} × 10^7.

B. EXCITED ELECTRONIC STATES OF STYRENE AND STILBENE DERIVATIVES

(1) A Model for the Excited States of Styrene and Stilbene

In devising a model for the excited states of alkenes conjugated to an aromatic nucleus, we must consider that the excitation may be localized on the alkene or the aromatic portion of the molecule. In some cases, the interaction of the alkene and the aromatic ring may be strong enough to vitiate attempts at considering the excitation to be localized. When the alkene and aromatic portions *can* be separated, the excitation usually resides in the group which has the lowest excitation energy (Section II–3–B–(3) below).

For example, the π,π^* states of stilbene may be considered to receive contributions from forms such as **6a** and **6b**.

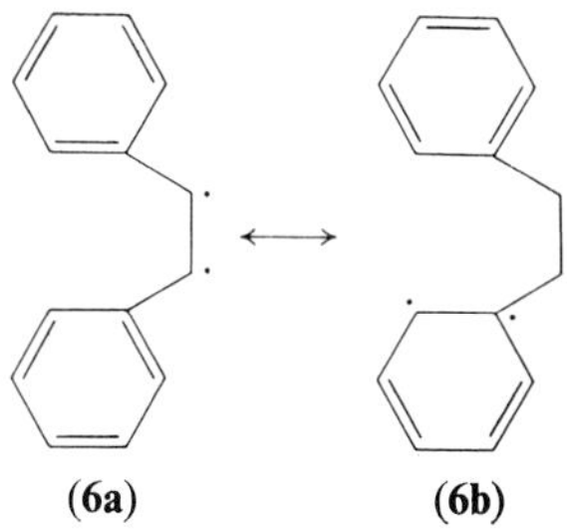

(6a)   (6b)

(2) Primary Processes of Conjugated Aromatics

Using the forms **6a** and **6b** as primitive models for the excited states of stilbene, the following primary processes are expected, among others: (*a*) cycloaddition to unsaturated groups;

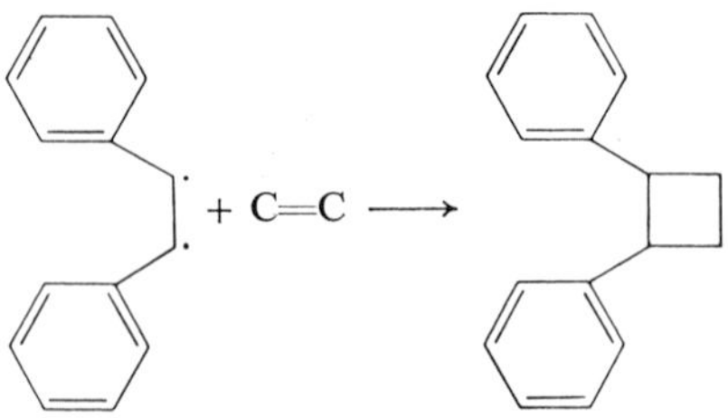

(b) intramolecular cycloaddition;

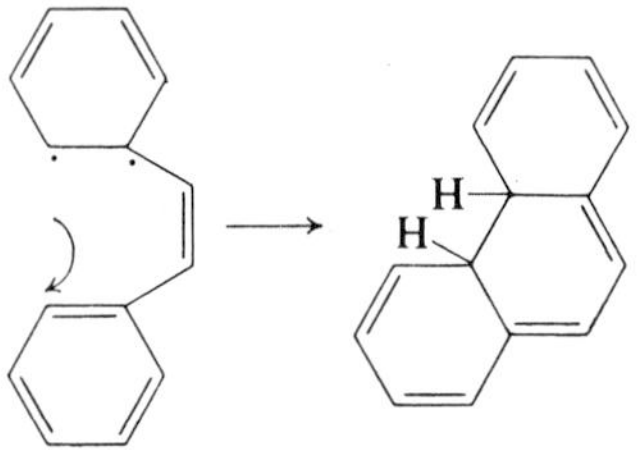

(c) cis–trans isomerization;

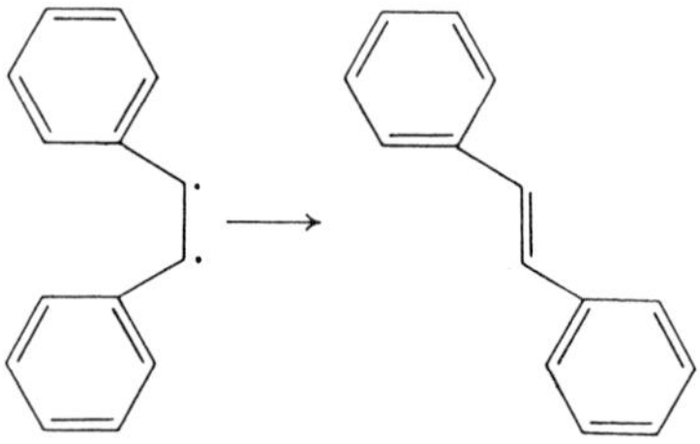

(3) Energy Diagrams for Conjugated Aromatics

The flexibility of conjugated aromatics in their excited states may result in short lifetimes for these species (204). Also the phenomenon called "non-

TABLE 3

Triplet Energies of Some Conjugated Aromatic Molecules

Compound	$E_3{}^a$	Reference
Phenylacetylene	72	212
Diphenylacetylene	62	211
Styrene	62	211
Stilbene	50	211
$C_6H_5CH=CH-CH=CHC_6H_5$	52	211

ᵃ Energies in kcal/mole.

vertical" energy transfer appears to be common for the more flexible conjugated aromatic molecules.

Some E_3 values for conjugated aromatic compounds are given in Table 3.

2. Photochemistry of Benzene and Catacondensed Derivatives

A. BENZENE AND ITS SIMPLE DERIVATIVES

(1) Benzene

Although benzene is relatively stable toward photochemical decomposition, numerous products are formed in low yields when benzene is photolyzed under various conditions. The "stability" of benzene toward photodecomposition may result from rapid reversible photovalence isomerizations (see below).

For example, benzvalene, 1, may be isolated in low yield by irradiation (2537 Å) of liquid benzene (213). Under somewhat different conditions,

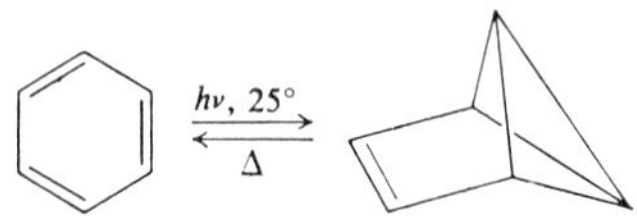

(1), ~0.01%

fulvene (2) and "Dewar" benzene (2a) are also produced from irradiation of benzene (214,215).

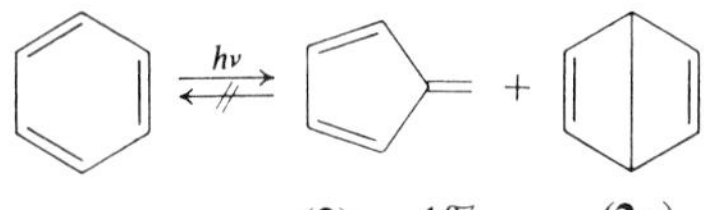

(2), ~1%   (2a)

The benzene nucleus may be added photochemically to a number of C≡C and C=C bonds resulting in synthetically useful cycloadditions (216,217).

Benzene and maleic anhydride form a weak complex in solution. Excitation of the complex with 3000 Å light or by energy transfer results in formation of the 2:1 maleic anhydride–benzene adduct 4 (218–222,229).

It is assumed, but not proven, that the photo-1,2-addition to form 3 is followed by a thermal 1,2-1,4-addition to yield 4.

The addition of maleic anhydride to alkyl benzene proceeds in moderate to low yields (223,224). Additions of the excited state(s) of benzene to unsaturated substrates occur in fair yields. Dimethyl acetylene dicarboxylate, 5, and benzene yield the cyclooctatetraene, 7, presumably via the bicyclooctatriene intermediate 6 (225,226).

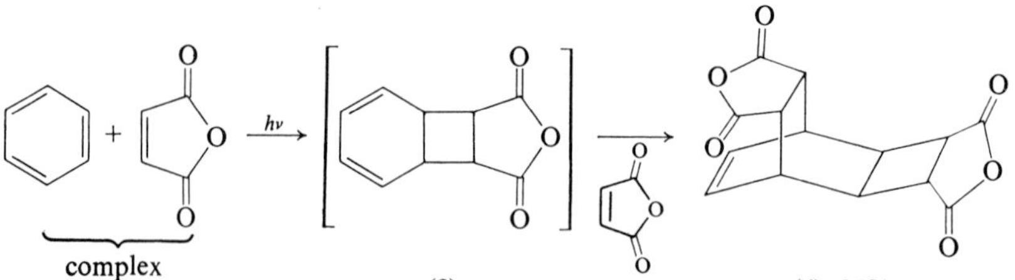

complex   (3)   (4), 95%

Methyl acetylenecarboxylate and phenylacetylene have also been added photochemically to benzene (225). Alcohols (and presumably other polar

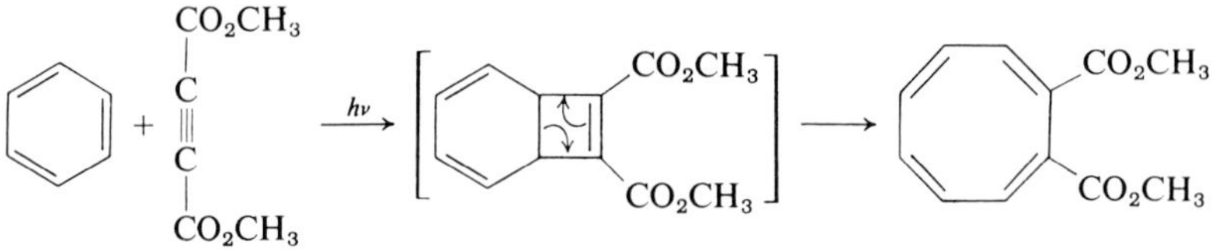

(5)   (6)   (7)

reagents) may be added to benzene to form interesting structures such as **8**. A trace of acid is required for efficient addition (227–229). Good yields of 1:1

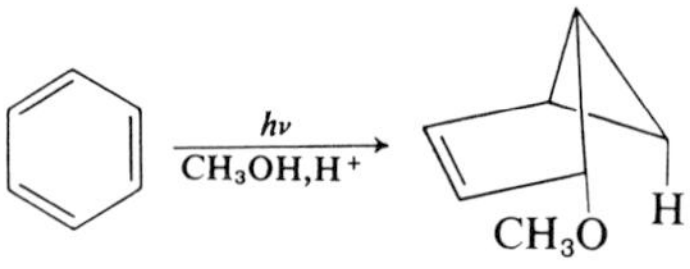

8

adducts are formed when benzene is irradiated in alkene solvents. The structure of the adducts indicates that either benzvalene or an excited state of benzene reacts with the olefin to yield structures such as **9** (230,231).

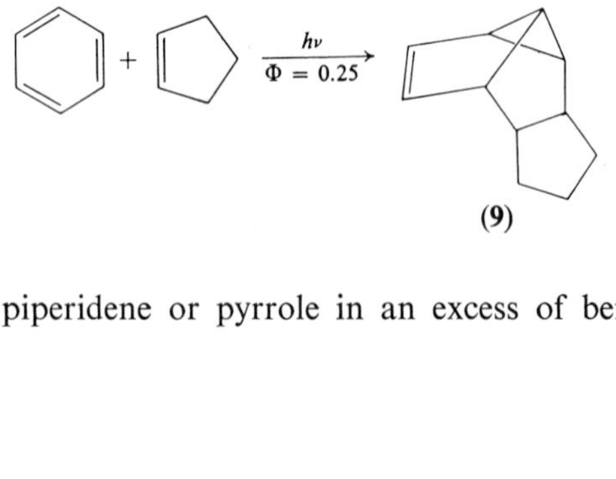

(9)

Irradiation of piperidene or pyrrole in an excess of benzene yields 1:1 adducts (232).

Irradiation of benzene in the presence of dienes results in the formation of a number of adducts. For example, irradiation of a butadiene–benzene mixture leads to the 2:2 adduct **11a** in good yield. The genesis of **11a** and **11b** is not known but it may involve a 1,4-1,4-addition to yield **10** which then undergoes (photosensitized?) dimerization (233,234).

Irradiation of a benzene–isoprene mixture results in formation of the related 2:2 adduct **13**. In addition, the 1:1 adduct **12** is formed.

(2) Alkyl Benzenes

Alkyl benzenes undergo rearrangements via transposition of the ring carbon atoms with the attached alkyl groups (235–239). Very probably these rearrangements proceed via benzvalene, bicyclo[2.2.0]hexadiene, and prismane intermediates. In the case of 1,3,5-tri-*tert*-butylbenzene, **14**, these remarkable structures may actually be isolated. A photoequilibrium occurs with the following photostationary state being produced by 2537-Å light (235–239).

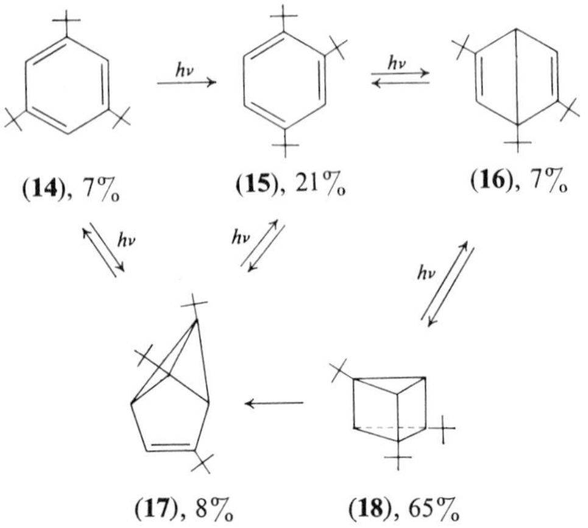

(14), 7%   (15), 21%   (16), 7%

(17), 8%   (18), 65%

Irradiation of the hydrocarbons, **21** and **22**, results in closure to the cyclopropanes **23** and **24** (240). This reaction has a close analogy in the rearrangement of **25a** to **25b** (241,242).

$$\text{PhC(CH}_3)_2\text{CH=CH--CH=C(CH}_3)_2 \xrightarrow{h\nu}$$

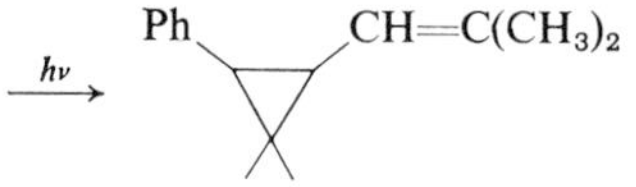

+ other products

cis + trans   cis + trans

(21)   (22)   (23)   (24)

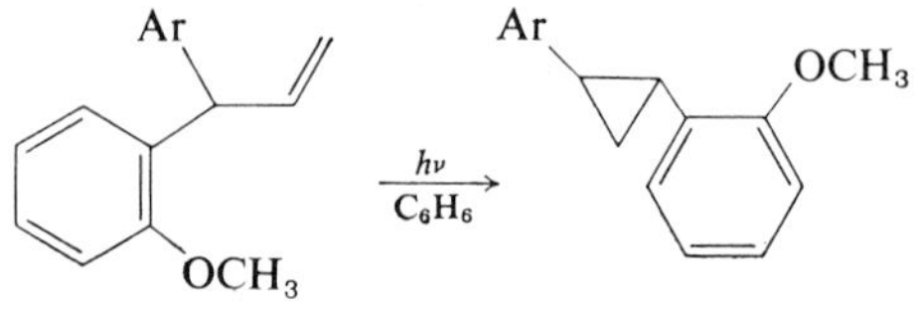

(25a)   (25b), 90%

(3) Benzenes with Small Ring Substituents

Irradiation of phenyl cyclopropane and its derivatives usually causes β-cleavage of the small ring as the important primary process. When one β bond is broken, geometrical isomerization or group migration may occur. For example, *trans*-1,2-diphenylcyclopropane, **26**, is reversibly converted to its *cis*-isomer, **27**, by direct or sensitized excitation (244). A remarkable feature of this reaction is the formation of *optically active* **26** when the optically active sensitizer **29** is employed (245). This result is strong evidence for the contact mechanism of energy transfer, since the transition state for energy transfer is highly dependent on the orientation of the partners involved.

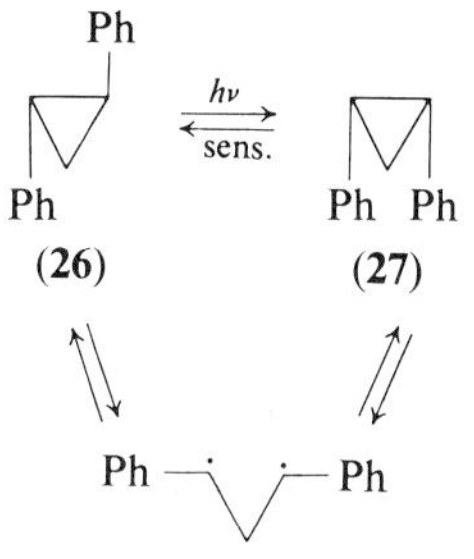

(26)   (27)

(28)

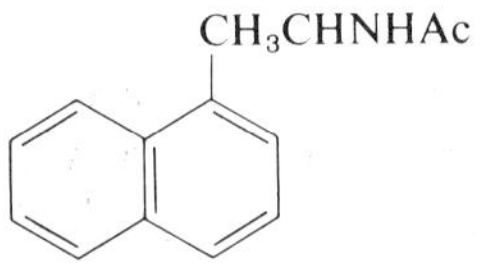

(29)

Irradiation of alkyl phenylcyclopropanes results in hydrogen migration to yield olefins (246–248). For example, irradiation of **30** yields **31** in good yield.

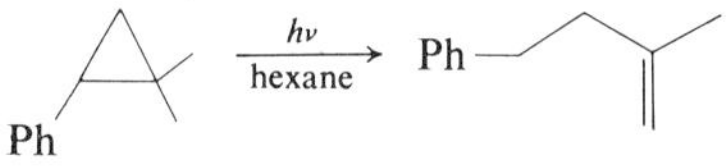

(**30**)   (**31**), 80%

In certain cases *bis* β-cleavage occurs to yield methylenes and olefins. These reactions offer an elegant method of producing methylenes under extremely mild and neutral conditions (249,250). For example, irradiation of 1,1,2,2-tetraphenylcyclopropane, **32**, in methanol yields **34** and **33**, whereas irradiation of **32** in 2-methyl-2-butene yields the cyclopropane **35**. Although the

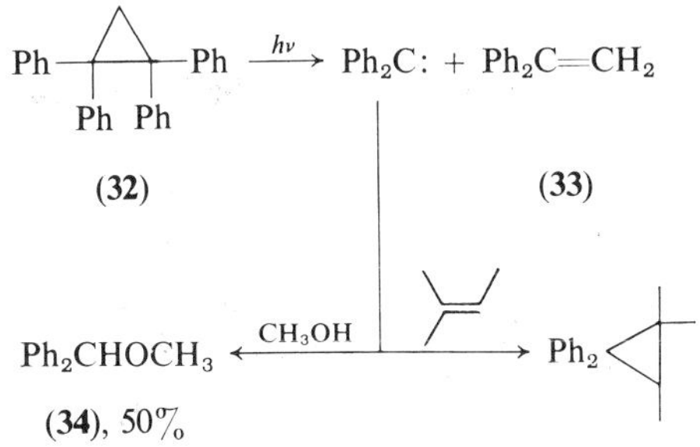

(**32**)   (**33**)

Ph_2CHOCH_3 $\xleftarrow{CH_3OH}$ Ph_2

(**34**), 50%

(**35**)

above reactions appear to possess the flavor of homolytic cleavages; 1,3-heterolytic addition may also occur. Thus irradiation of methanolic solutions of *trans*-1,2-diphenylcyclopropane yields **36** (251) in addition to the *cis* isomer **27**, the rearrangement product **37**, and the carbene adduct **38**.

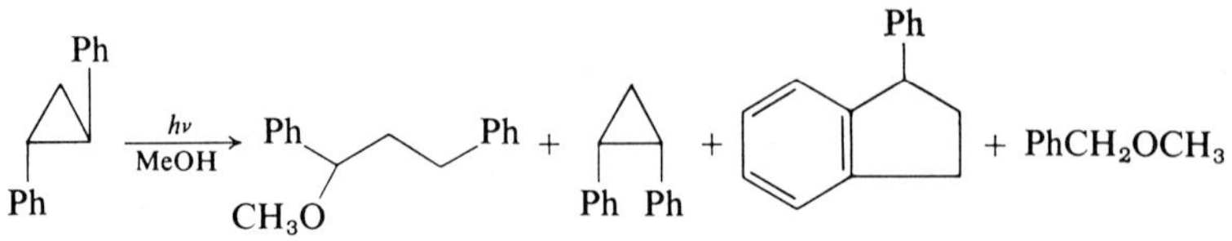

These reactions should be compared to the polar addition of alcohols and acids to benzvalene (228,229).

Irradiation of 1,2-dimethyl stilbene oxide and related compounds results in formation of carbenes and carbonyl compounds (252–255). The carbene thus generated may be added to various alkenes in 40–60% yield. Interestingly, a hydrogen shift to yield styrene does not compete with the addition of methyl phenyl carbene to olefins or alcohols. The yield of the cyclopropene may be

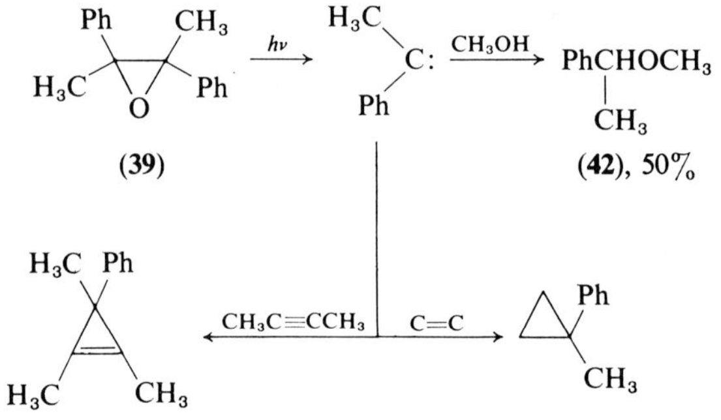

low because of its secondary photolysis to the indene **44** (252).

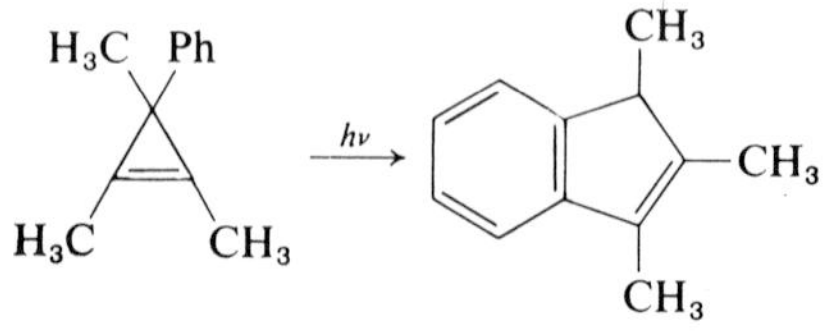

Irradiation of the oxazirane **44a**, in amine solvents yields **44b**, presumably via phenyl azide (256):

(**44a**)   (**44b**)

Irradiation of 1,2-*trans*-diphenylcyclobutane results in *cis–trans* isomerization and rearrangement to **48** (257). On the other hand, irradiation of *cis,trans*,

(**45**)   (**46**)

(**47**)   (**48**)

cis-1,2,3,4-tetraphenylcyclobutane results in smooth reversible cleavage to *trans*-stilbene (258).

Irradiation of benzonorbornadienes in the presence of acetophenone results in photosensitized formation of rearrangement products. The mechanism of these rearrangements may be related to the rearrangements of

(**49**)   (**50**)

norbornadiene and to barrelene and its derivatives (259). For example, photoisomerization of dibenzobicyclo[2.2.2]octatriene yields **52**. The reaction is photosensitized by acetone.

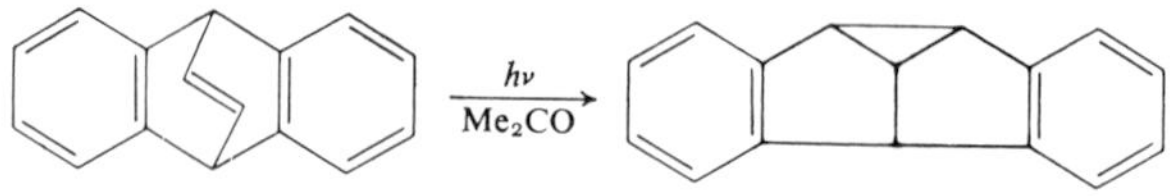

   (51)   **(52)**, 85%

(4) Phenols, Anilines, and Related Compounds

Irradiation of phenols and phenyl ethers often results in cleavage β (homolytic and heterolylic) to the aromatic nucleus (262–264).

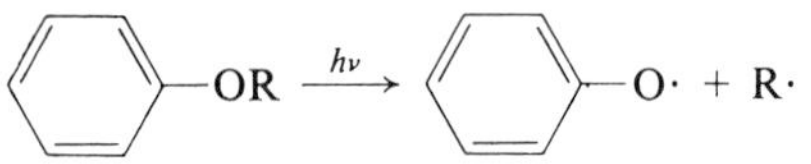

In the case of ring-substituted phenyl ethers, this cleavage results in formation of photo-Fries products and phenols (261–264).

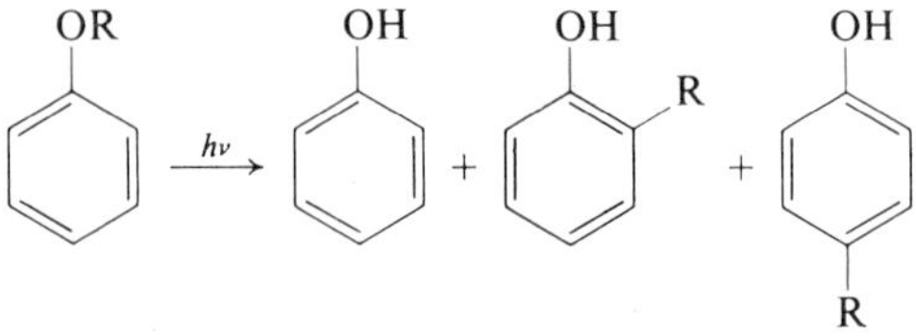

Heterolytic β-cleavage may also occur under favorable conditions. It appears that in contrast to the situation in ground-state substitution reactions, the electron-releasing or withdrawing effects of ring substituents are transmitted more effectively from the meta position than the para position. For example, irradiation of **53a** in aqueous dioxane results in smooth photosolvolysis to the alcohol **53b**, a reaction sequence indicative of ionic intermediates or transition states (265).

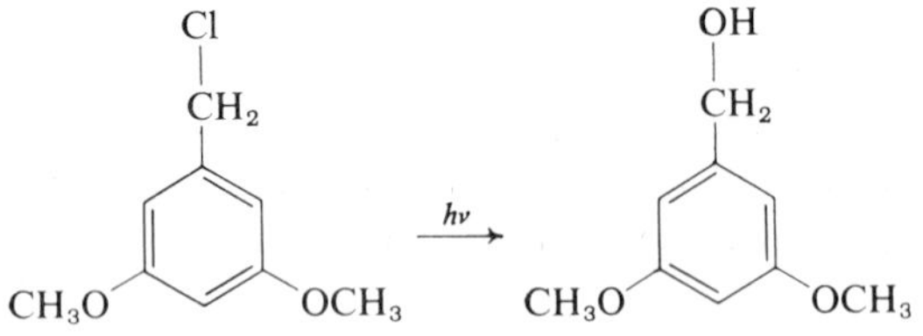

    (53a)   **(53b)**

Phenols are very strong acids in their excited-singlet states (267). The cyclization of **53c** to **53d** may be explained on the basis of an intramolecular protonation of the double bond followed by cyclization (268,269).

(53c)   (53d), 40–50%

Irradiation of diphenyl amines in the presence of oxygen leads to the formation of carbazoles (270–272). The mechanism would appear to involve the intramolecular attack of an excited benzene nucleus on its unexcited partner to lead to the intermediate **54** which then is dehydrogenated to yield **55**.

(54)   (55)

(5) Aromatic Halides

Photolyses of aromatic halides results in products to be expected from reaction of the radicals produced by cleavage of the Ar—X bond. Aromatic halides are particularly easily cleaved photochemically. For example, irradiation of iodobenzene in benzene leads to formation of biphenyl (273–275).

(55a)   (55b), 57%

(55c)

Intramolecular cyclizations and benzyne formation result when **55a** and **55c**, respectively, are irradiated (276,277).

(6) Sulfones

Benzocyclobutene **57** may be prepared by irradiation of **56** in the vapor phase (278). Similarly irradiation of **58** in solution results in formation of

(56)   (57)

1,2-diphenyl benzocyclobutene **59**.

(58)   (59)

B. POLYNUCLEAR AROMATICS

(1) Naphthalene and Derivatives

Except for anthracenes, the photochemistry of polynuclear aromatic compounds has not been extensively studied. Naphthalene is apparently stable to ultraviolet irradiation. Several examples of additions to the naphthalene nucleus are known, however. For example, irradiation of a solution of diphenylacetylene and naphthalene results in formation of the unusual adduct **60a** (280,281), via the initial adduct **60b** (281).

(60a)   (60b)

Attempts to add other unsaturated groups to naphthalene have been generally unsuccessful, except for a low yield of 1:1 adduct with maleic anhydride (282,283).

One example of a cyclic dimerization of a naphthalene is known, that of **61** to **62**. Why the reaction should go in this case but not in others is not clear (284,284a).

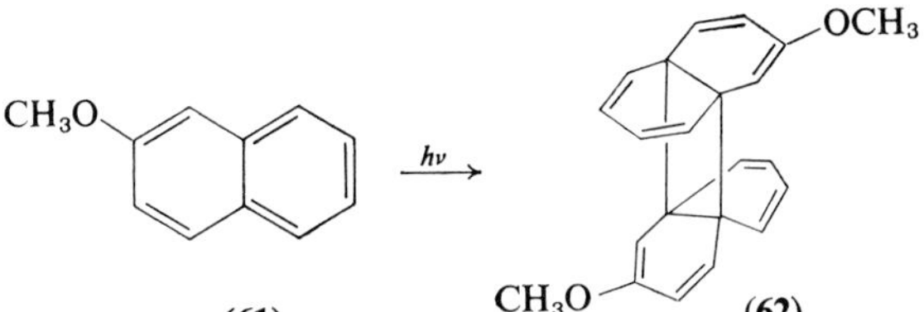

(61)   (62)

The naphthylene paracyclophane **62a** yields the interesting isomer **62b** (285).

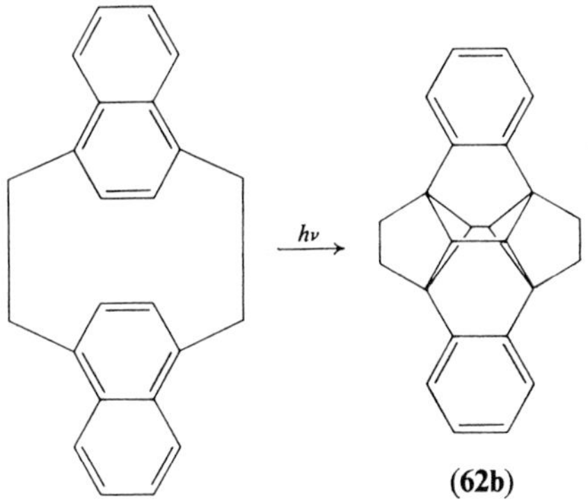

(62b)

(62a)

Although phenanthrene apparently does not dimerize photochemically, it does add maleic anhydride (286).

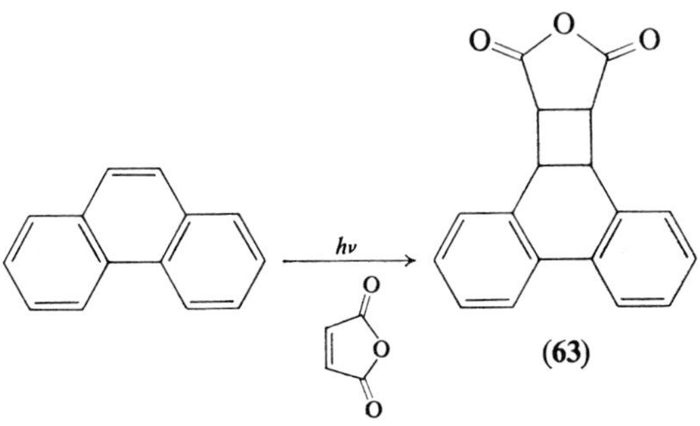

(63)

9,10-Dicyanophenanthrene, however, is reported to yield the dimer **64** (287).

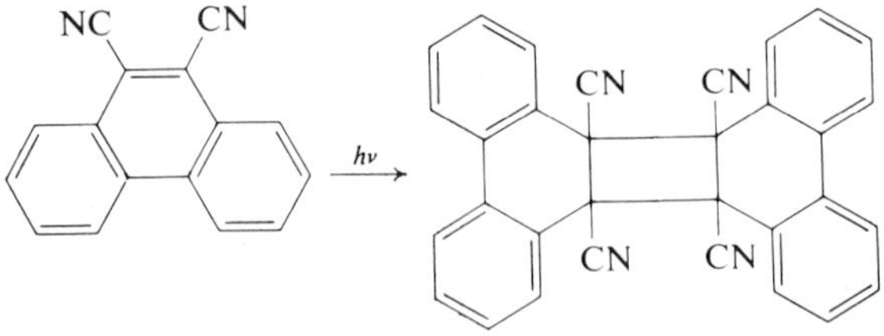

(64)

(2) Anthracene and Derivatives

Anthracene and its derivatives undergo photoadditions across the 9,10-position. Irradiation of degassed solutions results in formation of dianthracene, while irradiation of anthracene in the presence of oxygen results in formation of the peroxide **66** (288–291). The dimerization of the anthracene

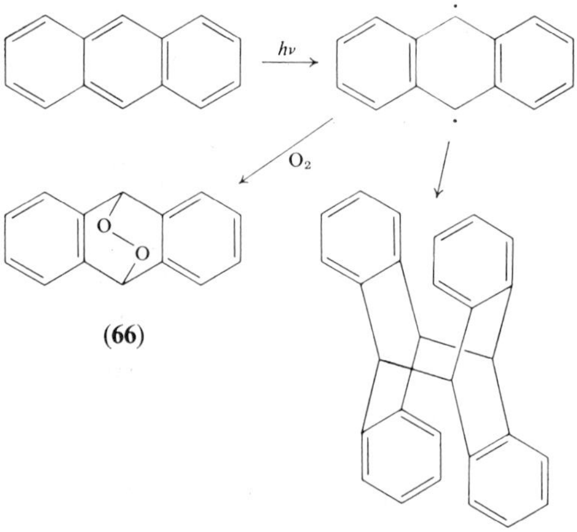

(66)

(65)

nucleus may also take place by an intramolecular mechanism (288,292). Naphthacene and other higher polycondensed aromatics apparently undergo similar photodimerization and addition reactions (293).

3. Photochemistry of Conjugated Aromatics

A. STYRENE AND STILBENE AND RELATED COMPOUNDS

(1) Styrene Derivatives

Irradiation of styrene results in polymerization (294) and dimerization (257). However, irradiation of substituted alkyl styrenes results in ring closure to cyclopropanes (295–297). This reaction is the reverse of the opening of cyclopropanes to olefins (Section II–1–A–(3)). Indene (3) is efficiently

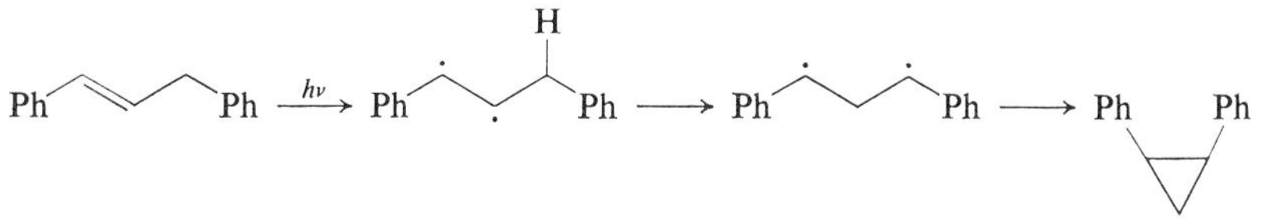

(2) (cis + trans)

dimerized head to head to the *trans*-cyclobutane 4 employing benzophenone

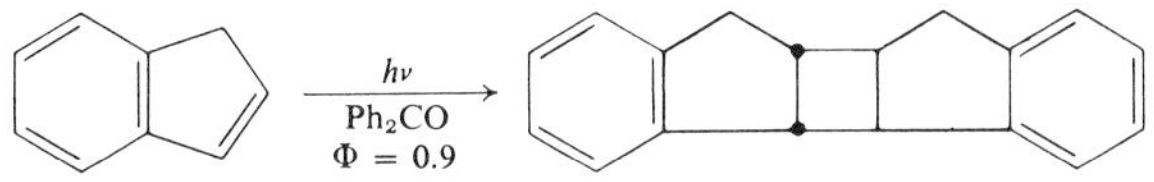

(3)   (4), 100%

as a sensitizer (298,299). Cross addition of indene to other molecules may also occur (300).

Styrene derivatives of general structure **4a** undergo ring opening to colored products such as **4b** (301,302).

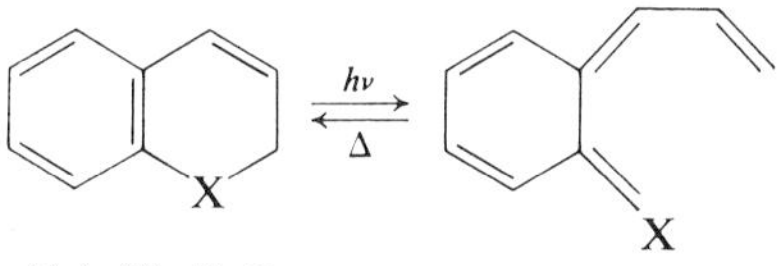

(4a), X=S, O   (4b)

Irradiation (303,304) of 1,2-divinylbenzene yields **4c** (compare the rearrangement of 1,3,5-hexatrienes, Section II–3–C–(1)).

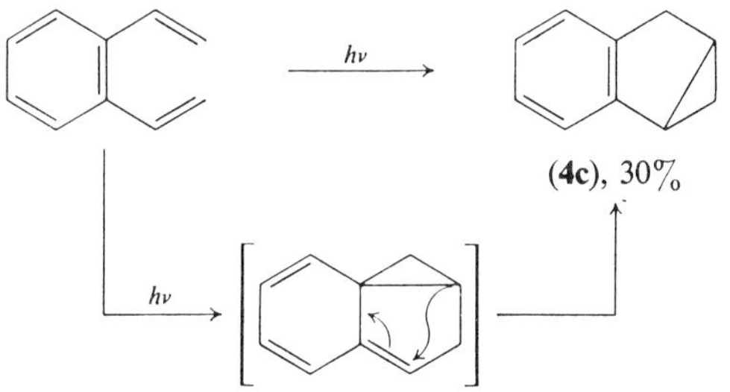

(4c), 30%

Acenaphthylene undergoes a solvent-dependent dimerization to yield the cyclobutane (305–307). Irradiation of 2-phenylthiophene results in

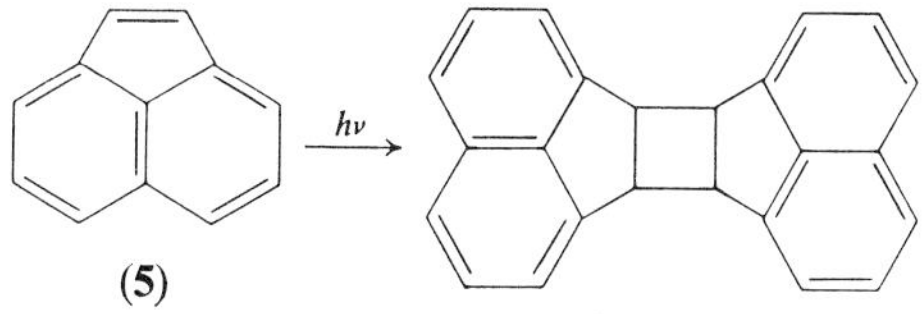

(5)

(6), *trans*
(7), *cis*

rearrangement to 3-phenylthiophene (308). Labeling experiments imply the

intermediacy of the valence shell expanded species **8**.

(8)

(2) Stilbene and Its Derivatives

The photochemistry of stilbene and its derivatives has been extensively studied. In addition to *cis–trans* isomerization, which appears to be a completely general reaction of acyclic stilbenes, two other important reactions are cyclization to yield dihydrophenanthrenes and dimerization to yield cyclobutanes. Both of the latter reactions appear to arise from S_1, although *cis–trans* isomerization apparently may occur from S_1 to T_1. The dihydro-

phenanthrene **11** may be detected spectrophotometrically (314–316).

Both stilbene and diphenylacetylene undergo photochemical addition to tetramethylethylene (317). In analogy to the dimerization of stilbene the

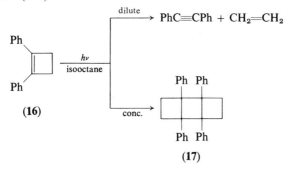

$$\text{PhCH}=\text{CHPh} + \text{Me}_2\text{C}=\text{CMe}_2 \xrightarrow{h\nu}$$

$$\text{PhC}\equiv\text{CPh} + \text{Me}_2\text{C}=\text{CMe}_2 \xrightarrow{h\nu}$$

triphenylcyclopropene dimer **13** apparently undergoes intramolecular cycloaddition followed by valence isomerization to yield **15** (318,319).

Irradiation of the diphenylcyclobutene **16** results in bis β-cleavage to diphenyl-acetylene and ethylene in dilute solution and dimerization to **17** in concentrated solution (321).

III. CARBONYL COMPOUNDS

1. General Considerations

A. EXCITED STATES OF ALDEHYDES AND KETONES

(1) A Model for the Excited States of Aliphatic Aldehydes and Ketones

Simple molecular orbital theory serves as a reasonable basis for the description of excited states of aliphatic aldehydes and ketones which are of interest

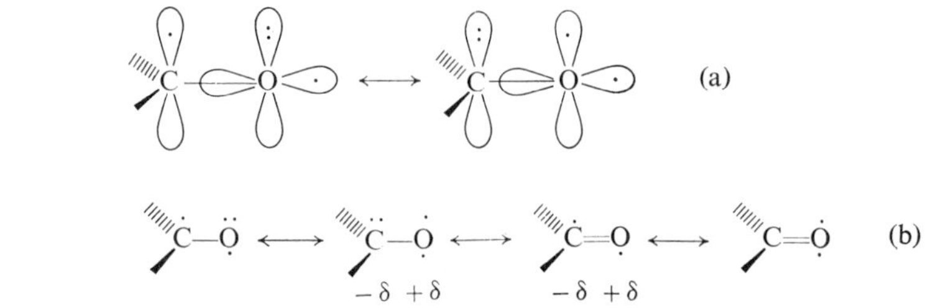

Fig. 7. Atomic orbital (a) description of the n,π^* state of an aldehyde or ketone and a valence bond (b) description of the same states.

to the organic photochemist. The lowest excited states of aliphatic aldehydes and ketones are generally assumed to be the π,π^* and n,π^* states, with the latter usually of lowest energy, and therefore the photochemically active singlet and triplet state. In terms of MO's, both S_1 (n,π^*) and T_1, (n,π^*) may be pictured as a system containing 2π electrons, one n electron and one π^* electron. A simple model which makes the same qualitative predictions as the MO description may be given in terms of the atomic orbitals on the carbon and oxygen of the carbonyl group (322,323) or in terms of valence structures (Fig. 7). Both of these descriptions predict that the n,π^* state should be a "bipolar" species in the sense that the carbonyl oxygen atom is a radical-like electrophilic species which has its main electron deficiency as a half-vacant orbital (a positive "hole") in the plane of the carbonyl function. The carbonyl carbon atom (or π system), on the other hand, should behave as a radical-like, nucleophilic species which derives reactivity from the presence of three electrons in the pi-system which is located above and below the plane of the carbonyl function.

If the excited states of aldehydes and ketones are roughly planar, then the stereoelectronic predictions of this simple model are given in Figure 8. Although formaldehyde is known to be puckered in its n,π^* state, this deformation derives largely from unusual bonding between its α-hydrogens and need not concern us here (324–330).

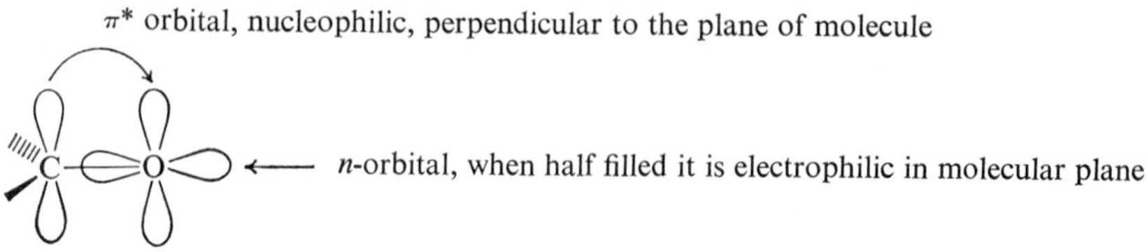

π^* orbital, nucleophilic, perpendicular to the plane of molecule

n-orbital, when half filled it is electrophilic in molecular plane

Fig. 8. Stereoelectronic reactivity relationships for a carbonyl n,π^* state.

(2) Primary Processes of Aliphatic Aldehydes and Ketones

The model for the n,π^* states of aldehydes and ketones presented above does not differentiate between the reactivities of singlet states and triplet states, since spin is not considered in deriving the model.

There are three general primary photochemical processes of the carbonyl function which are commonly encountered:

(a) cleavage of a bond α to the carbonyl function (α-cleavage);

$$\text{R}_2\text{C}\!-\!\ddot{\text{O}} \longrightarrow \text{R}\!-\!\text{C}\!=\!\ddot{\text{O}} + \text{R}\cdot$$

(b) abstraction by the oxygen atom of the n,π^* state from a suitable donor (hydrogen abstraction or photoreduction);

$$\text{R}_2\text{C}\!-\!\ddot{\text{O}} \;\; \underset{\text{H}-\text{R}}{\longrightarrow} \;\; \text{R}_2\text{C}\!-\!\ddot{\text{O}}\text{H} + \text{R}\cdot$$

(c) addition of the oxygen atom of the n,π^* state to an unsaturated linkage, usually a C=C or C≡C group (addition or oxetane formation).

$$\text{R}_2\text{C}\!-\!\ddot{\text{O}} + \text{C}\!=\!\text{C} \longrightarrow \left[\begin{array}{c} \text{R}_2\text{C}\!-\!\ddot{\text{O}} \\ | \\ \text{C}\!-\!\text{C} \end{array} \right] \longrightarrow \text{R}_2 \begin{array}{c} \text{O} \\ | \quad | \\ \text{C}\!-\!\text{C} \end{array}$$

Numerous other primary processes, especially those involving the π^* system, can be conceived and derived from this model and may eventually be discovered experimentally.

(3) Energy Diagrams for Aliphatic Ketones

The location of the energy levels of aliphatic carbonyl compounds generally cannot be obtained precisely from spectroscopic data because of the lack of structure in the absorption and emission spectra of these compounds (325).

An energy diagram for acetone, which we shall assume is a good model for other acyclic aliphatic aldehydes and ketones, is given in Figure 9. The important features of this diagram are: (a) the S_1 (n,π^*) state of acetone is relatively low in energy compared to other simple chromophores; (b) the T_1 (n,π^*) state of acetone is relatively high in energy compared to most chromophores (only simple benzene derivatives possess a higher E_3); (c) the lifetime of S_1 is long enough to allow participation in bimolecular processes of low

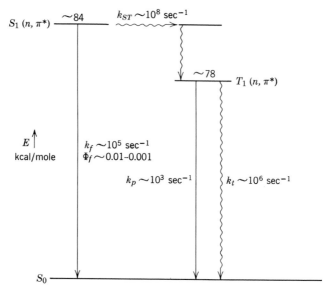

Fig. 9. Energy diagram for acetone.

activation energy. Because of their high E_3, aliphatic ketones are commonly employed as photosensitizers for unsaturated compounds possessing low absorption above 2800 Å.

B. EXCITED STATES OF AROMATIC ALDEHYDES AND KETONES

(1) A Model for the Excited States of Aromatic Aldehydes and Ketones

The model for the n,π^* state of alkyl aldehydes and ketones given above suffices for description of the photochemistry of aldehydes and ketones possessing lowest n,π^* states. We would expect that, although the primary processes should remain similar for aliphatic and aromatic carbonyl systems with lowest n,π^* states, the rate constants for these primary processes should vary with the nature of the aromatic moiety.

An important complication occurs, however, if an excited state associated with the aromatic group is strongly "mixed" into the lowest singlet or triplet. In the latter case, we expect the photochemistry typical of the n,π^* state to be modified or to disappear entirely. For example, if a π,π^* aromatic state is lower in energy than the carbonyl n,π^* state, reactivity may be more like that of a π,π^* state of a carbonyl function because of "coupling" or interaction of the π,π^* aromatic and n,π^* carbonyl states.

In general, however, the model for the n,π^* state of alkyl ketones and aldehydes given in Section III–1–A–(1) suffices as a description of aryl ketones and aryl aldehydes. It should be made clear at this point that we are dealing with models when we discuss or classify electronically excited states *in terms of the electron configuration which makes the major contribution to that state.* We must realize that these descriptions are only approximate. We know that, *in principle,* the n,π^* state of alkyl ketones possesses some π,π^* character. For example, the T_1 state should be described as

$$T_1 = a(n,\pi^*) + b(\pi,\pi^*)$$

where a and b are measures of the extent to which each configuration n,π^* or π,π^* contributes to the *actual state* T_1 of the molecule in question. For acetone, it would seem that $a \gg b$. The weighting of contributions of each configuration may be compared to the weighting of valence structures of ground-state molecules. The magnitude of the contribution of a given state depends on several factors, one of which is the *energetic separation* (for which the contribution varies inversely, as the square of the energy difference) of the configurations involved.

For aryl ketones the calculated energies of n,π^* and π,π^* configurations are much closer than for alkyl ketones so that the corresponding S_1 or T_1 states may not be so clearly described in terms of either configuration. Indeed, for certain substituted benzophenones and all naphthyl ketones and aldehydes, the lowest triplet is better classified as π,π^*. This classification implies that: (*a*) the excited carbonyl oxygen is not as electron deficient as it is in the n,π^* state, (*b*) the excitation energy is delocalized into the π system and may therefore not be available to overcome activation energies for reaction at the carbonyl moiety and (*c*) primary processes involving the π-system (or groups affixed to it) may occur.

In the case of certain aryl ketones and aldehydes possessing strong electron-releasing groups, a configuration which involves nearly complete transfer of an electron from the substituent to the carbonyl group is required to describe this excited state (structure **3a**, Fig. 10). This has the effect of reducing the electrophilicity of the carbonyl oxygen in the excited state and making it nucleophilic. States which are best described by such a model are called charge-transfer (CT) states.

Only in the case of n,π^* states is the triplet-excitation energy largely localized in the carbonyl group (331). In Figure 10 the three common types of T_1 states of aryl ketones are exemplified for benzophenone (**1**), 2-acetonaphthone (**2**) and 4-aminobenzophenone (**3**) in terms of major contributing structures.

Several points concerning these *models* can be made: (*a*) since alkyl ketones do not have the possibility of structures such as **1c** (π^* electron delocalized into the ring), we expect aryl ketones to be somewhat *less* reactive for primary processes which involve attack by an electrophilic carbonyl oxygen in the n,π^* state; (*b*) ketones with lowest π,π^* states have some radical but little

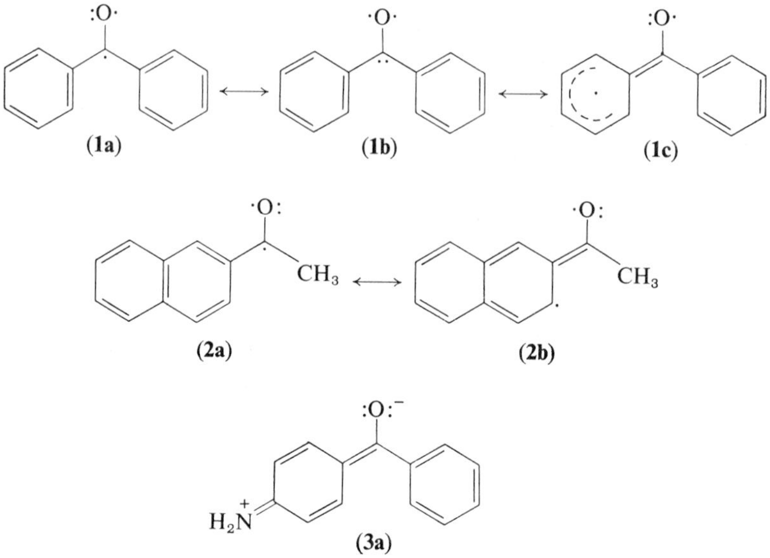

Fig. 10. Major contributing forms for n,π^* **(1)** π,π^* **(2)**, and CT **(3)** states.

electrophilic character on oxygen and have a large contribution from structures such as **2b** in which *the π^* as well as the π electron and electronic excitation are delocalized into the ring*; (c) ketones with lowest CT states are expected to have *both* new and different primary processes available (e.g., deprotonation as a strong acid) and low electrophilic (but possibly high nucleophilic) reactivity at the carbonyl oxygen.

Forms **1**, **2**, and **3** are intended to imply the decreasing order of reactivity of these excited states toward hydrogen abstraction and addition to C=C bonds (believed to be an electrophilic, radical attack by oxygen). That is, on the *basis of these structures only*, one would predict that the order of reactivity of the excited states of substituted benzophenones should be $n,\pi^* > \pi,\pi^* \gg$ CT. In fact, the reactivities of these compounds are one of the best lines of evidence for support of the postulated structures given in Figure 10. A warning is appropriate at this point. The forms depicted in Figure 10 are an attempt to describe the excited states of aryl ketones in terms of more familiar ground-state structures. Clearly, this approximation gives no particular significance to the large excess of electronic energy of the excited state and also *does not serve to differentiate singlet and triplet configurations* whose *reactivity* should be relatively unaffected by spin (332). Such an approximation has permitted the correlation of many of the known relative photochemical reactivities of various benzophenone derivatives and is therefore a useful, if unproven, device.

The above discussion assumed that the *rate constants for the primary photochemical processes will be similar for all* n,π^* *triplet states of aromatic ketones.* On the other hand, $T_1(\pi,\pi^*)$ or CT states *are presumed to be relatively inert toward the primary process of hydrogen abstraction and addition to* C=C *bonds.* This statement implies that the *rate constant for these processes will be one, two, or more orders of magnitude less than that of a typical* $T_1(n,\pi^*)$ *state.*

The energy of the T_1 state allows an immediate conclusion to be made concerning the efficiency of energy transfer to acceptors, if the triplet energies of the latter are known. (See Chapter on Energy Transfer, this volume).

The quantum yield for reaction, since it involves the *ratio* of the rate constant of reaction (which alone defines the reactivity) to the sum of competing rates, reflect only the efficiency of this competition. Thus, a state may be highly reactive toward a primary process but appear to be inert (as measured by the quantum yield) because of some faster deactivation. On the other hand, a long lifetime may result in an efficient reaction in spite of a relatively low inherent reactivity. An outstanding example of this concept is provided by the minor importance of singlet-state photochemistry of aryl aldehydes and ketones. This apparent lack of reactivity is certainly a reflection of the short lifetime of S_1 (limited by intersystem crossing to T_1) rather than a lack of inherent reactivity of S_1.

The nature and energy of the lowest triplet of simple aromatic ketones may usually be predicted by assuming that the energy of the carbonyl group is about 78 kcal and that this energy is lowered by ~ 4 kcal with each aryl substituent, unless the aryl moiety possesses a triplet much lower than 70 kcal. If this is the case, the carbonyl group can be considered to transfer its energy to the aryl moiety. For example, the triplet energy in benzophenone is located

excite here initially   energy transferred here
(π, π^*) (n, π^*)

on the carbonyl ($E_T \sim 70$) rather than the phenyl group ($E_T \sim 85$) because energy transfer from one to the other is exothermic only from the excited ring

excite here (r, π^*)

energy transferred here (π, π^*)

to the carbonyl. In the case of naphthyl ketones ($E_T \sim 60$), transfer from the carbonyl triplet occurs and the excitation resides on the ring.

(2) Energy Diagrams for Aromatic Ketones

The energy diagram for acetophenone is given in Figure 11. The rapid intersystem crossing rate is typical of all aryl aldehydes and ketones. Since a bimolecular reaction of S_1 would have to be nearly diffusion controlled in order to compete with the $S_1 \rightarrow T_1$ process, it is clear that, in general, *the photochemistry of aryl aldehydes and ketones will mainly involve T_1*. The rate of intersystem crossing from $T_1 \rightarrow S_0$ is about two orders of magnitude faster than that for diaryl ketones and may not be typical (see Figs. 12 and 13). The effect of this rapid decay rate is to reduce the efficiency, as measured by the quantum yield, of a highly reactive T_1 state. This can be seen clearly from the relationship below, where k_r is the rate constant for the reaction in

$$\Phi_r = \frac{k_r[T_1][S]}{k_r[T_1][S] + k_d[T_1]} \Phi_{ST}$$

question $[S]$ is the concentration of substrate, and k_d is the major competing path for destruction of T_1 (this may be a physical or chemical process). In the case of acetophenone, k_d is identified as k_t (in the absence of quenchers).

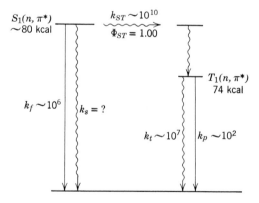

Fig. 11. Energy diagram for acetophenone, benzene solution at 25°C, based on data from Lewis and Turro (699), and Gilmore, Gibson, and McClure (700).

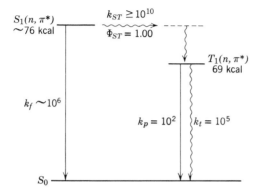

Fig. 12. Energy state diagram for benzophenone in benzene solution at 25°, based on data from Bell and Lipschitz (701).

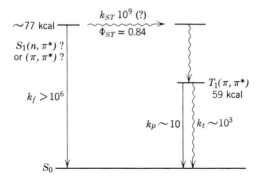

Fig. 13. Energy diagram for 2-acetonaphthone, based on data from Herkstroeter (702) and Ermolaev and Terenin (703).

NICHOLAS J. TURRO

TABLE 4

Energies and Configurations of the Lowest Triplet State of Some Aryl
Aldehydes (333–336)

Compound	E_3 [a]	T_1 [b]
Benzaldehyde	72	(n,π^*)
2-Hydroxybenzaldehyde	71	(n,π^*)
2-Naphthaldehyde	59.5	(π,π^*)
1-Naphthaldehyde	56	(π,π^*)
9-Anthraldehyde	40 [c]	(π,π^*)

[a] Energy of 0–0 $T_1 \rightarrow S_0$ transition, in kcal/mole.
[b] Assignment of major configurational contribution to T_1 based on
spectroscopic data.
[c] Assumed value based on energy of the anthracene triplet.

TABLE 5

Energies and Configurations of the Lowest Triplet States of Acetophenone
and Related Compounds at 77°K (337–342)

Compound	E_3 [a]	T_1 [b]
Propiophenone	75	n,π^*
Acetophenone	74	n,π^*
Phenylcyclopropyl ketone	74	n,π^*
4-Methylacetophenone	73	n,π^*
1,3,5-Triacetylbenzene	73	n,π^*
3-Cyanoacetophenone	73(70) [c]	n,π^*
3-Acetylpyridine	73(71) [c]	n,π^*
4-Chloroacetophenone	72	n,π^*
4-Methoxyacetophenone	72	π,π^*
4-Bromoacetophenone	71	n,π^*
3,5-Dimethylacetophenone	71	π,π^*
2-Acetylpyridine	71	n,π^*
Triphenylmethylphenylketone	71	n,π^*
4-Acetylpyridine	70	n,π^*
4-Acetylacetophenone	68	n,π^*
4-Aminoacetophenone	65	π,π^*
4-Acetylbiphenyl	61	π,π^*
1-Acetonaphthone	59	π,π^*
2-Acetonaphthone	56	π,π^*
3-Acetylpyrene	46	π,π^*

[a] Energy of 0–0 $T_1 \rightarrow S_0$ transition, in kcal/mole.
[b] Assignment of major configurational contributor to T_1, based on
spectroscopic data.
[c] Value in hydrocarbon solvent. Other value for solvents containing
polar molecules.

Note the similarity of Figures 11 and 12 with that of acetone (Section III–1–A–(3)). This correspondence implies that the (n,π^*) states are similar in both compounds (i.e., the benzene ring *does not* participate strongly in the *lowest* excited states).

The possibility of self-quenching should be considered when interpreting these diagrams. The rate constant k_t is usually measured under conditions where quenching of triplets (k_3) by ground-state molecules (K_0) of the same kind is negligible, i.e., at low concentrations of ketone (K). Under actual

$$K_3 + K_0 \xrightarrow{k_3} 2K_0 + \text{heat}$$

synthetic conditions the concentrations of substrates are considerably higher.

An energy diagram for benzophenone is given in Figure 12. It is quite similar to that of acetophenone and acetone. Two significant points should be noted, however. The triplet energy of benzophenone is 5 kcal *lower* than acetophenone and the triplet lifetime is about two orders of magnitude *longer*.

Finally, an energy diagram for 2-acetonaphthone, a molecule possessing a T_1 (π,π^*) state, is given in Figure 13. It is not known whether S_1 is n,π^* (they are probably very close in energy). The rate constant for intersystem crossing is speculative due to insufficient spectroscopic data. It should be

TABLE 6

Energies and Configurations of the Lowest Triplet State of
Benzophenones (343–348)

Compound	E_3[a]	T_1[b]
Xanthone	74	n,π^*
4,4′-Dimethoxybenzophenone	70	n,π^*
4,4′-Dimethylbenzophenone	69	n,π^*
Benzophenone	69	n,π^*
4,4′-Dichlorobenzophenone	69	n,π^*
2-Benzoylbenzophenone	69	n,π^*
4-Trifluoromethylbenzophenone	68	n,π^*
4-Hydroxylbenzophenone	68	n,π^*
4-Aminobenzophenone	67(63)[c]	n,π^* (CT)[c]
4-Cyanobenzophenone	66	n,π^*
Michler's ketone	61	CT or π,π^*
2-Naphthyl phenyl ketone	57.5	π,π^*
1-Naphthyl phenyl ketone	57.5	π,π^*
Fluorenone	53(?)	n,π^*(?)
Thiobenzophenone	40	n,π^*

[a] Energy of 0–0 $T_1 \rightarrow S_0$ transition in kcal/mole.

[b] Assignment of major configurational contribution to T_1, based on spectroscopic data.

[c] Value in isopropyl alcohol. Other value from hydrocarbon solvent.

noted that the energy of the triplet has dropped tremendously because of the presence of the naphthyl group. This implies the excitation is mainly associated with the hydrocarbon moiety and serves as a simple rationale for the difference in reactivity between n,π^* and π,π^* states. Finally, it should be pointed out that the triplet lifetime of compounds possessing T_1 (π,π^*) states is often much longer than that of T_1 (n,π^*) states. This effect tends to counteract the low reactivity of these states.

Tables 4, 5, and 6 can be employed to make effective structure–reactivity correlations. In this way, we can see the usefulness of spectroscopic information for the qualitative prediction of photochemical behavior. One can tell qualitatively, *by inspection* of these tables, whether a given aryl aldehyde or ketone will be reactive in the general primary processes of these compounds. For example, *all* of these compounds listed as possessing lowest n,π^* states are *presumed to be reactive toward hydrogen abstraction and addition to* C=C *bonds* (and in special cases α-cleavage).

C. EXCITED STATES OF CARBOXYLIC ACIDS AND RELATED COMPOUNDS

(1) Models for the Excited States of Carboxylic Acids and Related Compounds

The attachment of a heteroatom to a carbonyl group may profoundly affect the energy and structure of an excited state. The π^* system may now be delocalized over three atoms and the electronegativity of the heteroatom may greatly influence the energy required for n,π^* excitation (349). Insufficient data are available for the construction of a detailed model of the excited states of an acid, amide, ester, etc. Indeed it is not even known with certainty whether the lowest excited states are n,π^* or π,π^* in nature. However, inspection of the literature reveals that the α-cleavage and hydrogen-abstraction primary processes typical of an n,π^* state are known for carboxylic acids.

TABLE 7

Energy Data for Carboxylic Acids and Derivatives (350–352)

Molecule	$E_1{}^a$	$E_3{}^a$
CH_3CO_2H	135	—
$CH_3CO_2CH_3$	135	—
CH_3CONH_2	140	—
$C_6H_5CO_2H$	140	78
$C_6H_5CONH_2$	90	79
1-Naphthoic acid	—	58
2-Naphthoic acid	—	60

^{a} Energies in kcal/mole.

(2) Energy Tables for Carboxylic Acids and Derivatives

Some of the sparse data concerning the energy levels for carboxylic acids and derivatives are listed in Table 7. Essentially no data concerning rate constants for state interconversions are available.

2. Alkyl Aldehydes and Ketones

A. ALDEHYDES AND ACYCLIC KETONES

(1) Formaldehyde and Alkyl Aldehydes

The photochemistry of formaldehyde has been studied extensively in the vapor phase but not in solution (353). Acetaldehyde and propionaldehyde undergo α-cleavage, hydrogen abstraction, and cycloaddition to olefins. To date, however, quantitative information concerning these reactions has not been reported. Examples of each reaction follow (354–356).

$$CH_3CHO \xrightarrow{h\nu} CH_3\overset{.}{C}O + H\cdot \xrightarrow[RH]{h\nu} CH_3\overset{.}{C}H + R\cdot$$
$$\underset{OH}{|}$$

$$CH_2{=}CH(CH_2)_5CH_3 + CH_3\overset{.}{C}O \xrightarrow[CH_3CHO]{} CH_3\overset{O}{\overset{||}{C}}(CH_2)_7CH_3$$
$$\qquad (1) \qquad\qquad\qquad\qquad\qquad\qquad (2),\ 70\%$$

$$CH_3CHO + CH_2{=}CHC_6H_5 \xrightarrow{h\nu}$$

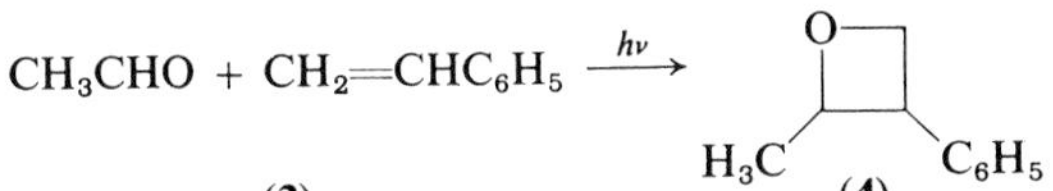

(3)

(4)

H_3C C_6H_5

The orientation of the addition of aldehydes to olefins indicates that Markownikoff addition is preferred. No evidence is available to determine whether the addition is a one-step or multistep process (354,357).

The cleavage process apparently is favored by structural features which stabilize the radical pair produced. Thus, if a secondary, tertiary, or resonance-stabilized radical is produced in addition to the formyl radical, and a good hydrogen donor is unavailable, cleavage may be the preferred process. A striking example of the specificity which is possible in these reactions is demonstrated by the nearly quantitative stereospecific photochemical conversion of laurolenal (5) to the cyclopentene 6 (358).* Labeling experiments have shown that the reaction is stereospecific.

---

* This article (358) is an excellent review of the photochemistry of aldehydes.

(5)   (6)

Long-chain alkyl aldehydes may undergo intramolecular γ-hydrogen abstraction followed by cyclization to a cyclobutanol or cleavage to acetaldehyde and an olefin. For example, irradiation of the optically active aldehyde **7** leads to the products **8**, **9**, and **10** (359,360). Apparently, some racemization of the starting material occurs also. However, the fact that the cyclobutanol **8** is optically active indicates that either a concerted cyclization (via a singlet state) or a rapid biradical closure (via a singlet or triplet state) is operative. If a triplet is involved, then presumably a biradical triplet of extremely short lifetime would be required.

(7), $R = (CH_2)_3CH(CH_3)_2$ (8), 20%

$$RCH_3C = CH_2 + CH_3CHO$$
(9)   (10)

(2) Acyclic Alkyl Ketones

The photochemistry of acyclic alkyl ketones is qualitatively similar to that of alkyl aldehydes, except that cleavage reactions seem to be less pronounced for straight-chain ketones (362). Acetone, for example, abstracts hydrogen atoms from hydrocarbons, alcohols, and ethers to yield radical pairs which may then proceed to various products depending on the reaction conditions (361).

(11)   (12)

At least two mechanisms appear to operate in the formation of oxetanes from alkyl ketones and ethylenes. For electron-rich ethylenes (polyalkyl-olefins, enol ethers, etc.) attack by the n,π^* ketone triplet apparently occurs and a biradical intermediate is produced which then collapses nonstereo-specifically to products (363). Energy transfer to the ethylene usually competes with the cycloaddition process.

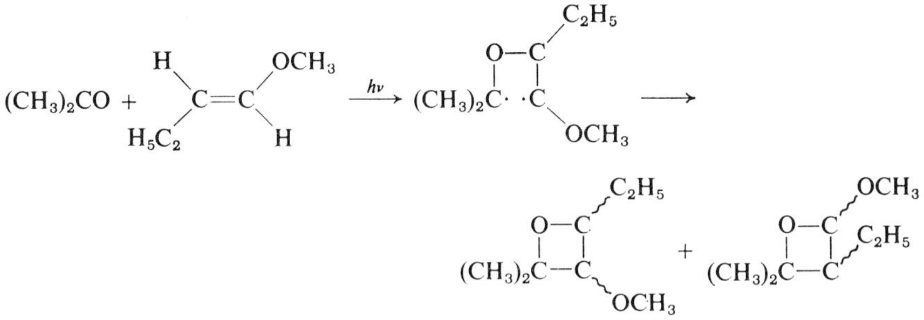

(13a), 50% cis
(13b), 50% trans

(13c) from alternate biradical

For electron-poor ethylenes (dicyanoethylenes, maleic anhydride, etc.) the n,π^* singlet apparently reacts with the ethylene to yield the oxetane in a stereospecific process (364). If the ethylene is not "sufficiently" electron poor, then only energy transfer to produce *cis–trans* isomerization occurs. Nearly

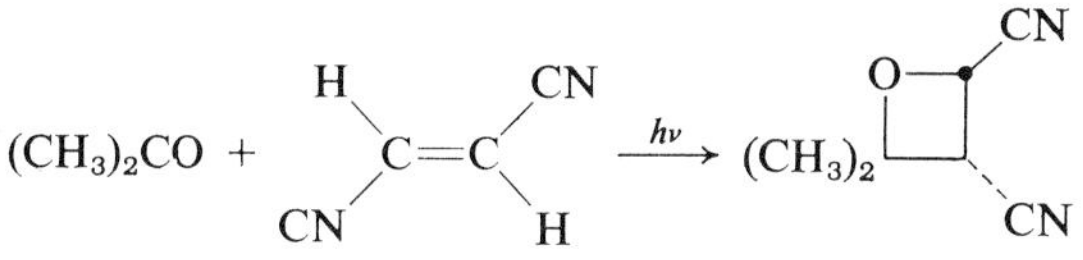

(14)

all alkyl ketones possessing γ-hydrogen atoms undergo an intramolecular hydrogen-atom transfer via a cyclic six-membered transition state. For

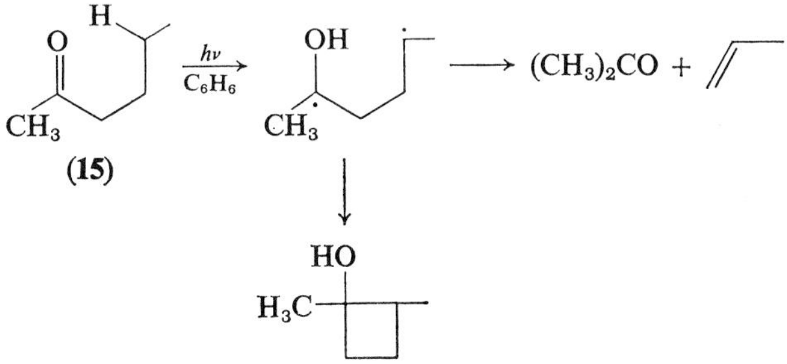

(15)

(16)

example, irradiation of 2-hexanone yields acetone and propene. The mechanism of this reaction has been studied and shown to proceed via *both* the n, π^* singlet and triplet states (365,366).

(3) Alkyl Ketones Containing α- or β-Substituents

The nature of the important primary photochemical processes of alkyl ketones may be modified by the presence of nonconjugated functional groups attached α or β to the carbonyl group. Although the ordinary primary processes of α-cleavage, hydrogen abstraction, and addition should occur, their relative rates may be influenced significantly by substituents. The substituents may also introduce new primary photochemical processes *or* new rapid deactivation paths.

For example, irradiation of 2-phenoxyacetone (369) in methanol introduces a new primary process of homolytic β-cleavage (367). This reaction may also be considered to be a primary process of the aromatic portion of the molecule

$$CH_3\overset{O}{\overset{\|}{C}}-CH_2-O-C_6H_5 \xrightarrow[CH_3OH]{h\nu} CH_3\overset{O}{\overset{\|}{C}}CH_2{}^{\cdot} + {}^{\cdot}O-C_6H_5 \longrightarrow$$

(17)

(18), 1%   (19), 17%   (20), 17%

(Section II–1–A–(2)). A wavelength dependence study of this reaction would help one to decide whether this is correct.

Nonconjugated enones are interesting because of the possibility of intramolecular energy transfer to the olefin from the excited carbonyl n,π^* state. Indeed, this process competes with α-cleavage in the case of *trans*-4-hexenone-2 (368). In contrast, irradiation of γ,δ-enones results in intramolecular energy transfer and oxetane formation, rather than α-cleavage. The γ,δ-enone 23 yields the oxetanes 24 and 25 (369,370). The major product results from anti-Markownikoff addition. However, it would not be surprising that perhaps entropy effects were operating to cause this reversal from intramolecular behavior (371).

(23)   (24), 40%   (25), 16%

Substitution of a phenyl group β to the carbonyl group facilitates α-cleavage and subsequent decarbonylation; i.e., 1,3-diphenylacetone yields 1,2-diphenylethane in good yield (372). These reactions are free radical in nature

$$C_6H_5CH_2COCH_2C_6H_5 \xrightarrow{h\nu} C_6H_5CH_2CH_2C_6H_5 + CO$$
$$\text{(26)} \qquad\qquad\qquad \text{(27), 81\%}$$

since photolyses of 1,1,3-triphenylacetone results in the ratio of ethanes expected from random coupling of benzyl and benzhydryl radicals. Thus, concerted loss of CO is not important in these cases.

$$C_6H_5CH_2COCH(C_6H_5)_2 \xrightarrow{h\nu} \overline{C_6H_5CH_2CO\cdot + \cdot CH(C_6H_5)_2}$$
$$\text{(28)}$$
$$\downarrow -CO$$
$$C_6H_5CH_2CH_2C_6H_5 \longleftarrow C_6H_5CH_2\cdot + \cdot CH(C_6H_5)_2$$
$$\text{(29), 20\%}$$
$$+ (C_6H_5)_2CHCH_2C_6H_5 + (C_6H_5)_2CHCH(C_6H_5)_2$$
$$\text{(30), 40\%} \qquad\qquad \text{(31), 20\%}$$

The photochemistry of halogen-substituted ketones in solution has not been studied in detail. The same primary processes as those for alkyl ketones, however, are expected, except that β-cleavage to halogen atoms and acetonyl radicals may occur (373). Recent work confirms this expectation (373)a.

B. CYCLIC KETONES

No new primary processes appear to be required to discuss the photochemistry of cyclic ketones (374). The nature of the secondary processes may be highly dependent on the structure of the starting ketone due to constraints that the cyclic structure places on the system.

Irradiation of solutions of cyclopropanones results in formation of an ethylene and CO as the only detectable products (375).

$$\xrightarrow[-78°, CH_2Cl_2]{h\nu} CH_2{=}CH_2 + CO$$

Although the loss of CO is the major photodecomposition path when cyclobutanone is irradiated in methanol, two other important processes occur, namely formation of ethylene and ketene and the rearrangement–addition product **34**. The mechanism of formation of **34** (376) is now known,

although rearrangement of the biradical **32** to the carbene **33** is a plausible

path. The yield of rearrangement product goes up rapidly as the α positions of cyclobutanone are alkylated (376).

Tetramethylcyclobutane-1,3-diones undergo both decarbonylation to yield cyclopropanones and cleavage to ketenes (377,378). Cyclopentanone under-

goes α-cleavage (379) followed by an intramolecular hydrogen shift to yield the unsaturated aldehyde **38a**. This reaction is common for cyclopentanone derivatives, even when the ketone is highly methylated so that decarbonylation might be expected (377). When hydrogen abstraction is hindered then

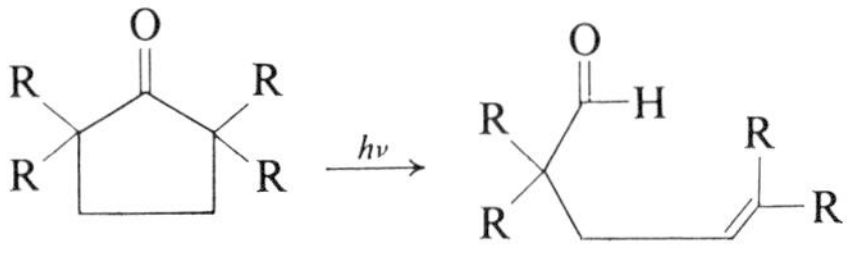

(37a), R=H
(37b), R=CH$_3$

(38a, b)

decarbonylation becomes important (380,381). The bicyclic ketone **39** and

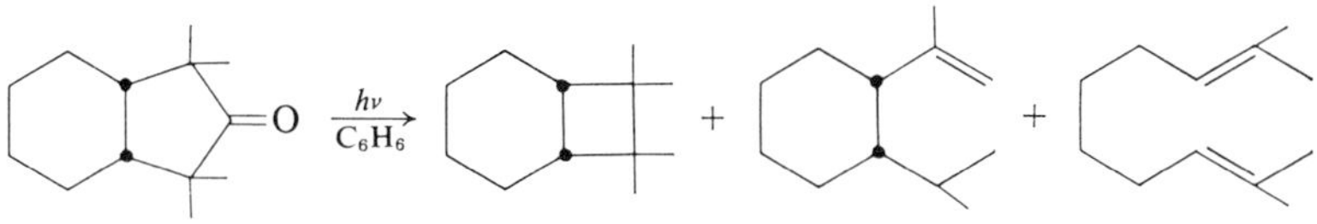

(39)   (40), 53%   (42), 27%

the benzocyclopentenone **43** demonstrate this effect (380,382,383).

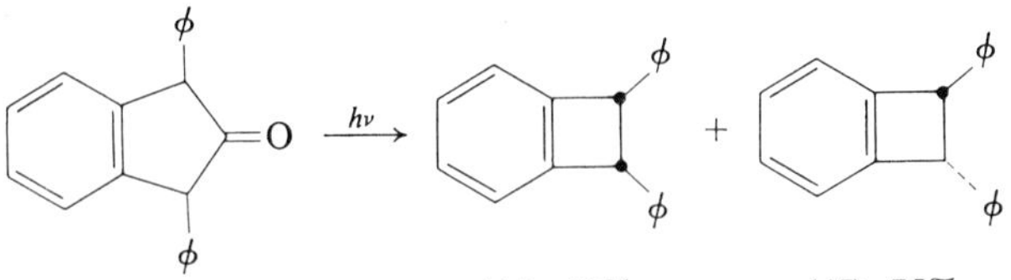

(43)   (44), 18%   (45), 75%

Cyclohexanone undergoes α-cleavage followed by one of several hydrogen shifts (384). The formation of **47** is analogous to the unsaturated aldehyde formation from cyclopentanones. Small amounts of 2-methylcyclopentanone are formed also (385). The ketene **48** may be trapped with nucleophiles

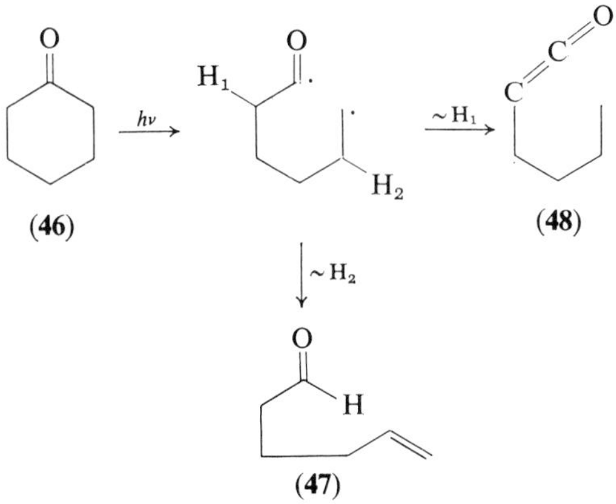

(46)   (48)

(47)

and, as a result, the photolyses of steroidal cyclohexanones have been employed to prepare carboxylic acid derivatives (381). 2,2,6,6-Tetramethyl-cyclohexanone undergoes net decarbonylation when irradiated in inert solvents. However, by analogy to 2,2,5,5-tetramethylcyclopentanone, an intermediate aldehyde which undergoes secondary decomposition may be involved (380).

Irradiation of isopulegone (52) results in formation of the isomeric cyclobutanols 53 and 54 (386).

3. Aryl Aldehydes and Ketones

A. ARYL ALDEHYDES

(1) Benzaldehyde

The photochemistry of aryl aldehydes is qualitatively similar to that of alkyl aldehydes except that α-cleavage is rarer. For example, irradiation of benzaldehyde in 2-methyl-2-butene results in hydrogen abstraction to yield the alcohols 1 and 2 and addition to the C=C bond to yield the oxetanes 3 and 4 (387–389).

(2) Naphthaldehydes and Anthraldehydes

Naphthyl aldehydes possess T_1 (π,π^*) states, in general, and are therefore expected to be relatively inert to the normal photoreactions of the excited carbonyl function (390). It is found, for example, that 1-naphthaldehyde is resistant to photoreduction in common hydrogen-donating solvents such as isopropyl alcohol. The more reactive hydrogen donor tri-n-butyltin hydride (6) does effect photoreduction, however (391,392).

Both 1- and 2-naphthaldehydes react with 2-methyl-2-butene to yield oxetanes (387). Although the net quantum yield is low, good overall yields are possible (presumably because of the inertness of these compounds toward α-cleavage and photoreduction). Again, the relative lack of orientational

selectivity of product formation demonstrated in oxetane formation by benzaldehyde occurs.

Since it appears that the electronic excitation in T_1 for naphthylaldehydes is in the π system, one may expect photochemistry involving the aromatic nucleus (so far unreported) (393). Furthermore, S_1 may be n,π^* (this is difficult to determine from available spectral data). The inefficient oxetane formation noted above may be a reaction of S_1 (n,π^*) which is expected to be *reactive* but short-lived, thus offering a possible explanation for the low quantum yield.

As expected, 9-anthraldehyde [T_1, (π,π^*)] is relatively inert toward photoreduction (394,395). However, it does undergo photoaddition to 2-methyl-2-butene in a *wavelength dependent reaction* (a rarity in solution photochemistry).

With light of wavelength lower than ~4100 Å, oxetane formation occurs (a reaction characteristic of the excited carbonyl group) while light of wavelength greater than ~4100 Å effects dimerization to yield **11** (a reaction characteristic of the excited π system of anthracene) (396). This result

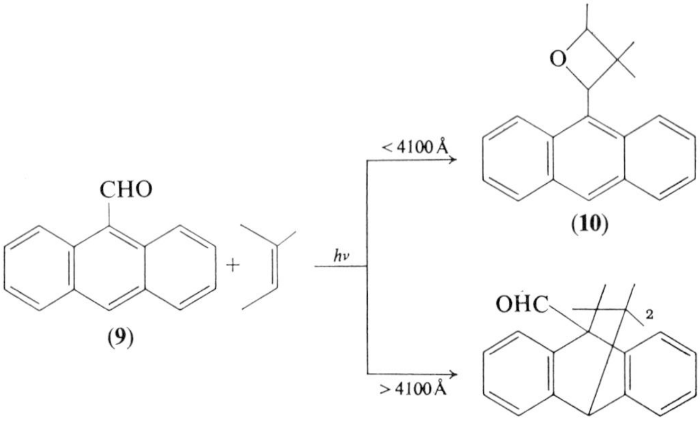

(9)

(10)

(11), head to tail dimer

suggests that either (a) only the T_2 (n,π^*) reacts to form oxetane (i.e., it is not formed with $h\nu > 4100$ Å) and not T_1 (π,π^*) or (b) intersystem crossing to T_2 and T_1 is wavelength dependent and does not occur with $h\nu > 4100$ Å. The latter possibility implies that S_1 (π,π^*) dimerizes more rapidly than it crosses to T_1 (π,π^*), and the latter state when formed by $h\nu > 4100$ Å reacts inefficiently to form oxetane. Energy transfer experiments designed to excite only T_1 (π,π^*) have helped to resolve this point (394).

9-Anthraldehyde is not photoreduced by the common hydrogen-donor solvents (isopropyl alcohol, cyclohexane, etc.). Even with the powerful hydrogen donor tributyltin hydride the quantum yield for photoreduction is low. A wavelength effect has not been sought in this case.

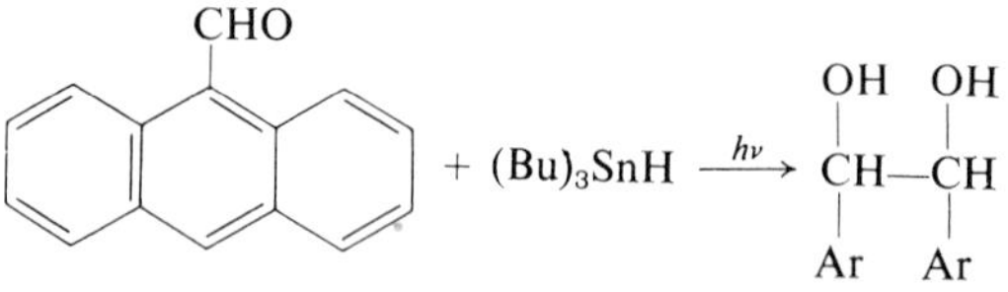

(9)

(12), Ar=Anthracyl

B. ARYL ALKYL KETONES

Acetophenone, like benzaldehyde, shows little or no tendency to undergo α-cleavage. Thus, hydrogen abstraction and addition to unsaturated bonds are the only important primary photochemical processes expected for alkyl aryl ketones.

Irradiation of acetophenone in isopropyl alcohol, toluene, or α-methyl-benzyl alcohol as solvent results in formation of the pinacol 13 (397–399).†

$$C_6H_5COCH_3 + RH \xrightarrow{h\nu} C_6H_5\underset{\underset{OH}{|}}{C}(CH_3)\underset{\underset{OH}{|}}{C}(CH_3)C_6H_5$$

$$(13), > 70\%$$

Substitution in the benzene nucleus of an alkyl aryl ketone with an electron-donating group (e.g., methyl, methoxy, amino, etc.) will lower the energy of the π,π^* states while raising the energy of the n,π^* states (400–402). Aceto-phenone possesses a triplet (π,π^*) state very close to its T_1 (n,π^*) state (403). Substitution of methyl groups or other electron-releasing groups on the benzene ring of acetophenone causes an inversion of the configuration so that T_1 is now π,π^*. Indeed, polymethyl and methoxy-substituted acetophenones exhibit much lower quantum yields for photoreduction by isopropyl alcohol (404).

Acetophenone undergoes addition to $C=C$ (405) and $C\equiv C$ (406) bonds to yield oxetanes or related products, but hydrogen abstraction is sometimes an important side reaction.

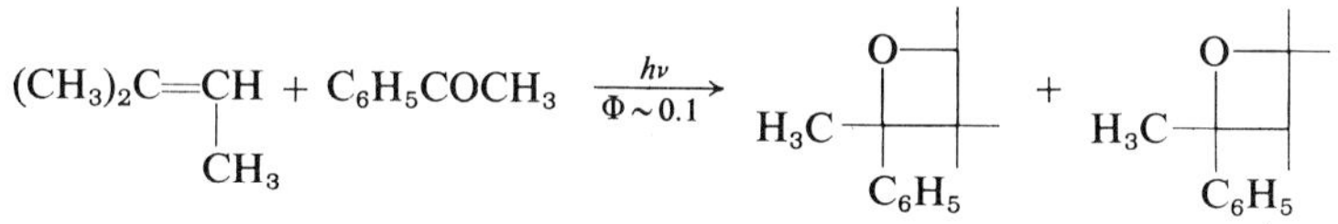

$$(CH_3)_2C\underset{\underset{CH_3}{|}}{=}CH + C_6H_5COCH_3 \xrightarrow[\Phi \sim 0.1]{h\nu}$$

(14), 90%   +   (15), 10%

$$C_6H_5COCH_3 + C_4H_9C\equiv CC_4H_9 \xrightarrow{h\nu}$$

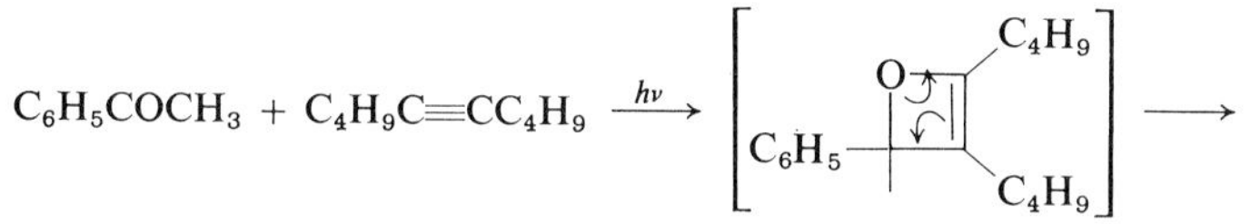

(16)

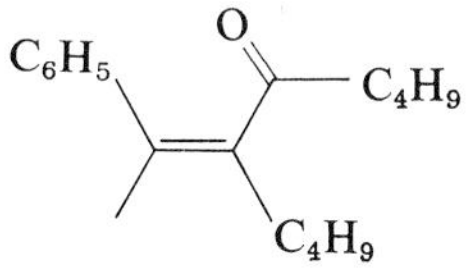

(17)

When 2-methylacetophenones are irradiated, intramolecular hydrogen abstraction occurs, as shown by deuterium labeling experiments. These

† For an interesting photoreaction of acetophenone which is induced by a trace of phenol, see ref. 399.

molecules are relatively stable toward intermolecular hydrogen abstraction as a result of this intramolecular deactivation path. However, intermolecular photoreduction does occur (407). This reaction is a variation of the γ-hydrogen abstraction reaction of alkyl ketones (408). In addition to the

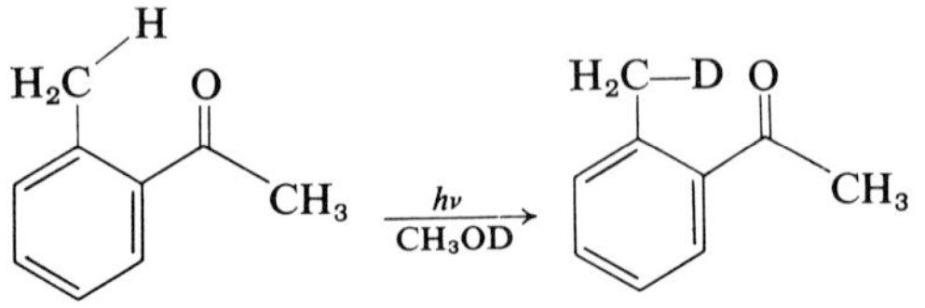

two primary photochemical processes, energy transfer to unsaturated bonds is a common process for acetophenone derivatives. This is due to the relatively high triplet energy of acetophenone ($E_3 = 74$ kcal/mole) and its simple derivatives. As a result, acetophenone does not efficiently form oxetanes with olefins possessing triplet energies less than 74 kcal/mole, because of efficient competition from energy transfer (see Table 6, Section III–1–B–(2)).

For example, irradiation of acetophenone and norbornene ($E_3 < 74$ kcal/mole) results in dimerization of the norbornene (via energy transfer) rather than oxetane formation (409).

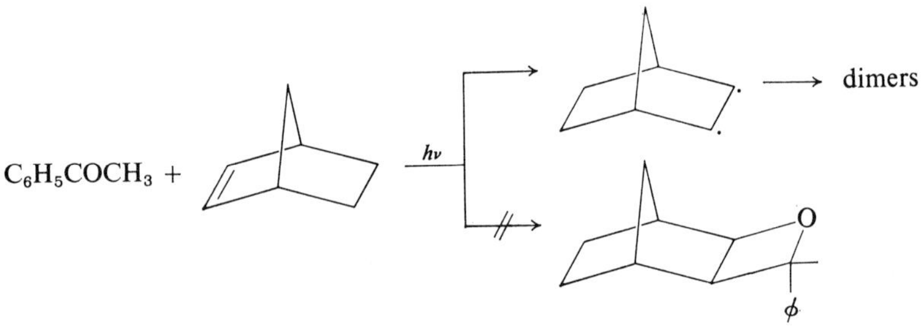

(18)

Butyrophenone undergoes an efficient but solvent dependent photochemical γ-hydrogen abstraction to produce acetophenone, ethylene, and the cyclo-

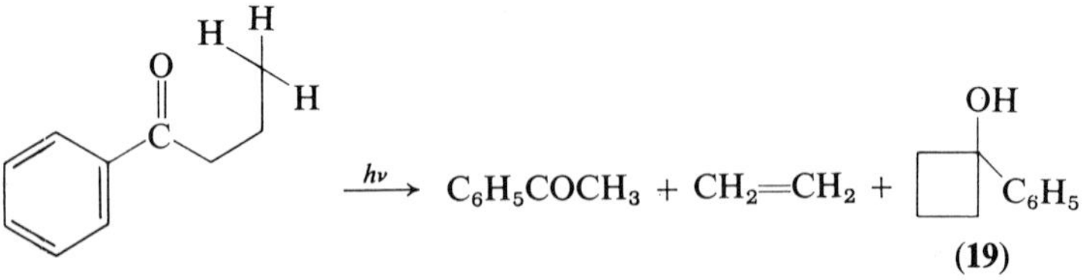

(19)

butanol 19 (410,412). The rate constant for the hydrogen abstraction from the T_1 state is $\sim 10^6$ sec. Intersystem crossing ($k_{st} \sim 10^{10}$) precludes a significant yield of abstraction from S_1.

Substitution of an alkoxy or dialkylamino function on the α-carbon does not appear to affect the intramolecular hydrogen abstraction process. For example, irradiation of the alkoxyketone **20** results in formation of the oxetanol **21** (411), while irradiation of β-diethylaminoacetophenone yields the phenylazetidin-3-ol **23** (414).

$$(20) \qquad (21),\ 34\%$$

$$(22) \qquad (23),\ 26\%$$

Substitution of functional groups on the alkyl chain or on the phenyl ring may affect the primary processes of the n,π^* excited state or even make the lowest excited state π,π^* or charge transfer in nature. In addition, these new functional groups may themselves add new primary photochemical processes.

For example, 4-bromobutyrophenone undergoes cleavage of the Ar—Br bond to lead to butyrophenone (415).

Irradiation of compounds having a small ring adjacent to the carbonyl group generally results in cleavage of the small ring in competition with the usual primary processes (416). For example, irradiation of *trans*-1,2-dibenzoylcyclopropane **24** results in reversible isomerization (417). In addition to isomerization, rearrangement may occur. Photosensitization by benzophenone leads to reduction products.

$$(24) \qquad \qquad (25)$$

Irradiation of the epoxyketone **26** results in formation of the dione **27**, by a sequence of steps which is typical for such compounds (418). The α-keto-

$$C_6H_5CO-CHCHC_6H_5 \xrightarrow{h\nu} C_6H_5CO\overset{\cdot}{C}H-CHC_6H_5 \longrightarrow C_6H_5COCH_2COC_6H_5$$

$$\underset{O}{\diagdown\diagup} \qquad\qquad \underset{\cdot O}{|}$$

$$(26) \qquad\qquad\qquad\qquad\qquad\qquad (27)$$

azirine **28** undergoes wavelength-dependent changes of the small ring (419) to yield **29** and **30**.

C. DIARYL KETONES

(1) Benzophenone and Alkyl Derivatives

The photochemistry of diaryl ketones is analogous to that of alkyl aryl ketones, i.e., S_1 is generally too short-lived to participate efficiently in any of the usual primary photochemical processes and T_1, when n,π^* in nature, is reactive toward hydrogen abstraction and addition to unsaturated bonds. Again, this reactivity may be masked by rapid reversible intramolecular decay processes or by energy transfer (417).

Hydrogen abstraction by benzophenone and its derivatives is one of the most extensively studied primary photochemical processes. Benzophenone will abstract a hydrogen atom from nearly any molecule containing a C—H bond including benzene (391), although the rate of abstraction varies widely depending on the particular molecule. The O—H bond is more resistent to abstraction, but the N—H, Sn—H, and S—H bonds are quite reactive. Factors which tend to weaken the C—H bond or make it more nucleophilic (more electron rich) facilitate the reaction. It appears that the abstraction process involves attack on the X—H bond by the electrophilic half-filled n-orbital of the n,π^* triplet state. Although S_1 may also be reactive, its short lifetime ($< 10^{-10}$ sec^{-1}) precludes efficient hydrogen abstraction.

The reaction of benzophenone with alcohols generally results in formation of benzpinacol. Since the mechanism for hydrogen abstraction involves the intermediacy of ketyl radicals, the latter may be intercepted by appropriate radical traps (407,420–422). The ketyl radical is a potential hydrogen donor.

$$(C_6H_5)_2\dot{C}OH \longrightarrow (C_6H_5)_2COHCOH(C_6H_5)_2$$

$$(C_6H_5)_2C{=}O \xrightarrow[R_2CHOH]{h\nu} (C_6H_5)_2\dot{C}{-}OH \xrightarrow{NF_2NF_2} (C_6H_5)_2\overset{\displaystyle NF_2}{\underset{\displaystyle |}{C}}OH$$

Indeed, the dimethyl ketyl radical produced in the primary process from benzophenone triplet and isopropyl alcohol is capable of reducing ground-state benzophenone to the benzhydryl ketyl radical. This reaction accounts for the fact that at high light intensities or at high isopropyl alcohol concentrations (for which the concentration of dimethyl ketyl radical is at a maximum) the quantum yield for benzophenone photoreduction approaches two; i.e., a triplet benzophenone abstracts one hydrogen and the dimethyl ketyl radical thereby produced reduces a second molecule of benzophenone. Ketyl radicals are also implicated in "chemical sensitization" by ketones (427).

$$(C_6H_5)_2C{=}O + (CH_3)_2CHOH \rightarrow (C_6H_5)_2\dot{C}OH + (CH_3)_2\dot{C}OH$$
$$(C_6H_5)_2C{=}O + (CH_3)_2\dot{C}OH \rightarrow (C_6H_5)_2\dot{C}OH + (CH_3)_2C{=}O$$
$$2(C_6H_5)_2\dot{C}OH \rightarrow (C_6H_5)_2COHCOH(C_6H_5)_2$$

Irradiation of benzophenone in the presence of amines results in photo-reduction, although the mechanism may be different from photoreduction in alcohols (425).

Benzophenone is reactive toward addition to C=C bonds although energy transfer to the ethylene, as is hydrogen abstraction (especially if allylic hydrogens are available) are generally competing processes (405,406,409). Irradiation of isobutylene solutions of benzophenone results in formation of oxetanes in good yield (387,409). As we have seen earlier, the photochemical reactions of benzophenone in solution occur through the lowest triplet n–π^* state, and are characteristic of attack by an electron-deficient oxygen. The attack of benzophenone triplets on isobutylene would be expected to occur preferentially at the less-substituted carbon on the basis of both steric effects and because of the greater electron density on the less-substituted carbon. Thus, the preferred formation of **31a** may be explained by a kinetically

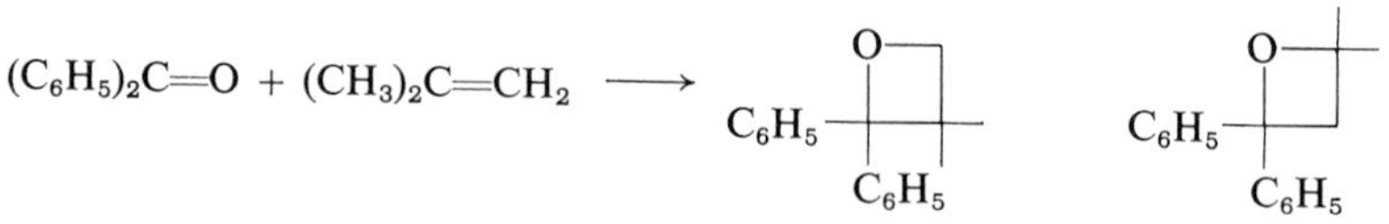

$$(C_6H_5)_2C{=}O + (CH_3)_2C{=}CH_2 \longrightarrow$$

(**31a**), 90%   (**31b**), 10%

controlled addition of the excited carbonyl oxygen on the C=C bond. Another point of view is that the *stability* of the possible biradical inter-mediates determines the structure of the predominant product. In this case, the predominant isomer of the oxetanes formed is correctly predicted from consideration of the more stable biradical (ground-state) intermediate. This implies that a two-step reaction occurs and that the relative stabilities of the "one-bond" biradicals determine the relative ratio of the final products. Attack of the $n{-}\pi^*$ triplet state of benzophenone on isobutylene could produce any one or more of the four biradical intermediates **32**, **33**, **34**, and **35**. The most stable of these biradicals is expected to be **32**, because of stabilization of the odd electron centers by the maximum number of phenyl and methyl groups. The next lowest energy biradical should be **33**, while **34** and **35** (which involve alkoxy radicals) should be of highest energy. The preference of formation of **31a** and **31b** may thus also be explained in these terms. Collapse of intermediate biradicals has been invoked as a mechanism for the "chemical sensitization" of *cis-trans*-isomerization (427).

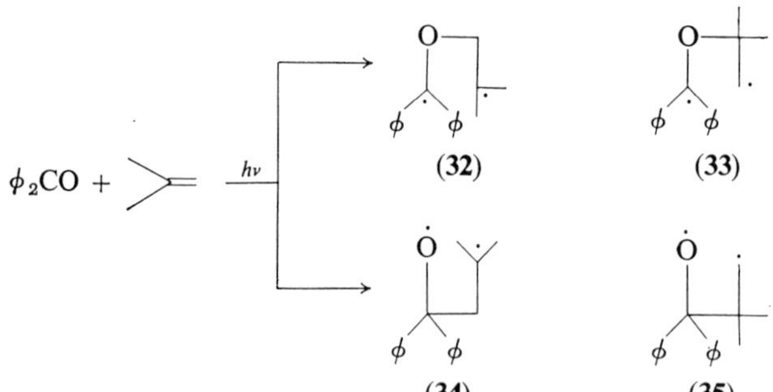

$$\phi_2CO +$$ hv

(**32**)   (**33**)

(**34**)   (**35**)

In contrast to the situation with acetophenone, benzophenone adds to norbornene to form an oxetane. If it is assumed that the norbornene triplet lies at about 72 kcal/mole above its ground state then these results are nicely rationalized since energy transfer from benzophenone to norbornene should be slow, allowing oxetane formation to compete (409,426). Benzophenone does not add efficiently to dienes or electron-poor ethylenes, because energy transfer competes favorably with cycloaddition to the C=C bond (364,428).

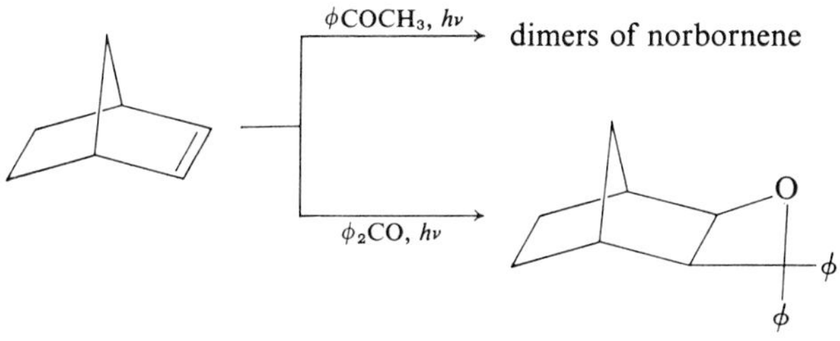

(36), 80%

Substitution of the benzene rings of benzophenone affects the primary photochemical processes in three significant ways: (a) by introduction of new primary processes which may compete with photochemistry of the n,π^* triplet; (b) by modification of the electron density of the oxygen atom of the n,π^* state as a result of electron withdrawing or releasing ring substituents; and (c) by introduction of new states, such that T_1 is no longer n,π^* (but rather π,π^* or charge transfer). As a result, the efficiency of hydrogen abstraction and oxetane formation may be significantly affected by ring substitution (420).

(2) Substituted Benzophenones

We have seen how ring substitution can lead to very different reactivities for acetophenone derivatives. Similarly, the reactivity of ring-substituted benzophenone derivatives toward hydrogen abstraction and additions to C=C bonds is markedly dependent on the nature of the ring substituents (Table 8). Electron-releasing substituents lessen the reactivity toward the usually electrophilic primary processes of the n,π^* state by increasing the electron density at the carbonyl oxygen atom. In some cases the substituent may "switch" the T_1 state from reactive n,π^* to a less reactive π,π^* or charge transfer (CT) state. As a result, the configuration of T_1 may be different in different solvents!

For examples, ketones **37**, **38**, **39**, and **40** are inert toward both hydrogen abstraction from isopropyl alcohol and (except for **39**) addition to C=C bonds (e.g., isobutylene).

(37) 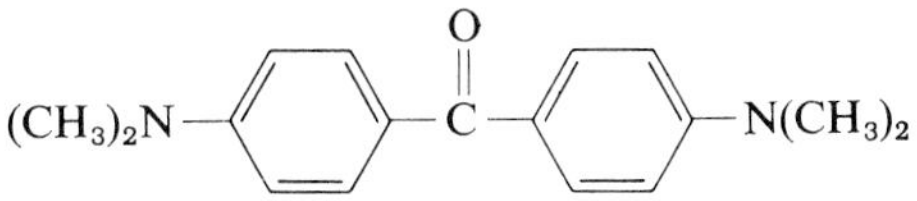 (38)

(39)   (40)

From emission spectra it is clear, for example, that the T_1 state of **37** is *different* in hydrocarbon solvents from that in polar solvents. This difference is reflected in the photolysis of **37** in cyclohexane (T_1 apparently n,π^*) in which a fairly rapid reaction ($\Phi \sim 0.2$) occurs and in isopropyl alcohol (T_1 is apparently π,π^* or CT) in which the ketone is inert (431–433). Although the reaction expected in these solvents is photoreduction, it has been claimed that in fact this process is not responsible for disappearance of **37** in cyclohexane but recent work has confirmed that hydrogen abstraction products are formed. Irradiation of **37** in isopropyl alcohol containing HCl (to protonate the amine function) leads to efficient photoreduction. In this case the lowest triplet is n,π^* and the electron-withdrawing —NH_3+ group probably enhances the reactivity of this state.

These results imply that oxetane formation should be significantly affected by solvent changes for those ketones which show large solvent effects for photoreduction.

TABLE 8

Quantum Yields for Photoreduction of Substituted Benzophenones in Isopropyl Alcohol and Cyclohexane (429–433)

Ketone	$(CH_3)_2CHOH$	T_1	C_6H_{12}	T_1
Benzophenone	1.0	n,π^*	0.5	n,π^*
4-Fluorobenzophenone	1.0	n,π^*	—	n,π^*
4-Chlorobenzophenone	1.0	n,π^*	—	n,π^*
4-Bromobenzophenone	1.0	n,π^*	—	n,π^*
4-Phenylbenzophenone	0.1	π,π^*	0.05	π,π^*
4,4′-Dimethyoxybenzophenone	1.0	n,π^*	—	n,π^*
4-Hydroxybenzophenone	0,02	n,π^*	0.9	n,π^*
3-Aminobenzophenone	0.00	CT or π,π^*	0 03	CT or π,π^*
4-Aminobenzophenone	0.03	CT or π,π^*	0.20	?
4,4′-Dimethylaminobenzophenone	0.00	CT or π,π^*	0.60	n,π^*
2-Benzylbenzophenone	0.01	n,π^*	—	n,π^*
2-Hydroxybenzophenone	0.01	?	—	—
2-t-Butylbenzophenone	2.0	n,π^*	—	—
2-Aminobenzophenone	0.01	?	—	—
2-Methoxybenzophenone	2.0	n,π^*	—	—
2-Methylbenzophenone	0.05	n,π^*	—	—

Fluorenone (426) may also form oxetanes in a process (434,435) which partially involves triplet states (435a). However this ketone does apparently undergo the primary process of addition to C=C bonds. Usually, the expected oxetane is not isolated, but instead derivatives of dibenzfulvene are obtained.

Xanthone (427), unlike thioxanthone **46** does not form an oxetane with benzofuran **44**, but instead transfers triplet energy to the latter, causing dimerization (435). Since benzophenone ($E_t = 69$) forms an oxetane with **44** the triplet energy of **44** is probably about 72 kcal.

The effects of switching substituents can reduce the reactivity of substituted benzophenones by means other than "state switching":

1. By introducing a *new primary process.*
2. By accelerating internal conversion or reaction from S_1 (i.e., inhibiting triplet formation).
3. By causing reaction to be reversible.
4. By accelerating intersystem crossing from T_1 to S_0.

The lack of reactivity of **39** and **40** toward hydrogen abstraction may be due to either (3) or (4). It has been found that the pinacols of **39** and **40** (prepared by nonphotochemical methods) cleave to the ketones when irradiated in the presence of acetone (436–438).

$$\text{ArCOHCOHAr} \xrightarrow[\text{Me}_2\text{CO}]{h\nu} \text{Ar}_2\text{CO} + \text{Me}_2\text{CHOH}$$

$$\textbf{(48)} \text{ or } \textbf{(49)}$$

(**48**) Ar = xanthyl

(**49**) Ar = fluorenyl

Examples of inhibition of *intermolecular reactivity* as a result of (*1*) are given below (429–432):

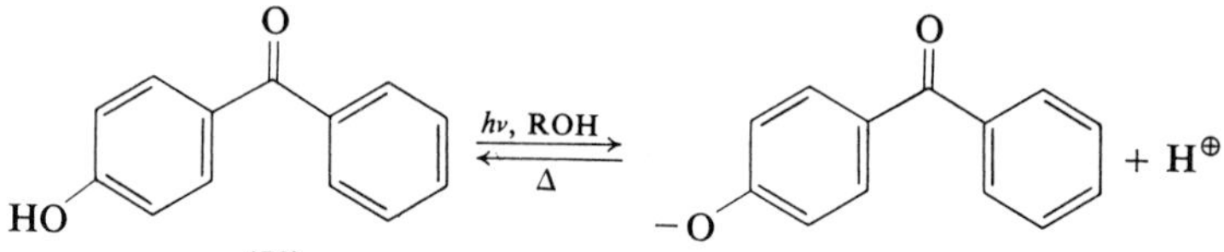

(**50**)   (**51**)

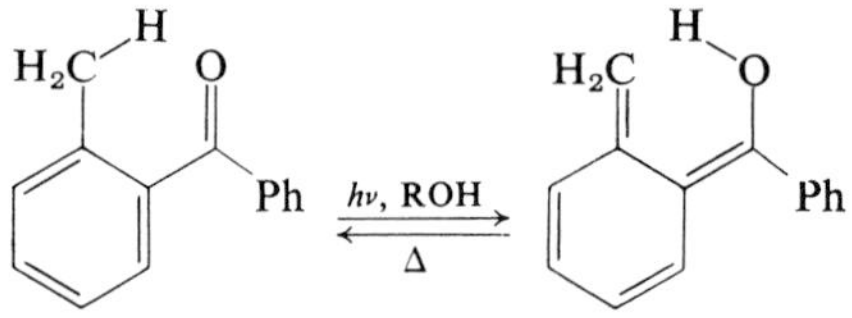

(**52**)   (**53**)

Thus, while ketone **50** does not abstract hydrogens from isopropyl alcohol (i.e., because ionization occurs at a faster rate than hydrogen abstraction), a rapid photolysis of **50** occurs in cyclohexane ($\Phi \sim 1$).

It is presumed, but has not been demonstrated, that this photolysis involves hydrogen abstraction.

The lowest triplet of **52** in alcohol and hydrocarbon solvents appears to be n,π^*, so that state switching is probably not the cause of lack of reactivity in isopropyl alcohol. 2-Alkylbenzophenones appear to undergo intramolecular hydrogen abstraction to yield the unstable enol **53**. This species rapidly reverts back to the original ketone. Since the process is highly reversible, many quanta can be absorbed without significant net reaction of ketone (439).

2-Hydroxylbenzophenones, which are inert toward photolysis in solution, have several possibilities for lowering of reactivity. Thus, T_1 may be π,π^* or a photoionization may occur. In addition, hydrogen bonds are believed to inherently enhance the rate of radiationless transitions (437). Therefore, S_1 may be particularly short-lived due to a rapid $S_1 \rightarrow S_0$ conversion, or T_1 may experience rapid deactivation to the ground state (440–442). Whatever the reason, 2-hydroxybenzophenones are *not* efficient energy transferring agents (443). This implies a low concentration of triplets (due to lack of formation or speed of destruction).

The enolization of 2-alkylbenzophenones has been employed as a method for diene syntheses. For example, irradiation of ketone **54** in the presence of dimethyl acetylene dicarboxylate yields the adduct **56** (408).

The ortho-vinyl benzophenone **56a** undergoes photocyclization to **56b** in benzene and to **56c** in methanol (445) cf. **54** → **54b**, p. 167.

(3) Naphthyl Aryl Ketones

Naphthyl and anthracyl ketones possess π,π^* T_1 states. As a result, the efficiencies of primary processes of hydrogen abstraction and addition are low. However, these molecules are sometimes even more stable toward other processes so that a good yield of photoproduct may be produced in spite of the low efficiency of the reaction.

1- and 2-Naphthyl phenyl ketones are reported to be inert to photoreduction in isopropyl alcohol (446). Presumably, a more potent hydrogen donor such as tri-n-butyltin hydride or an amine will photoreduce these compounds (425).

Interestingly, 2-phenyl naphthyl ketone forms an oxetane (57) with a low efficiency but high yield with 2-methyl-2-butene (447).

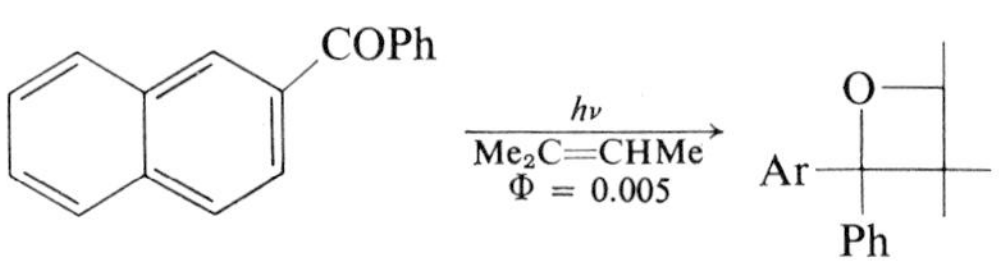

$$\xrightarrow[\substack{Me_2C=CHMe \\ \Phi\ =\ 0.005}]{h\nu}$$

(57), Ar = naphthyl, 62%

The diketone 58 undergoes an intramolecular photopinacolization in isopropyl alcohol (448). It should not be surprising if examples of photo-

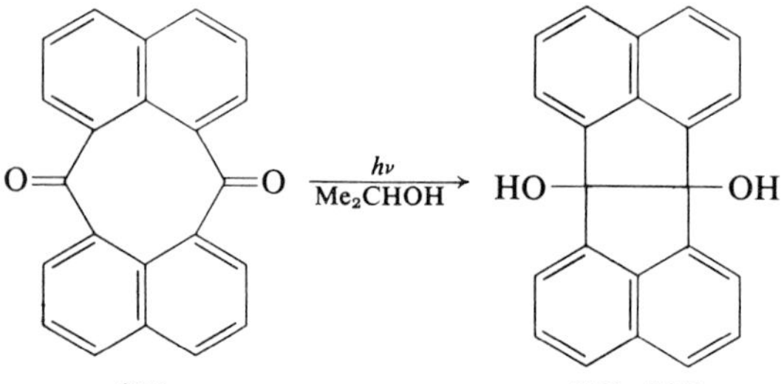

$$\xrightarrow[Me_2CHOH]{h\nu}$$

(58) (59), 55%

reductions involving the aromatic nucleus are discovered for naphthyl aryl ketones, since the π,π^* excitation may be considered to be mainly localized in the ring, away from the carbonyl function.

D. THIOKETONES

Reported photochemical reactions of thioketones are relatively few. It appears that the T_1 state is n,π^* but the energy ($E_3 \sim 40$) is rather low due to a n,π^* excitation of sulfur which involves a $3p$ rather than a $2p$ electron on oxygen.

Irradiation of thiobenzophenone at 2537 Å (but not at $h\nu > 3600$ Å) in alcohol leads to photoreduction. This peculiar effect is not understood.

Reduction may involve hydrogen abstraction by the T_1 (n,π^* state) by analogy to the behavior of benzophenone. The abstraction step may involve the thio-carbonyl carbon (449). Irradiation of thiobenzophenone in the presence

$$Ph_2C{=}S + RH \xrightarrow{h\nu} Ph_2CHSH + \text{other products}$$

of olefins apparently leads to cycloaddition elimination to form 1,1-diphenyl-alkenes, again possibly formally analogous to the addition to C=C bonds by benzophenone (450).

$$Ph_2CS + CH_2{=}CHC_2H_5 \xrightarrow{h\nu} \left[\begin{array}{c} CH_2{-}S \\ | \quad\quad | \\ CH{-}CPh_2 \\ | \\ C_2H_5 \end{array}\right] \longrightarrow \begin{array}{c} CH_2{=}S + \\ CH{=}CPh \\ | \\ C_2H_5 \end{array}$$

Irradiation of 4,4'-dimethyleaminothiobenzophenone results in a dimerization–cleavage reaction. The role of boron may be to cause "state switching" so that an n,π^*-like state is lower. This then attacks the ground state C=S bond (451).

$$Ar_2C{=}S{\cdots}B(Bu)_3 \xrightarrow{h\nu} Ar_2C{=}\overset{*}{S}{\cdots}B(Bu)_3$$

$$Ar_2C{=}\overset{*}{S}{\cdots}B(Bu)_3 \longrightarrow \left[\begin{array}{c} Ar_2C{-}SB(Bu)_3 \\ | \quad\quad | \\ Ar_2C{-}SB(Bu)_3 \end{array}\right]$$

$$\longrightarrow Ar_2C{=}CAr_2 \atop 100\%$$

Thioketones are oxidized to ketones and SO_2 by irradiation in the presence of O_2 (452). The photochemistry of thiobenzophenone is qualitatively analogous to that of benzophenone. No detailed mechanistic studies of this and related systems have been made (453,454).

4. Carboxylic Acids and Related Compounds

A. VINYL AND AROMATIC ESTERS

The solution photochemistry of aliphatic carboxylic acids and esters has not been studied in detail. In general, these compounds do not have significant absorption beyond 2500 Å, so that quartz equipment is required. It is not known whether the lowest excited states of these compounds are n,π^* or π,π^*.

Irradiation of vinyl esters such as **1** results in α-cleavage followed by rearrangement to a 1,3-dione. Since the dione **2** is enolic, it competes with

$$\underset{\substack{||\\ CH_2 \\ \textbf{(1)}}}{\overset{O}{CH_3\overset{||}{C}OCCH_3}} \xrightarrow{h\nu} \overline{CH_3\overset{\cdot}{C}O + \overset{\cdot}{O}\underset{\substack{||\\CH_2}}{CCH_3}} \longrightarrow \underset{\textbf{(2)}, 30\%}{CH_3COCH_2COCH_3}$$

the starting material for the exciting light and the reaction is "quenched" by this internal filter.

Although the rearrangements presumably involve cage recombination of the radicals produced by α-cleavage, occasionally the radicals escape the cage and products such as **3** and **4**, which are expected of kinetically free radicals, result in addition to the 1,3-diones (455–458).

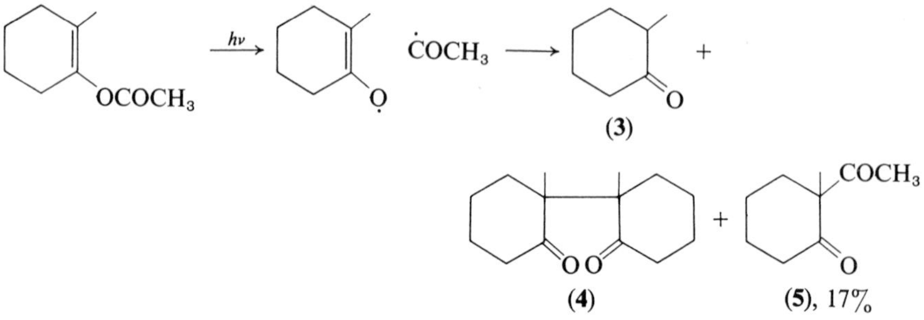

(3)

(4)   (5), 17%

Enol lactones apparently also undergo α-cleavage followed by various paths for stabilization of the resulting radical pair. Since the radical pair

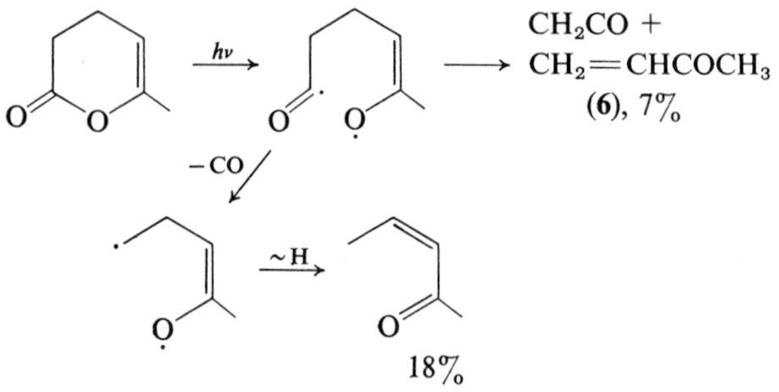

$CH_2CO +$
$CH_2{=}CHCOCH_3$
(6), 7%

18%

cannot become kinetically free in the case of lactones, new decomposition paths may occur as shown above (459). Similar photo-Fries reactions occur

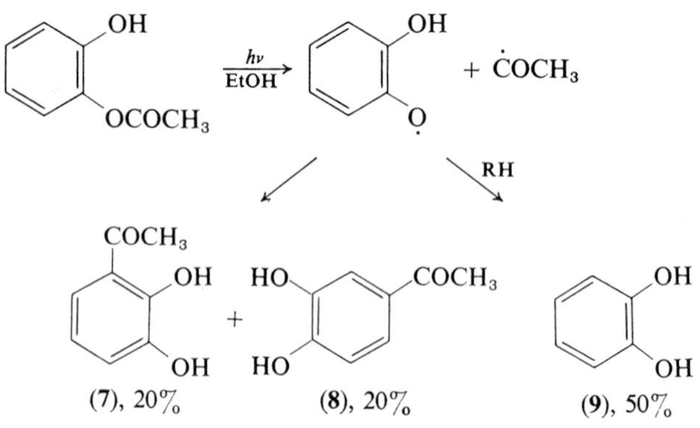

+ $\dot{C}OCH_3$

RH

(7), 20%   (8), 20%   (9), 50%

when phenyl esters are irradiated. Clearly, the hydrogen-donating ability and viscosity of the solvent and the temperature will influence the ratio of Fries rearrangement to kinetically free radical products, if the proposed mechanism is the correct one (460,461). Recent work indicates that the photo-Fries occurs via a singlet state and is insensitive to solvent (461a).

Vinyl esters and phenyl esters of benzoic acid and its derivatives also undergo the photo-Fries rearrangement mechanism. Occasionally, the photo-Fries rearrangement offers a path to products under mild conditions so that the photoconversion is the method of choice. For example, the photo-Fries has been employed as an important step in the total synthesis of grieseofulvin **10**. Aluminum chloride failed as a thermal catalyst in this reaction (462).

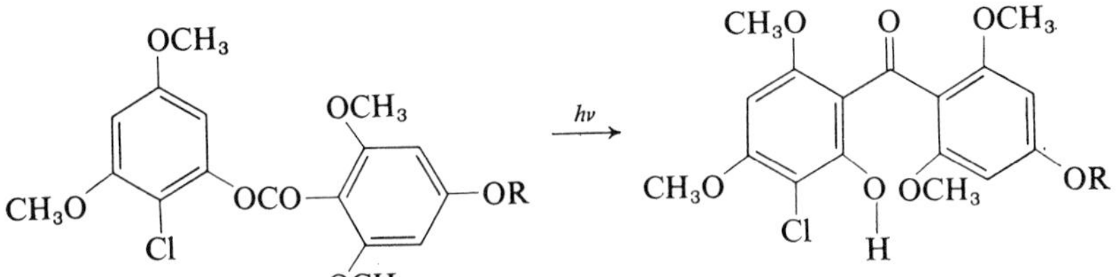

(10), 15%

As in the case of vinyl and phenyl esters of aliphatic acids, these rearrangements cannot be taken to high conversions because of the intense absorption

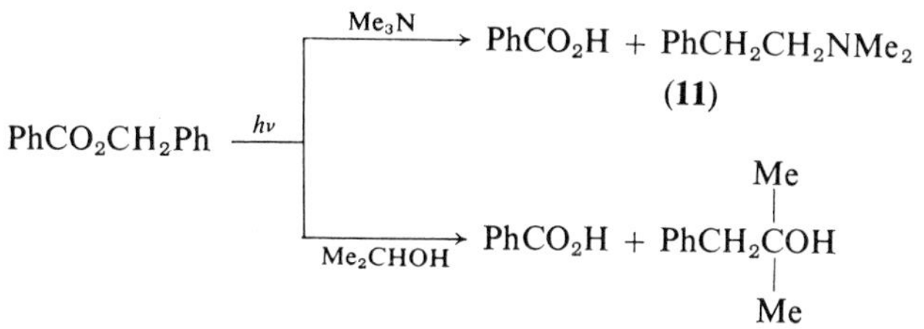

$PhCO_2CH_2Ph$ $\xrightarrow{h\nu}$

$\xrightarrow{Me_3N}$ $PhCO_2H + PhCH_2CH_2NMe_2$

(11)

$\xrightarrow{Me_2CHOH}$ $PhCO_2H + PhCH_2\underset{Me}{\overset{Me}{\underset{|}{\overset{|}{C}}}}OH$

(12)

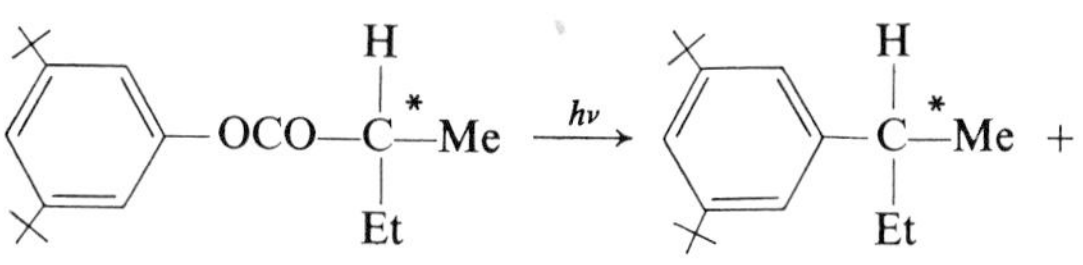

(12a)   (12b), 20%

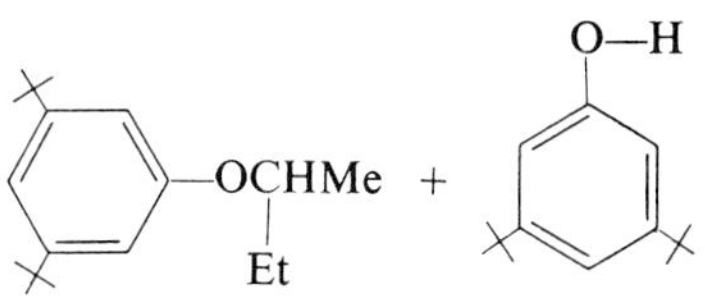

(12c), 3%   (12d), 75%

characteristic of the products. Irradiation of benzyl benzoate in aliphatic alcohol or amine solvents results in benzylation. For example, irradiation of benzyl benzoate in triethyl amine yields benzoic acid and the amine **11**, while isopropyl alcohol yields the alcohol **12** (463).

The optically active ester **12a** undergoes photodecarboxylation to yield the optically active hydrocarbon **12b**, in addition to other products (464).

B. AMIDES

The photochemistry of amides is similar to that of esters in that α-cleavage appears to be the dominant primary process (465). For example, irradiation of formamide in benzene results in amidation of the benzene ring. The reaction is "sensitized" by acetone (466). The mechanism of sensitization may be either energy transfer to the amide or abstraction of a hydrogen atom.

$$
\underset{\text{HCNH}_2}{\overset{\text{O}}{\|}} \xrightarrow[\text{Me}_2\text{CO}]{h\nu} \text{H}\cdot + \underset{\overset{\bullet}{\text{C}}\text{NH}_2}{\overset{\text{O}}{\|}} \xrightarrow{\text{C}_6\text{H}_6} \text{PhCONH}_2
$$

Formamide may be added to C=C bonds photochemically, probably also by a cleavage-addition mechanism. For example, formamide and norbornene

(13), 87%

yield the exoadduct **13** in good yield. Aromatic anilides also undergo photo-Fries type rearrangements.

(14), 14%   (15), 12%   (16), 6%

C. ACID HALIDES

Only a few photoreactions of acid halides are known. Again, α-cleavage seems to be the most important primary process for these compounds. Thus, irradiation of acetyl bromide in ether results in acetylation of the α-position of the ether.

$$CH_3COBr \xrightarrow[Et_2O]{h\nu} CH_3COCHOCH_2CH_3$$
$$\underset{CH_3}{|}$$
$$(17), 20\%$$

D. ACETYL CYANIDE

Irradiation of acetyl cyanide in the presence of various olefins results in oxetane formation. Contrary to the behavior of acetone, which does not add to norbornene to form oxetanes, acetyl cyanide does (471). This result implies either a lower triplet energy for acetyl cyanide compared to acetone or a much faster rate of cycloaddition. Since acetyl cyanide also adds to styrene derivates to form oxetanes, the rate constant for oxetane formation (or formation of a complex which results in an oxetane) is competitive with energy transfer.

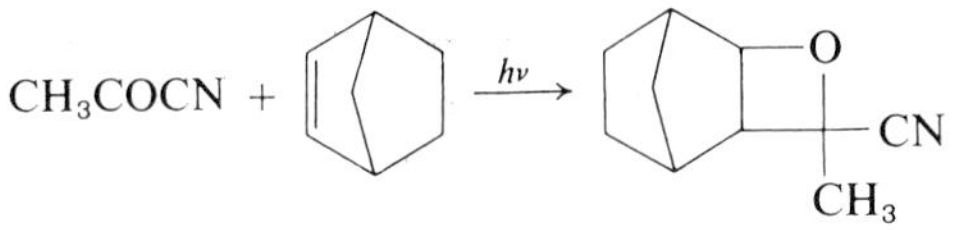

$$CH_3COCN + \text{(norbornene)} \xrightarrow{h\nu} \text{(oxetane adduct)} \begin{matrix} CN \\ CH_3 \end{matrix}$$

(18) + (19) (isomers), 77%

$$CH_3COCN + Ph_2C{=}CH_2 \xrightarrow{h\nu} \underset{Ph\ CH_3}{\overset{O}{Ph\underset{|}{|}CN}}$$

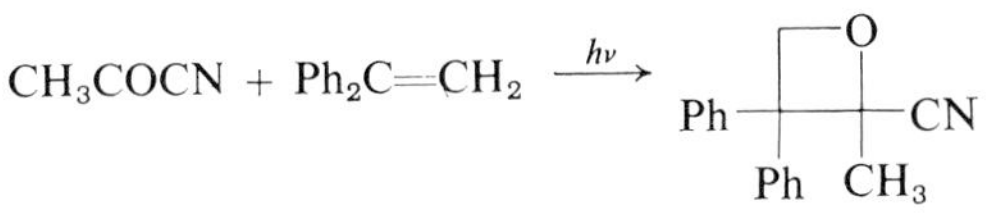

(20), 52%

E. SILYL KETONES

Irradiation of methyl triphenylsilylketone 21 in ethanol leads to different products in the presence and absence of base (472). The reaction in base is reminiscent of the carbene formation which occurs when cyclobutanones are irradiated (Section III–2–A–(4)).

$$Ph_3SiCOCH_3 \xrightarrow[EtOH]{h\nu} Ph_3SiOEt + Ph_3SiOH$$
$$(21)$$

$$(21) \xrightarrow[\substack{EtOH \\ base}]{h\nu} Ph_3Si\cdot\overset{\cdot}{C}OCH_3 \longrightarrow Ph_3Si{-}O{-}\overset{\cdot\cdot}{C}{-}CH_3$$

$$\xrightarrow{EtOH} Ph_3SiO{-}\underset{CH_3}{\overset{OEt}{\underset{|}{\overset{|}{CH}}}}$$

F. KETENES

Very little has been reported on the photochemistry of ketenes in solution. The photolysis of ketene in the vapor phase, however, has received considerable attention. Both the singlet and triplet states of ketene appear to be involved, and the latter may be quenched by inclusion of a suitable acceptor. The major reaction in the vapor phase appears to be loss of carbon monoxide (473).

$$CH_2{=}C{=}O \xrightarrow[\text{vapor}]{h\nu} \dot{C}H_2{-}\dot{C}{=}O \rightsquigarrow S_0$$

$$S_1 \text{ or } T_1$$

$$\downarrow$$

$$:\dot{C}H_2 + CO$$

Such a reaction would appear to be initiated by the π^* electron between the carbon atoms. If this is so, one might expect that the primary processes of a $C{=}C$ double bond (modified somewhat by the fused $C{=}O$) may be applicable to the photochemistry of ketenes. Thus, the photochemistry of ketene in solution seems to involve mainly hydrogen abstraction and cycloaddition reactions.

The cyclic ketene **22** undergoes efficient decarbonylation in inert solvents to yield the hydrocarbons **23** and **24**. Carbon suboxide undergoes photolysis

| (22) | (23) | (24) |

to CO and the carbene **25** in the vapor phase, but appears to be relatively inert to photolysis in solution.

Diphenylketene (**26**) apparently undergoes photochemical cleavages, hydrogen abstraction, and cycloaddition reactions, as judged by the nature

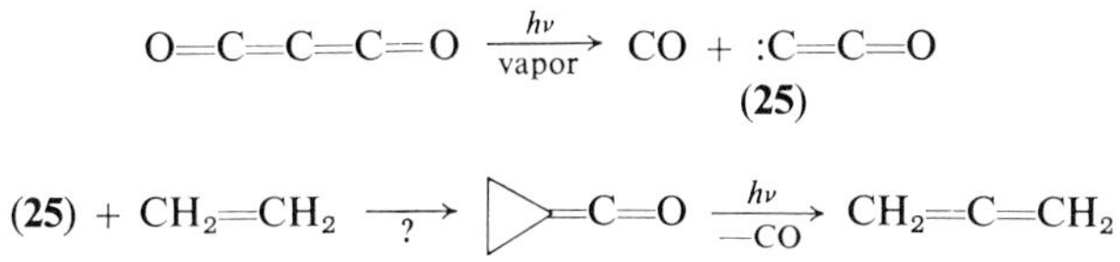

$$O=C=C=C=O \xrightarrow[\text{vapor}]{h\nu} CO + :C=C=O$$
$$(25)$$

$$(25) + CH_2=CH_2 \xrightarrow{?} \triangleright=C=O \xrightarrow[-CO]{h\nu} CH_2=C=CH_2$$

of the products produced. For example, irradiation of **26** in the presence of 1,1-diphenyl ethylene yields 1,1,2,2-tetraphenylcyclopropane. It is claimed that the tetraphenylcyclobutanone **27** does not yield this product when

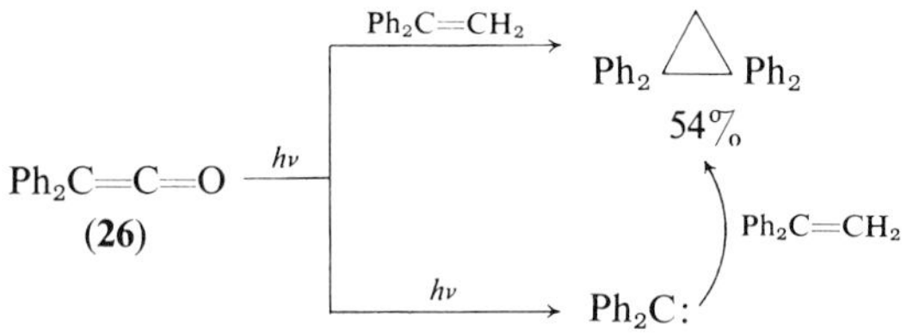

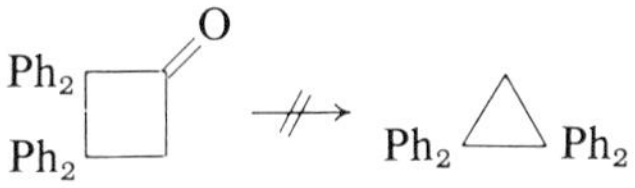

irradiated (477). In hydrogen donating solvents, reductive decarbonylation occurs (477).

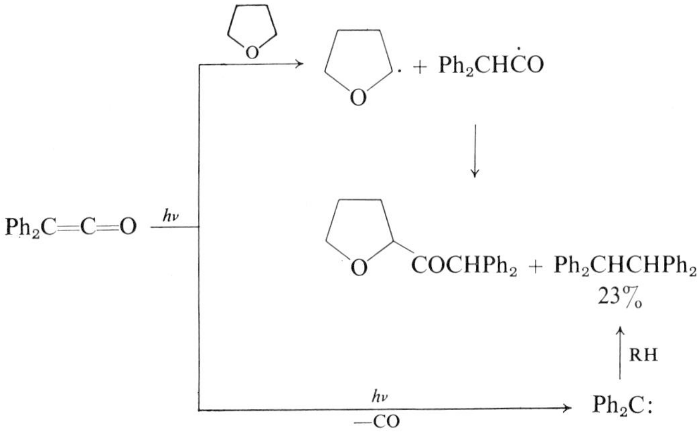

Benzophenone is also a minor product of the above reaction. In benzene, however, it is *the major product in the absence of oxygen*! This result may in part derive from a cycloaddition followed by decomposition. The high yield of benzophenone demands that the other product be recycled as an oxygen source.

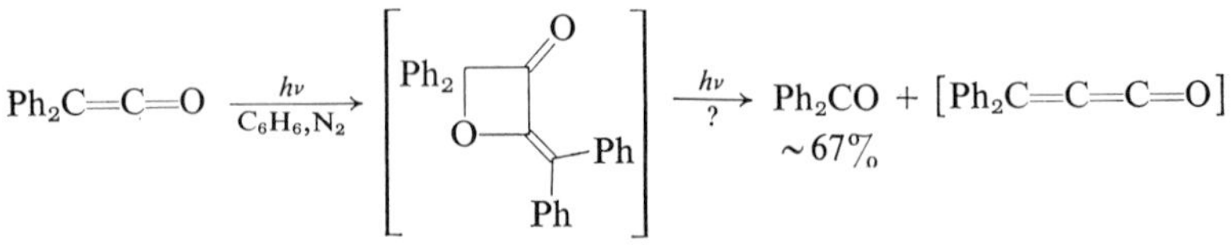

$$Ph_2C=C=O \xrightarrow[C_6H_6,N_2]{hv} \left[\begin{array}{c} Ph_2 \overset{O}{\boxed{}} \\ O \quad\overset{\displaystyle}{\diagdown}\text{-Ph} \\ Ph \end{array} \right] \xrightarrow[?]{hv} Ph_2CO + [Ph_2C=C=C=O]$$
$$\sim 67\%$$

Irradiation of dimesitylketene **28** in cyclohexane results in a low yield of the ethylene **29**. This reaction involves either cleavage to yield the carbene which then attacks a ketene to produce a cyclopropanone or dimerization via photochemical cycloaddition to yield a dione which is subsequently photolyzed to **29**.

$$R_2C=C=O \xrightarrow{hv} R_2C=CR_2$$
$$\quad(28) \qquad\qquad (29)$$

$$R = \begin{array}{c} CH_3 \\ \text{—}\!\!\diagup\!\!\diagdown\text{—}CH_3 \\ CH_3 \end{array}$$

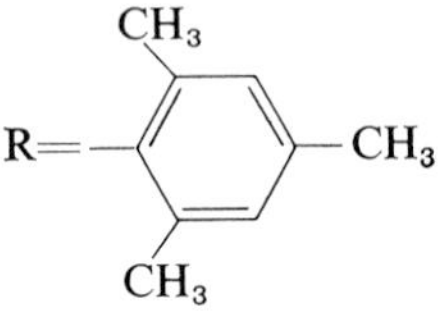

IV. CONJUGATED ENONES, DIONES, AND RELATED COMPOUNDS

1. General Considerations

A. EXCITED STATES OF ENONES AND RELATED COMPOUNDS

(1) Models for the Excited States of Enones

Although a wealth of photochemistry of enones is known, the nature of their lowest excited states is not known with certainty, but may be deduced from the reactions of excited enones. An immediate problem concerns the geometry of enone excited states which may exist in either a planar or twisted form (479). The lack of emission data on enones forces the configuration of the lowest triplet states of these compounds to remain in doubt. As was the case for ketones, we would expect different photochemistry from the n,π^* and π,π^* states of enones.

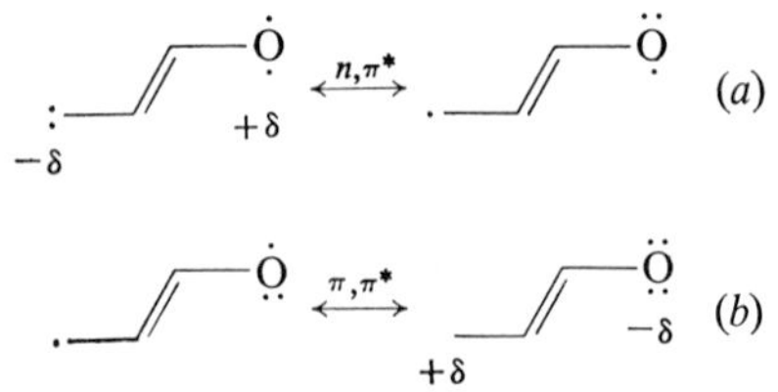

Fig. 14. Valence bond descriptions of the n,π^* (a) and π,π^* (b) states of an enone.

Tentative descriptions of the n,π^* and π,π^* states of an enone, if the excited state remains planar, are given in Figure 14. It is possible that the planar model may not be an accurate description of the lowest excited states of enones. Like conjugated dienes, enones have the possibility of relaxing to *twisted* S_1 and T_1 states. These relaxed states may resemble a carbonium ion fused to an allyl anion.

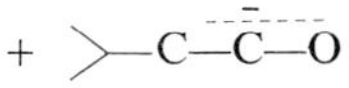

$$+ \quad \rangle\!\!-\!\!C\!\!-\!\!\overset{\scriptscriptstyle -}{C}\!\!-\!\!O$$

(2) Primary Processes of Enones

Since the enone chromophore possesses some of the properties of both carbonyl and diene groups, we might expect that the photochemistry of an enone will be somewhat analogous to that of a ketone or diene. For example, the primary processes of α-cleavage, hydrogen abstraction and addition, which are characteristic of a diene, may occur (Eqs. (4), (5), and (6)). The reactions of the enone excited state might be expected to exhibit greater polar character than those of the corresponding diene.

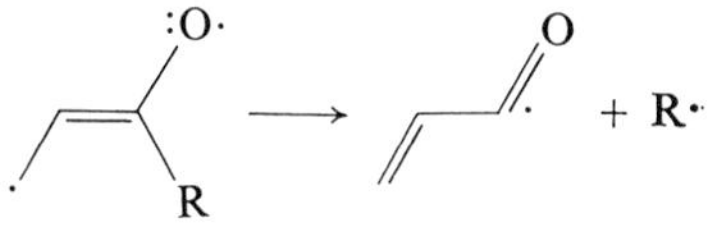

(1)

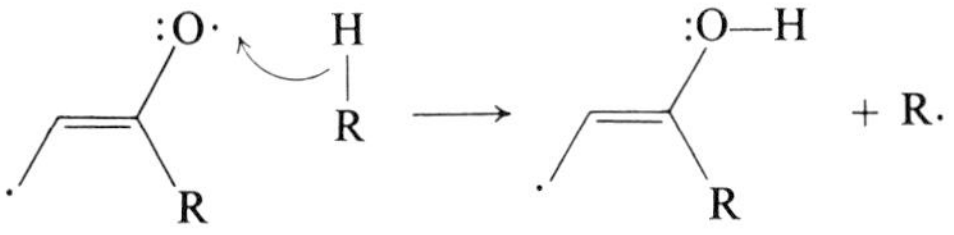

(2)

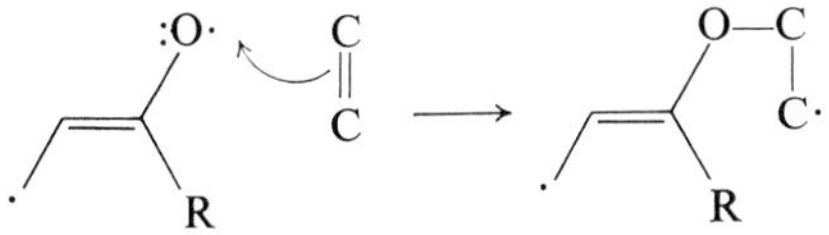

(3)

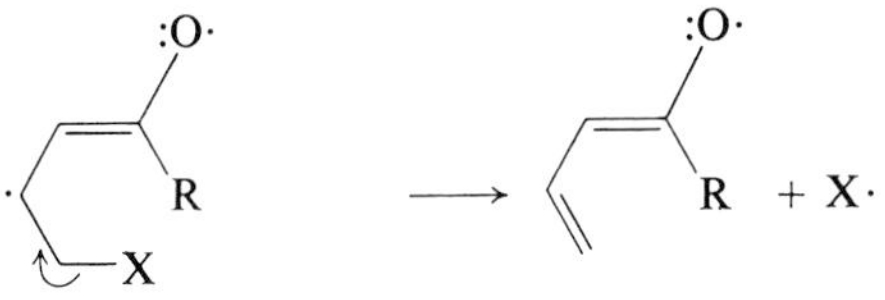

(4)

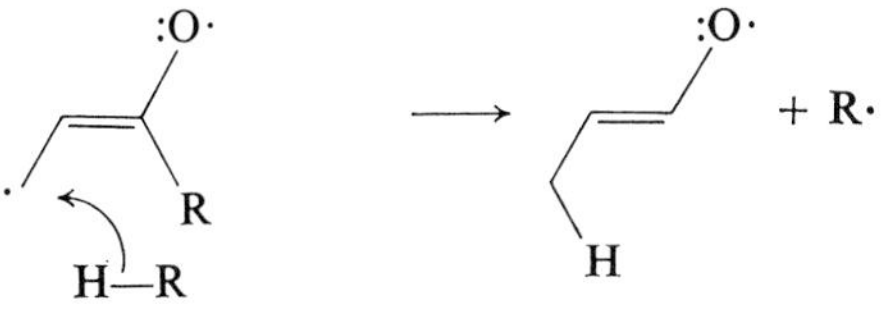

(5)

$$(6)$$

$$(7)$$

TABLE 9

Triplet Energies of Some Enones and Derivatives

Compound	$E_3{}^a$	Ref.	Compound	$E_3{}^a$	Ref.
$CH_2=CHCHO$	~69	480		71	485
	~71	481		68	485
	69	482		67	485
	62	483		62	484

^{a} E_3 in kcal/mole.

Although these reactions have been depicted as occurring in a homolytic fashion, heterolytic or polar processes may also lead to the same results. Further conjugation of the double bond should not introduce any fundamental differences in the expected chemistry of these excited states, so that the vinylogous principle may be employed to describe the excited states of dienones, etc.

(3) Energy Diagrams for Enones

Enones generally do not exhibit phosphorescence spectra. However, quenching studies have indicated the effective triplet level of an enone from which energy transfer occurs. Table 9 lists some triplet energies of enones and related compounds. Although the lifetimes of enone triplets seem to be extremely short, very limited data concerning these lifetimes are available.

B. EXCITED STATES OF UNSATURATED CARBOXYLIC ACIDS AND DERIVATIVES

(1) Models for the Excited States of Unsaturated Acids and Derivatives

Very little is known concerning the nature of the excited states of conjugated acids and their derivatives. The bulk of reported photoreactions of these compounds involve additions across the C=C bond, indicating a π,π^* excited state. Some reactions of the C=O bond are known, but these are rare.

Thus, a working model for maleic anhydride would be

(2) Primary Processes

As indicated above, the major primary photochemical processes of conjugated acids and their derivatives are additions. These are mainly cycloadditions or dimerizations. α-Cleavage reactions are rare for these compounds although reactions related to oxetane formation have been observed.

(3) Energy Level Diagrams

Hardly any data on the energies, lifetimes, etc., are available for conjugated acids and derivatives. Since sensitization can be effected by benzophenone for many of these compounds, it is probable that their triplet energies lie lower than 68 kcal.

C. EXCITED STATES OF α-DIKETONES

(1) Models of the Excited States for α-Diketones

The lowest S_1 and T_1 states of simple α-diketones are generally n,π^* states although promotion of an n-electron to a π^* orbital might be expected to lead to net C_2—C_3 *bonding* in the n,π^* state. Spectral analysis of biacetyl leads to a contrary conclusion (486). As a result, the general chemistry of α-dicarbonyls seems to be more similar to that of the isolated carbonyl group than a 1,4-conjugated biradical, with the exception of certain concerted 1,4-addition and intramolecular additions.

(2) Primary Processes of α-Diketones

Qualitatively, the same primary processes shown by simple alkyl ketones are predicted by the model of the n,π^* state of alkyl α-diketones given above. Quantitatively, the reaction rates should be modified by the necessary interaction of the reacting excited carbonyl and its neighbor, and the much lower energy of the n,π^* states.

(3) Energy Diagrams for α-Diketones

α-Diketones display remarkable resistance to intramolecular triplet quenching. As a result, biacetyl and its simple derivatives show moderately strong phosphoresence even in fluid solution. An energy diagram for biacetyl is given in Figure 15. Some data on the excited states of α-diketones and derivatives are given in Table 10.

TABLE 10

Compound	Φ_{st}	E_1 [a]	E_3 [a]	k_t [a]
CH_3COCO_2H	0.67	80	68	—
$CH_3COCO_2C_2H_5$	0.5	—	65	—
$C_6H_5COCO_2H$	—	76	63	—
$C_6H_5COCO_2C_2H_5$	—	—	62	—
$C_{10}H_7COCO_2C_2H_5$	—	—	57	—
CHOCHO	—	63	56	—
$CH_3COCOCH_3$	0.99	65	55	1×10^3
$C_6H_5COCOC_6H_5$	0.87	65	51(54)	2×10^4
Camphorquinone	—	57	50	3×10^3
Phenanthrenequinone	—	55	49	—

[a] E_1 and E_3 in kcal/mole, k_t in sec^{-1}.

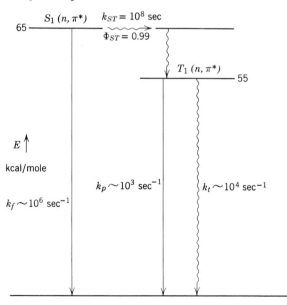

Fig. 15. Energy diagram for 2,3-butanedione.

D. EXCITED STATES OF BENZOQUINONE AND DERIVATIVES

(1) Models for the Excited States of Benzoquinones

The photochemistry of benzoquinones seems to derive from both n,π^* and π,π^* states. The n,π^* state of benzoquinone can be represented as

and the π,π^* state as

While these descriptions are qualitatively adequate, quantitative predictions as to which site will actually be the most reactive are not possible at present.

(2) Primary Processes of Benzoquinones

The primary processes of benzoquinone, as predicted by the above models, may be related to the primary processes of a ketone or to the primary processes of a C=C group, depending on whether the reactive state is n,π^* or π,π^*.

Thus, one can imagine hydrogen abstraction and oxetane formation from the n,π^* state. The π,π^* state, on the other hand, may undergo similar

reactions at the C=C bond.

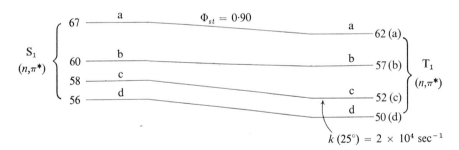

(3) Energy Diagrams for Benzoquinones

The singlet and triplet energies of benzoquinones and some derivatives are given in Figure 16. The features which reduce the reactivity of benzophenone and derivatives, such as intramolecular hydrogen abstraction and the intrusion of charge transfer states, also modify the reactivity of benzoquinone and derivatives.

S_1
(n,π^*)

67 — a — $\Phi_{st} = 0.90$ — a — 62 (a)
60 — b — b — 57 (b)
58 — c — c — 52 (c)
56 — d — d — 50 (d)

T_1
(n,π^*)

$k\,(25°) = 2 \times 10^4\ \mathrm{sec}^{-1}$

Fig. 16. Singlet- and triplet-state energies (in kcal/mole) of 1,4-quinones: (*a*) anthraquinone; (*b*) naphthoquinone; (*c*) duroquinone; (*d*) benzoquinone (497–500).

2. α,β-Unsaturated Alkyl Ketones and Aldehydes

A. ACYCLIC ENONES

As indicated above, enols and enones undergo photochemical primary processes characteristic of both C=C and C=O groups. The acyclic α,β-unsaturated alkyl enones do not require the inclusion of a "polar" type of primary process (see, however, Section II–B).

Irradiation of 2-butenal, **1**, yields both oxetanes and cyclobutanes when irradiated in the presence of 2-methyl-2-butene. As in the case of dienes (see Section I–3–A–(1)) 1,2-addition seems to be preferred as none of the 1,4-adduct, **4**, was isolated (501).

Intramolecular additions of the C=C bond of the excited enol or enone to an isolated C=C bond are also known. For example, citral **5** undergoes rearrangement to **7** and **8**. Both products may be derived from the inter-mediate **6** (502,503).*

Cis–trans isomerization is a common and probably general primary process of α,β-unsaturated carbonyl compounds. In addition, ketones possessing a hydrogen atom on the carbon γ to the carbonyl group may undergo Type II intramolecular hydrogen abstraction. However, this reaction is apparently not general, since numerous α,β-unsaturated ketones which possess this structural feature fail to give evidence of Type II abstraction.

* 1,5-Dienes exhibit a tendency to close to five-membered rings.

For example, the ketone **9** undergoes *trans–cis* photoisomerization followed by Type II abstraction which results in deconjugation to a β,γ-unsaturated ketone. Other conceivable products such as **14**, **15**, and **16** have not yet been reported (504,505).*

Presumably a "homoallylic" seven-membered transition state obtains the conversion of **17** to **20**. To date, a methyl abstraction by the carbonyl oxygen has not been observed.

* For an example which may involve an excited state or intermediate related to **16**, see ref. 505.

Hydrogen abstraction by the oxygen atom of the excited enone system may lead to reduction of the carbonyl function or reduction of the C=C bond. Irradiation of the steroidal enone **24** in ethanol (507) results in reduction of the C=C bond, although the primary photochemical process is probably the formation of the allylic ketyl radical **25**, which may then abstract a hydrogen atom or couple with another radical.

The *trans*-enone **27a** is converted to the *cis*-isomer **27b**, which undergoes photocyclization to **27c** and **27d** (508).

B. CONJUGATED CYCLIC ENONES

(1) Small Ring Enones

The photochemistry of cyclic enones displays less radical character than that of acyclic enones. Molecular rearrangements typical of polar ground-state reactions are more common. The C=C bond of the excited enone bond is highly reactive toward addition to other unsaturated groups. α-Cleavage is rare for enones except for small ring ketones. For example, diphenylcyclo-propenone (509,510) and the cyclobutenone **28** (511,512) undergo facile photocleavage.

(2) Cyclopentenone and Derivatives

The most important photoreactions reported to date for cyclopentenone and its simple derivatives are additions to C=C bonds (513–519). Cyclopentenone dimerizes to yield a solvent-dependent mixture of the cyclobutanes **31** and **32** (513). In the presence of an excess of ethylenes, the cross addition products form in good yield (514,515). The mechanism of the dimerization reaction appears to proceed via the triplet enone (520–522).*

Intramolecular closure of cyclopentenone derivatives provide the method of choice for closure to "cage" compounds in many cases. For example, a cubane precursor **35** was prepared by closure of the dienone **34** (523,513).

Irradiation of the cyclopentenone **35a** results in ring contraction to yield **35b** (525).

Bicyclo[3.1.0]hexenes generally undergo facile cleavage of the 4,6-cyclopropane bond followed by rearrangement to a stable isomer, usually a phenol or a cyclohexadienone.

---

* It has been proposed that the reactive triplet may be T_2 (522).

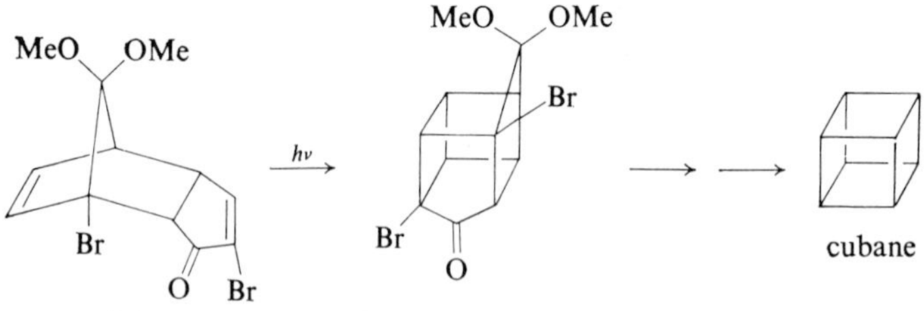

(34)   (35)   cubane

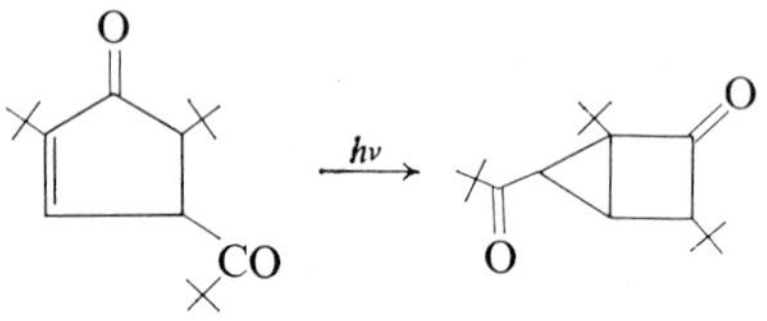

(35a)   (35b)

For example, irradiation of the enone **36** results in the formation of phenol (**37**). However, irradiation of lumisantonin **38** results in formation of the cyclohexadienone **39** (527). Finally, irradiation of **40** results in formation of **41** (528). The asterisk indicates a plus, dot, or minus (i.e., it is noncommittal about the polarity of the excited state).

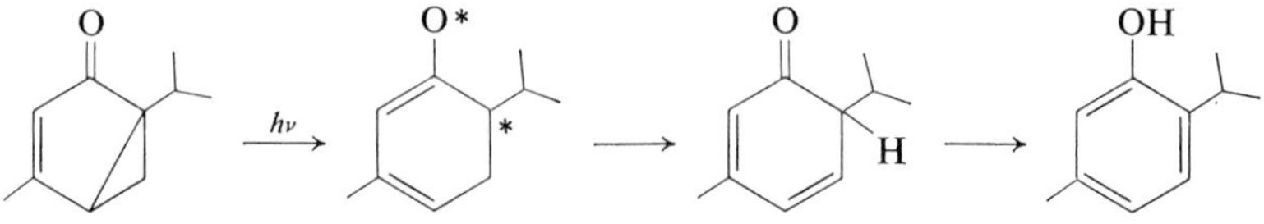

(36)   (37), 100%

An argument for dipolar species is also derived from the fact that irradiation of 6-phenyl-6-*p*-cyanophenylbicyclo[3.1.0]hex-3-en-2-one causes only

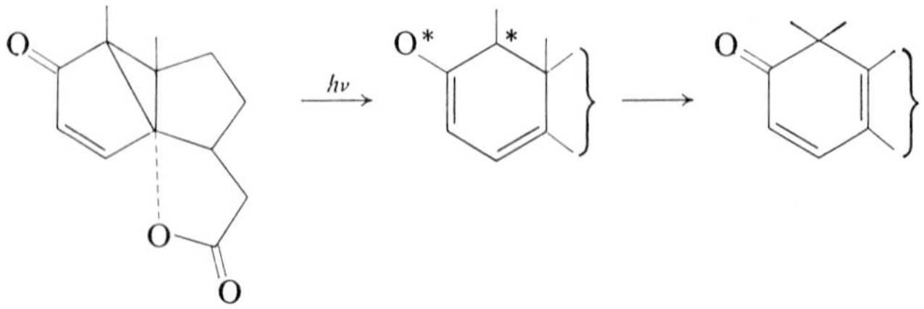

(38)   (39)

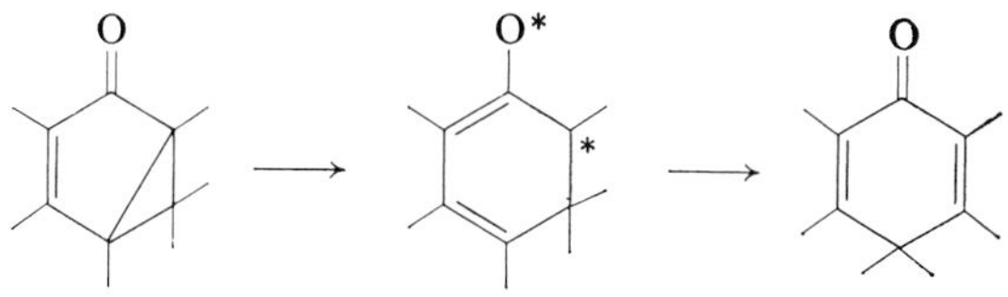

(40) (41)

phenyl migration. This indicates migration to an adjacent carbon with cationic character (529).

(3) Cyclohexenones

The reactivity and selectivity of conjugated cyclohexenone in cyclo-additions are qualitatively parallel to those of cyclopentenones. Thus, 2-cyclohexenone undergoes dimerization and cross-cycloaddition reactions (530).

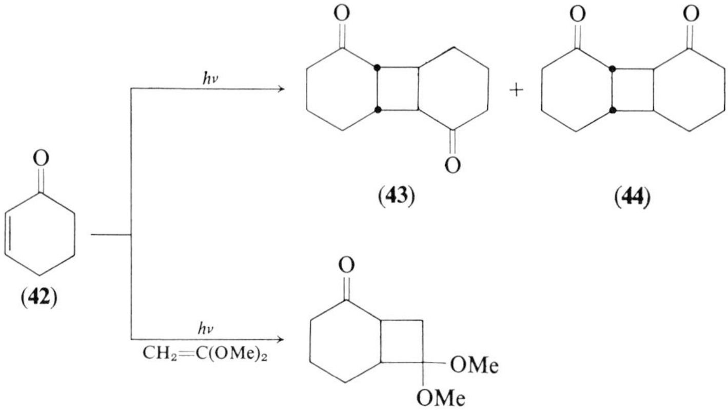

(42) (43) (44)

(45)

The orientation of the adducts formed with *electron*-rich olefins is analogous to that shown for **30**. However, isobutylene yields a considerable amount of the 7,7-dimethyl isomers **47** and **48**. The occurrence of the ketones **46** and **49** suggests the intermediacy biradical intermediates in these cycloadditions. This hypothesis is in agreement with the observation that *cis-* and *trans-*2-butene yield the same mixture of adducts, indicating that loss of stereo-chemistry occurs in some intermediate (530,531). Available evidence points to a π,π^* triplet mechanism for these reactions (532).

In inert solvents, cyclohexenones undergo molecular rearrangements. For example, 4,4-dimethylcyclohexen-2-one (**51**) undergoes rearrangement to the bicyclo[3.1.0]hexanone **52** (533).

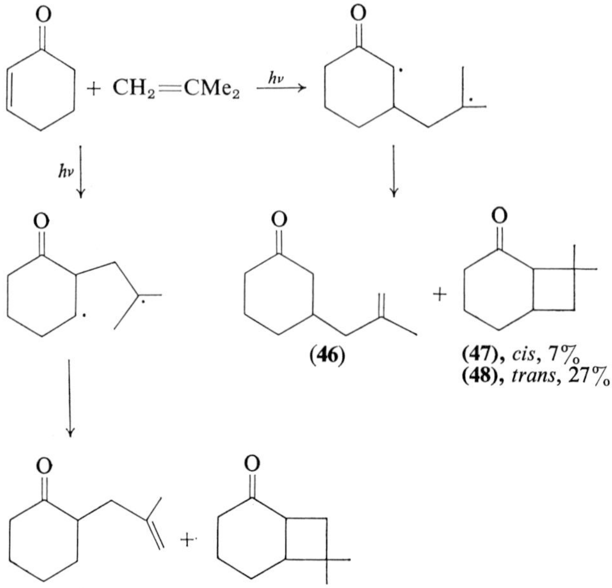

(46)

(47), *cis*, 7%
(48), *trans*, 27%

(49)   **(50)**, 6%

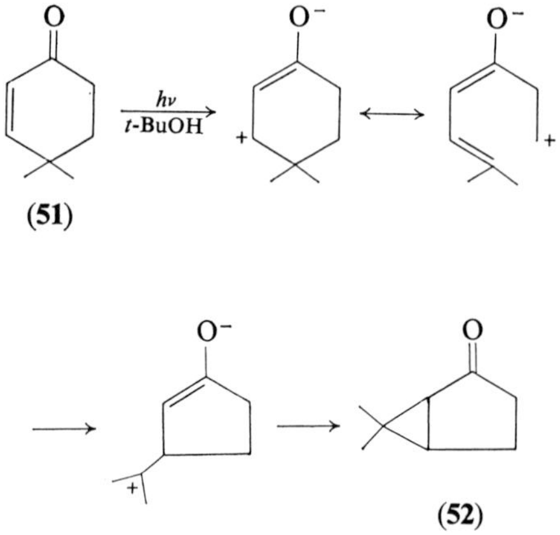

(51)

(52)

A formally related rearrangement to a bicyclo[3.1.0]hexanone occurs simultaneously with group migration when the 4,4-diarylcyclohex-2-enone is irradiated. Since *p*-cyanophenyl and *p*-methoxyphenyl show similar migratory aptitudes, migration to a "radical-like" adjacent carbon is a possible step. However, studies with optically active compounds demonstrate that "free" radical intermediates cannot be involved (534–537).

(53), R = pCNC$_6$H$_4$ (54a)   (54b)
or pCH$_3$OC$_6$H$_4$

Intramolecular cycloadditions of alkenylcyclohexenones are also known. For example, irradiation of carvone yields carvonecamphor (538). Irradiation

(55)   (56), 50%

of optically active verbenone results in cleavage of the C—C bond β to the excited C=C bond and 1,3-migration to yield optically active chrysanthenone (58).

(57)   (58), 75%

C. 2-CYCLOHEPTENONE AND 2-CYCLOOCTENONE

The strained *trans*-cyclic enones **60** and **62** may be produced from the *cis*-cyclic enones **59** and **61** (539–541). These results may be pertinent to the photochemistry of cyclohexenones, i.e., the intermediates in cyclohexenone photochemistry may possess a structure similar to *trans*-2-cyclohexenone.

(59)   (60)

(61)   (62)

3. α,β-Unsaturated Acids and Derivatives

A. CINNAMIC ACID AND DERIVATIVES

Many α,β-unsaturated acids and their derivatives undergo the photo-chemical primary processes of *cis–trans* isomerization. Cyclobutane formation also occurs in fluid solution and the solid state. The factors controlling the stereochemistry of these cycloadditions are not worked out for reactions in fluid solid, but for those reactions occurring in the solid (crystal) state a correlation exists between the structure of the dimers and the structure of the crystal. As an example, the photodimerization of two crystal modifications (α and β) of *trans*-cinnamic acid produces two stereoisomeric dimers, one formed from each crystal form. The α-form yields α-truxillic acid **2** while the β-form yields β-truxinic acid **4** (546,547).

It has been shown that the crystal lattice of the α-form contains pairs of molecules lined up head-to-tail with the distance between the reactive carbon atoms about 4 Å (547). The β-form, on the other hand, has a crystal structure with pairs of molecules lined up head-to-head with a similar distance separating the C=C bonds. These are the optimum reaction conditions since a minimum of lattice distortion occurs as a result of dimerization. It has been found that when the C—C distance between reaction centers is larger than 4 Å, the dimerization does not occur (542).

α,β-Unsaturated lactones and lactams also undergo photodimerization to cyclobutanes. For example, coumarin undergoes both sensitized and direct dimerization and cross addition reactions (548–550).

$$(5) \quad \xrightarrow[\text{Me}_2\text{C}=\text{CMe}_2]{hv} \qquad (9)$$

Irradiation of aryl-substituted cinnamic acids yields lactones, perhaps via intramolecular oxete formation, followed by rearrangement. A similar reaction occurs with related amides (551).

(11) $\xrightarrow[\text{C}_6\text{H}_6]{hv}$ (12) or (13)

(14), 79%

4. Dienones

A. LINEAR, CROSS-CONJUGATED DIENONES

Cross-conjugated dienones undergo reactions related to those of conjugated enones. For instance, dibenzylacetone undergoes dimerization to cyclobutanes in a solvent-dependent reaction (552,553). Intramolecular hydrogen abstraction and solvent-addition reactions are also known for these compounds (554,555).

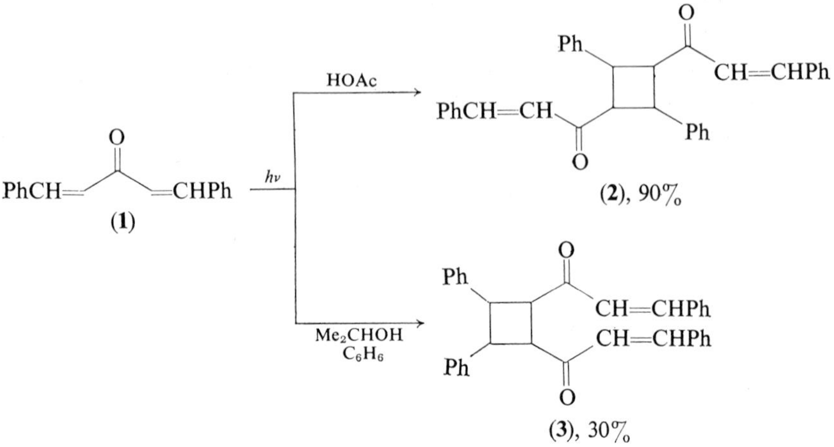

(2), 90%

(3), 30%

B. CYCLOHEXA-2,5-DIENONES

The photochemistry of a wide variety of cyclohexa-2,5-dienones has been studied (556–562). Except when the 4-position bears a labile substituent, these molecules generally undergo molecular rearrangements characteristic of polar ground-state species. It may be that a "biradical-like" (n,π^* ?) state precedes the polar rearranging species. For example, irradiation of 4,4-diphenylcyclohexa-2,5-dienone **4** results in formation of the bicyclo[3.1.0]-hexenone **5**. A possible mechanism involves excitation of **4** to the n,π^* (biradical) singlet state which then converts to the triplet state (supported by sensitization studies) which in turn forms a species which may be represented by the bipolar species **4a**. The latter is thought to rearrange to **4b**, which then collapses to the product (557,561,562). Species of the type **4a** are useful in

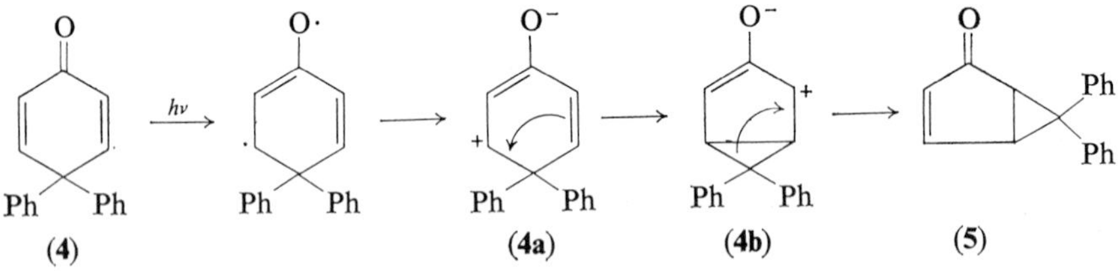

rationalizing the polar-like photochemical reactions of cyclohexa-2,5-dienones.

Another important reaction of cyclohexa-2,5-dienones is the elimination of a 4-substituent as a radical (563). For example, the dienone **6** undergoes elimination of a CCl_3 group when irradiated in ether. It should be noted that hydrogen abstraction followed by radical expulsion also rationalizes this pathway. In benzene, however, rearrangement to the bicyclo[3.1.0]hexenone 8 occurs (564,565). Finally, irradiation of 6 in isobutylene results in formation of the oxetane 9 (566).

C. LINEAR CONJUGATED DIENONES

Linear conjugated dienones are known to undergo dimerization, hydrogen abstraction, and intramolecular addition reactions (567–591). Each of these reactions has an analogy in diene chemistry. The dienic acid 10 undergoes photo-rearrangement to the allene 11, comparable to a reaction (571) known for trienes (Section I–3–2–(1)).

D. CYCLOHEXA-2,4-DIENONES AND RELATED COMPOUNDS

Disubstituted cyclohexa-2,4-dienones commonly undergo photochemical cleavages and rearrangements. For example, irradiation of 12 in the presence

of water yields **15**, the acid derived from the ketene cleavage products **13** and
14 (572).

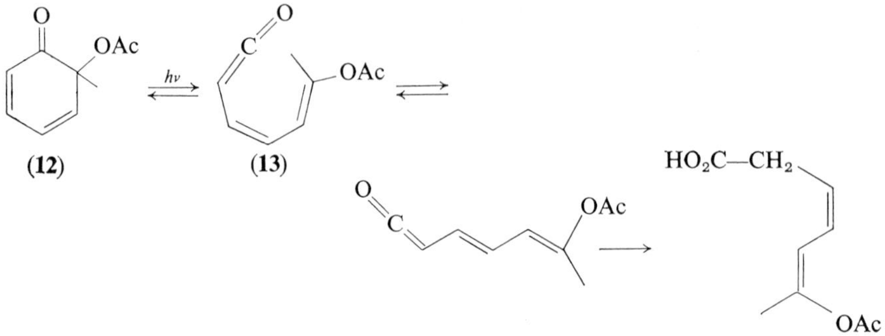

(12)　　　　　　　**(13)**

(14)　　　　　　　　　　　**(15), 80%**

The ketene formation is thermally reversible, so that in the absence of a
nucleophile a slower but irreversible cleavage leading to aromatization
occurs (572). Rearrangements of cyclohexa-2,4-dienones are not as common

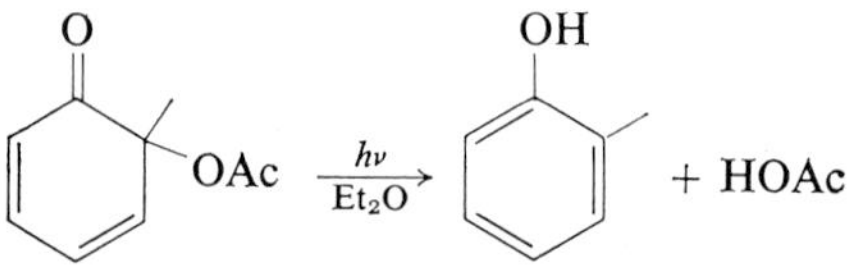

(16)　　　　　　　**(17)**

as they are for cyclohexa-2,5-dienones, presumably because of the more
rapid cleavage reactions which are possible. Nonetheless, the dienone **18**
rearranges to the bicyclo[3.1.0]hexanone **19** in good yield (573–576).

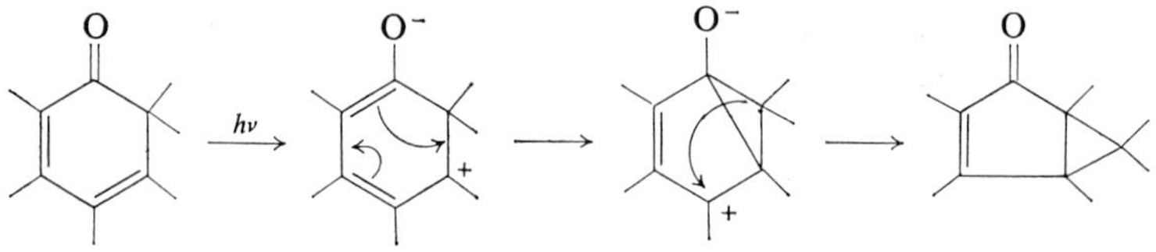

(18)　　　　　　　　　　　　　　　　　　**(19), 80%**

E. TROPONES

Irradiation of tropone and its derivatives results in interesting bimolecular
dimerizations. For example, tropone (**20**) yields **21**, in what appears to be a
triplet dimerization. Notice that this 6 + 4 electron cycloaddition should not
be a concerted photoreaction (577–579).

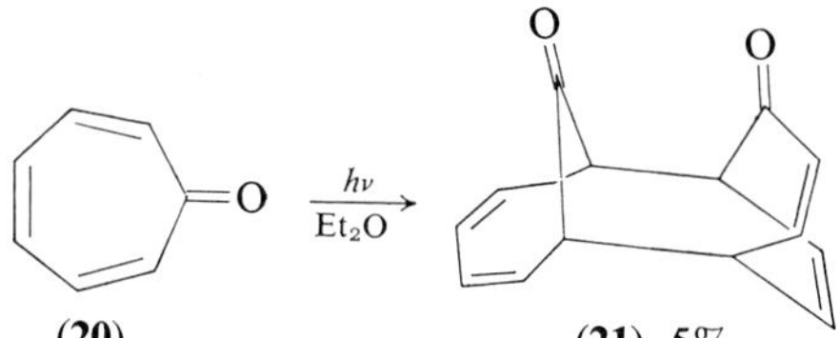

(20)   (21), 5%

5. Enediones and Related Compounds

Dibenzoylethylene undergoes an interesting rearrangement to the enol ether **3** when irradiated in alcoholic solutions (*cis–trans* isomerization also occurs). The reaction occurs mainly in the n,π^* singlet state and represents an addition to the unsaturated benzene ring followed by rearrangement (582,583).

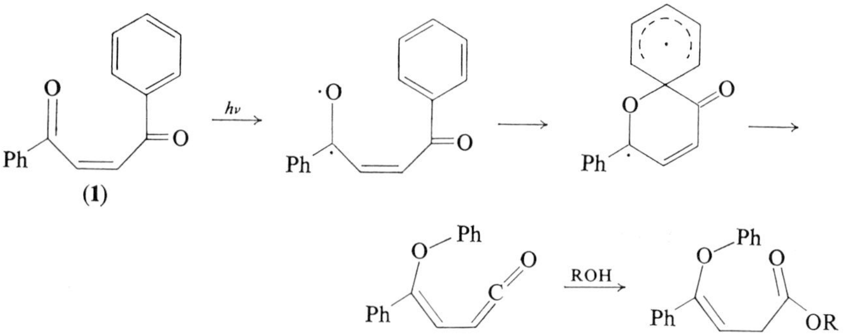

(1)

(2)   (3)

2-Methoxy-6-phenyltropone, **4**, undergoes a novel 1,8-addition to yield **5** (580).

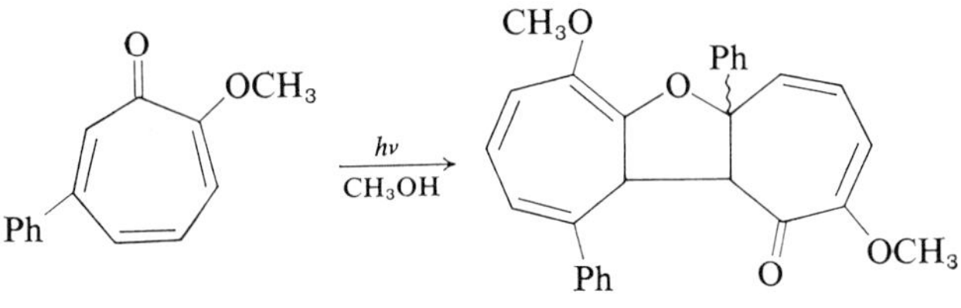

(4)   (5)

In dilute solution, **4** yields the expected valence isomer **6** (581).

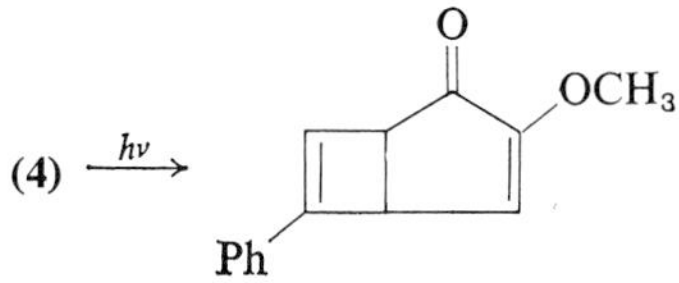

(4) $\xrightarrow{h\nu}$

(6), 75%

In the presence of benzophenone as photosensitizer, **1** undergoes photo-reduction to dibenzoylethane **7**. This reaction may involve energy transfer

$$\text{PhCOCH=CHCOPh} \xrightarrow[\substack{R_2\text{CHOH} \\ Ph_2\text{CO}}]{h\nu} \text{PhCOCH}_2\text{CH}_2\text{COPh}$$

$$\text{(1)} \qquad\qquad\qquad\qquad\qquad\qquad\qquad \text{(7)}$$

from benzophenone to yield a triplet of **1** which then undergoes photo-reduction (in contrast to the rearrangement of singlet **1**) or may involve reduction of ground state **1** by $Ph_2\text{COH}$ radicals. Diels-Alder adducts of benzoquinone cyclize to cage isomers on ultraviolet irradiation (584,585).

(**8a**), X = —CH$_2$—   (**9**), 80–90%
(**8b**), X = —C$_2$H$_4$—

6. Maleic and Fumaric Acids and Derivatives

A. ACYCLIC DERIVATIVES

In addition to *cis–trans* isomerization, maleic and fumaric acids and esters undergo additions to unsaturated linkages. For example, irradiation of dimethyl maleate and cyclohexene yields, after hydrolysis, a mixture of isomeric cyclobutanes **2** and the adduct **3** (586–588). Irradiation of dimethyl-

(**1**)   (**2**)   (**3**)

fumarate in the solid phase yields the dimer **5** (589).

(**4**)   (**5**)

B. MALEIC ANHYDRIDE AND DERIVATIVES

Maleic anhydride and its derivatives undergo photoaddition to olefins (590–594). These reactions seem to be general and the yields are often good. They are often more efficient under sensitized conditions.

Maleic anhydride undergoes photodimerization (591) and cross cyclo-addition to a large number of olefin substrates (one example of which is given below). The addition of maleic anhydride to aromatic molecules has received considerable attention (see Section II–2–A–(1)).

Similarly, alkyl, dialkyl, halo and dihalo maleic anhydrides undergo cycloaddition reactions to yield cyclobutanes, as do malimides (591a).

7. α-Dicarbonyl and Related Compounds

A. BIACETYL DERIVATIVES

α-Diketone triplets possess the exceedingly rare property of being sufficiently long-lived to phosphoresce in fluid solution. The photochemistry of these compounds closely parallels that of monoketones. Intramolecular reactions involving the π-system are not known.

Irradiation of biacetyl in the presence of isopropyl alcohol yields the pinacol **2** and acetone (598,599). 2,3-Pentanedione undergoes Type II hydrogen

$$CH_3COCOCH_3 \xrightarrow[\text{M}_2\text{eCHOH}]{hv} CH_3\overset{\overset{\text{OH}}{|}}{\underset{\cdot}{C}}COCH_3 + Me_2\dot{C}OH \longrightarrow$$
(1)

$$\begin{array}{cc} \overset{\text{OH}}{|} & \overset{\text{OH}}{|} \\ CH_3C\!\!-\!\!\!-\!\!\!CCH_3 & + Me_2CO \\ \overset{|}{CO} & \overset{|}{CO} \quad (3), 100\% \\ \overset{|}{CH_3} & \overset{|}{CH_3} \\ & (2), 95\% \end{array}$$

abstraction followed by cyclization. This appears to be a general reaction of branched α-diketones. Yields are higher when a secondary or tertiary hydrogen is located on the γ-carbon.

(4)   (5), 45%

α-Cleavage products do not appear to occur with diketones, but irradiation of the α-keto ester **6** at 80° yields a hydroxy ketene (isolated as **7**) and acetone.

$$\longrightarrow \begin{array}{c} Me_2CO \\ + PhC(OH)\!\!=\!\!C\!\!=\!\!O \\ \Big\downarrow ROH \\ PhCHOHCO_2R \\ (7) \end{array}$$

(6)

At room temperature, **6** undergoes photoreduction to form the pinacol **8** (611). α-Cleavage reactions are also common primary processes of α-dicar-

$$(6) \quad \xrightarrow[\text{ROH}]{h\nu} \quad \begin{array}{c} \text{OH} \\ | \\ \text{Ph}-\overset{}{\text{C}}\text{CO}_2\text{CHMe}_2 \\ | \\ \text{Ph}-\overset{}{\text{C}}\text{CO}_2\text{CHMe}_2 \\ | \\ \text{OH} \quad \textbf{(8)} \end{array}$$

bonyl acids. Irradiation of benzoylformic acid in water yields benzaldehyde, but photoreduction occurs in hydrogen-donating organic solvents (600).

$$\text{PhCOCO}_2\text{H} \xrightarrow[\text{H}_2\text{O}]{h\nu} \text{PhCHO} + \text{CO}_2$$

Benzocyclobutanedione **9** undergoes several interesting photoreactions which seem to originate from the primary process of cleavage of the CO—CO bond. Irradiation of **9** in boiling ethanol yields the adduct **12**. The latter may be rationalized as arising from the carbene precursor **11**. This carbene may also dimerize or be trapped with olefins. In the presence of maleic anhydride, the Diels-Alder adduct **15** is formed (601,602).

(9)   **(10)**   **(14)**

(11)   **(12)**, 39%

(13), 65%

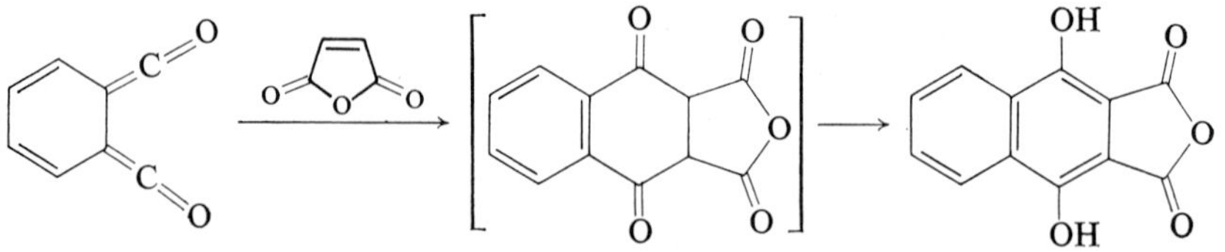

(14) → **(15)**, 67%

Although oxetane formation has not been reported for biacetyl òr alkyl α-diketones, aryl α-diketones undergo two modes of cycloaddition with olefins to form both oxetanes and dioxenes. For example, irradiation of phenanthrenequinone **16** and furan yield the dioxene **18**. The factors controlling which mode of addition occurs are not well established (603–605).

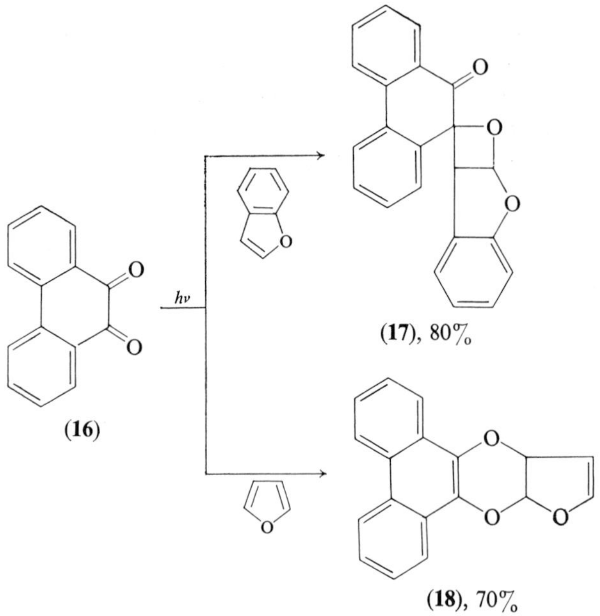

(16) $\xrightarrow{h\nu}$

(17), 80%

(18), 70%

B. BENZOQUINONE

Benzoquinone and its derivatives display photochemical reactivity at both the carbonyl function and the ring double bond. The reactions which are known imply that the excited states of benzoquinones are radical-like in nature (606).

Benzoquinone abstracts hydrogen atoms from suitable donors. Irradiation of benzoquinone in the presence of acetaldehyde, for example, leads to formation of the acetophenone **21** in addition to hydroquinone (607).

1,4-Benzoquinone forms oxetanes in good yields when irradiated in the presence of unhindered olefins (608–610). For example, **19** and 1,5-*cis,cis-*

(**19**)   (**20**), 15%

(**21**), 67%   (**22**)

cyclooctadiene, **23**, yields the oxetane **24** (608,609). Acetylenes and dienes may also be added to the carbonyl function. Interestingly, 2,3-dimethylbuta-diene adds 1,4 to the C=O bond (611,612).

(**19**)   (**23**)   (**24**), 90%

Alkylated 1,4-benzoquinones dimerize across the C=C bond and add olefins across the same bond photochemically. Oxetane formation is less important for the substituted benzoquinones perhaps because, in plane attack by the *n*-orbital of the *n,π** state, on the *π*-system of the olefin is required (613,614).

Di-*t*-butylbenzoquinones undergo photochemical rearrangements and addition of alcoholic solvents. The mechanism of these rearrangements may

(25)   (25a), 40%

(26)   (27), ~80%

be analogous to Type II hydrogen abstraction followed by cyclization to the spirocyclopropane **29** which may, in turn, either rearrange or add solvent (615,616).

C. NAPHTHOQUINONES AND ANTHRAQUINONES

No new primary processes appear to be required to rationalize the photochemistry of 1,4-naphthoquinones or 9,10-anthraquinones.

Thus, 1,4-naphthoquinone undergoes photoreduction, photodimerization, and cross additions of olefins to the C=O and C=C bond (617–619). Anthraquinone undergoes photoreduction to anthrahydroquinone **38**. Substituents on the α-positions of anthraquinone serve to affect the photo-

(32) → C₆H₆ → **(33)**

(32) → Me₂CHOH → **(34)**

(32) → **(35)** + **(36)**

reduction of anthraquinones if an intramolecular hydrogen abstraction can occur. Thus, 1-alkyl, 1-amino, and 1-hydroxyanthraquinones are inefficient at intermolecular hydrogen abstraction, presumably because of the efficiency of intramolecular (reversible) abstraction (620,621).

(37) $\xrightarrow[\text{Me}_2\text{CHOH}]{h\nu}$ **(38)**

Irradiation of anthraquinone in the presence of olefins results in cyclo-addition to form oxetane (622).

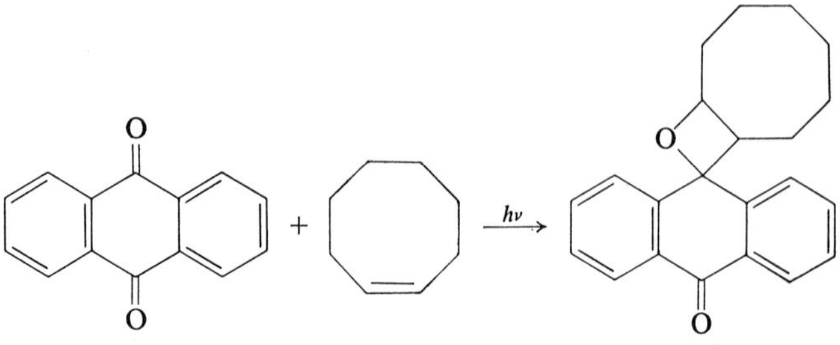

(39)

V. NITROGEN-CONTAINING CHROMOPHORES

1. General Considerations

A. EXCITED STATES OF SOME NITROGEN-CONTAINING CHROMOPHORES

(1) Models and Primary Processes for the Excited States of Nitrogen-Containing Chromophores

Several of the nitrogen-containing chromophores that have received photochemical attention shall be mentioned in this section.

The azine group resembles the carbonyl group in some of its general electronic characteristics. Unfortunately, it is not known whether the lowest electronic state of this group is generally n,π^* or π,π^*, or how the major configuration of the S_1 or T_1 state varies with substituents. A working model for an azine must therefore presuppose both types of reactivity, as shown below.

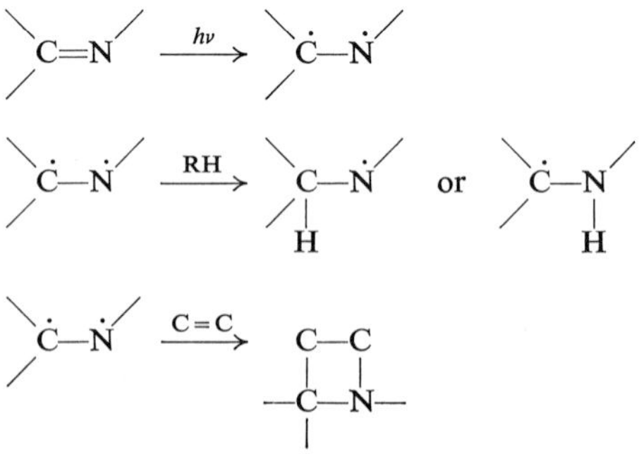

$$\underset{B}{\overset{A}{>}}C=N\overset{X}{\underset{}{}} \;\underset{h\nu}{\rightleftarrows}\; \underset{B}{\overset{A}{>}}\dot{C}-\dot{N}\overset{X}{\underset{}{}} \;\underset{h\nu}{\rightleftarrows}\; \underset{B}{\overset{A}{>}}C=N\overset{}{\underset{X}{}}$$

$$\underset{R}{\overset{}{}}\dot{C}-\dot{N}< \;\longrightarrow\; -\underset{.}{C}=N< \;+\; R\cdot$$

The azo group generally possesses a lowest $S_1(n,\pi^*)$ state. However, the configuration of T_1 is not known, in general. The bulk of the known photochemistry of azo compounds can be rationalized on the basis of a biradical structure (which, unsatisfactory as it is, is supposed to describe the n,π^* or π,π^* state).

$$\underset{R}{\overset{R}{>}}N=N\overset{R}{\underset{}{}} \;\underset{h\nu}{\rightleftarrows}\; \underset{R}{\overset{R}{>}}\dot{N}-\dot{N}\overset{R}{\underset{}{}} \;\rightleftarrows\; \underset{R}{\overset{R}{>}}N=N\overset{}{\underset{R}{}}$$

$$\underset{R}{\overset{R}{>}}\dot{N}-\dot{N}\overset{R}{\underset{}{}} \;\longrightarrow\; R-N=\dot{N} \;+\; R\cdot$$

$$\underset{R}{\overset{R}{>}}\dot{N}-\dot{N}\overset{R}{\underset{}{}} \;\overset{RH}{\longrightarrow}\; \underset{R}{\overset{R}{>}}\dot{N}-\underset{}{N}\overset{H}{\underset{}{}}-R$$

$$\underset{R}{\overset{R}{>}}\dot{N}-\dot{N}\overset{R}{\underset{}{}} \;\overset{C=C}{\longrightarrow}\; \underset{R}{\overset{R}{>}}N-N\overset{C-C}{\underset{R}{}}$$

The diazo and azide linkages are similar electronically and display related photochemistry. Although hydrogen abstraction and cycloaddition reactions of diazo and azide groups should be possible, to date cleavage to eliminate N_2 seems to be preferred.

$$R_2C\overset{+}{=}N\overset{-}{=}N \;\overset{h\nu}{\longrightarrow}\; R_2\dot{C}-N=\dot{N} \;\longrightarrow\; R_2C\colon \;+\; N\equiv N$$

$$RN\overset{+}{=}N\overset{-}{=}N \;\overset{h\nu}{\longrightarrow}\; R-\dot{N}-N=\dot{N} \;\longrightarrow\; RN\colon \;+\; N_2$$

The nitro group parallels the carbonyl function in its photochemistry. This may result from the fact that the lowest singlet and triplet of alkyl and simple aromatic nitro compounds possess n,π^* configurations. The nitrite

$$R-N\overset{O}{\underset{O}{}} \;\overset{h\nu}{\longrightarrow}\; R-N\overset{O}{\underset{O}{}} \;\longrightarrow\; R\cdot \;+\; \dot{N}O_2$$

$$R-N\overset{\nearrow O}{\underset{\searrow O}{}} \quad \xrightarrow{RH} \quad R-N\overset{\nearrow O}{\underset{\searrow OH}{}}$$

$$R-N\overset{\nearrow O}{\underset{\searrow O}{}} \quad \xrightarrow{C=C} \quad R-N\overset{\nearrow O}{\underset{\searrow O-C}{}} C$$

and nitroso groups undergo cleavage reactions, predominantly.

$$R-O-N{=}O \xrightarrow{h\nu} R-O-\dot{N}-\dot{O} \longrightarrow RO\cdot + \dot{N}O$$

$$R-N{=}O \xrightarrow{h\nu} R-\dot{N}-\dot{O} \longrightarrow R\cdot + \dot{N}O$$

(2) Energy Diagrams for Nitrogen-Containing Chromophores

Only a few scattered reports of the triplet energies or lifetimes of chromophores containing the nitrogen function have been published. Some of these data are tabulated in Table 11.

TABLE 11

Energy Data for Some Unsaturated Nitrogen Compounds[a]

Compound	$E_1{}^a$	$E_3{}^a$	Ref.
$C_6H_5CH{=}NC_6H_5$	82	—	623, 632
$PhN{=}\overset{+}{N}{=}\overset{-}{N}$	99	78	630
$\overset{-}{C}H_2{-}\overset{+}{N}{\bar{=}}\overset{-}{N}$	67	—	629
(bicyclic azo compound)	84	63	624, 627, 628
$O-N{=}N-O$	67	45	632, 626
$C_6H_5NO_2$	—	59	631
CH_3ONO	73	—	633
Pyridine	100	82	632, 634
Quinoline	90	60	632,634
Acridine	—	44	634

[a] Energies in kcal/mole.

2. Photochemistry of Azines and Related Compounds

A. AZINES

The photochemistry of azines has not been extensively studied. Hydrogen abstraction and *cis–trans* isomerization reactions are known (635–637).

$$Ph_2C{=}NCH_3 \xrightarrow[Me_2CHOH]{h\nu} Ph_2CHNHCH_3$$

Indazoles, pyrazoles, and isoxazoles undergo a photosensitized transposition of ring atoms (638,639). See p. 216 for a related reaction. Some of these molecules are photochromic if the hydrogen abstraction reaction is intramolecular and reversible (640).

A photochemical Beckmann rearrangement to yield **6** has been reported to occur when **4** is irradiated in acetic acid. This reaction may involve a photochemical protonation (641) or oxaziran intermediate.

Irradiation of the imine, **6a**, originally reported to yield the dimer **6b** (642), has been found to actually yield **6c** (642a).

B. AZO COMPOUNDS

Irradiation of alkyl azocompounds in fluid solution generally results in *cis–trans* isomerization in addition to α-cleavage to radicals. In the case of azomethane, the *cis*-isomer may be detected spectroscopically (643).

$$\begin{array}{ccc}
CH_3 & & \\
\diagdown & & \\
N{=}N & \xrightleftharpoons{h\nu} & N{=}N \\
& & \diagup \quad \diagdown \\
\diagdown CH_3 & H_3C & CH_3 \\
(7) & & (8)
\end{array}$$

Azobisisobutyronitrile **9** is cleaved into the radical pair **10** by light. Some of the radicals escape the cage to become free while others recombine to yield **11** and the ketenimine **12** (644,645).

$$Me{-}\underset{\underset{CN}{|}}{\overset{\overset{Me}{|}}{C}}{-}N{=}N{-}\underset{\underset{CN}{|}}{\overset{\overset{Me}{|}}{C}}{-}Me \xrightarrow{h\nu} 2\ Me{-}\underset{\underset{CN}{|}}{\overset{\overset{Me}{|}}{C}}\cdot + N_2 \longrightarrow$$
$$\qquad\qquad (9)\qquad\qquad\qquad (10)$$

$$Me{-}\underset{\underset{CN}{|}}{\overset{\overset{Me}{|}}{C}}{-}\underset{\underset{CN}{|}}{\overset{\overset{Me}{|}}{C}}{-}Me\ +\ Me_2C{=}C{=}N{-}\underset{\underset{CN}{|}}{\overset{\overset{Me}{|}}{C}}{-}Me$$
$$\qquad\qquad (11)\qquad\qquad\qquad\qquad (12)$$

Irradiation of diethylazocarboxylate (presumably *trans*) does not cause elimination of nitrogen, instead *trans–cis* isomerization to the reactive *cis* form occurs. In the presence of good hydrogen donors 1:1 adducts such as **15** result (646,647). Irradiation of **13** in the presence of C=C or C=C—C=C

$$EtO_2CN{=}NCO_2Et \xrightarrow[\text{dioxane}]{h\nu} \bigl[\text{1,4-dioxane ring}\bigr] + EtO_2CNH \longrightarrow \bigl[\text{dioxane ring with }NNHCO_2Et, CO_2Et\bigr]$$
$$\quad (13)\qquad\qquad\quad (14)\qquad\qquad EtO_2CN\cdot$$
$$\qquad\qquad\qquad\qquad\qquad\qquad\qquad\qquad (15),\ 50\%$$

groups yields cycloaddition products (647).

$$R{-}N{=}N{-}R \xrightarrow[\text{CH}_2{=}\text{CHOEt}]{h\nu} \bigl[\text{azetidine ring with OEt, N{-}N, R, R}\bigr]$$
$$\quad (13),\ R\ =\ EtOCO\qquad (16)\qquad\qquad (17)$$

Azobenzene undergoes both direct (649,650) and sensitized (648) *cis–trans* isomerization but not loss of nitrogen. In the presence of a strong oxidizing agent **18** undergoes cyclization to the diazaphenanthrene **20**, but at a rate much slower than that of *cis–trans* isomerization (651,652).

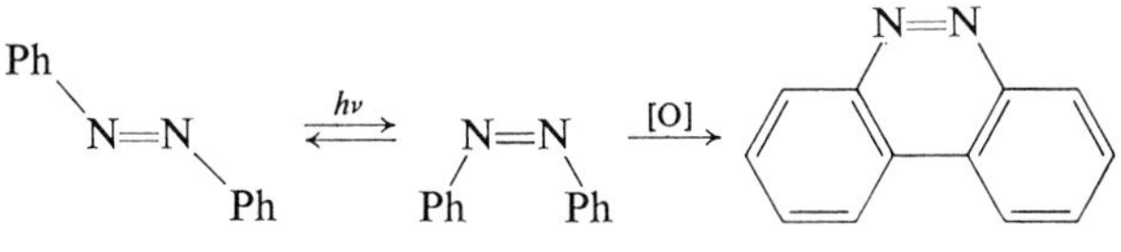

(18) (19) (20)

Cyclic azoalkanes generally lose nitrogen, upon photolysis, to produce cyclopropanes (in the case of pyrazolines) in synthetically useful yields. The

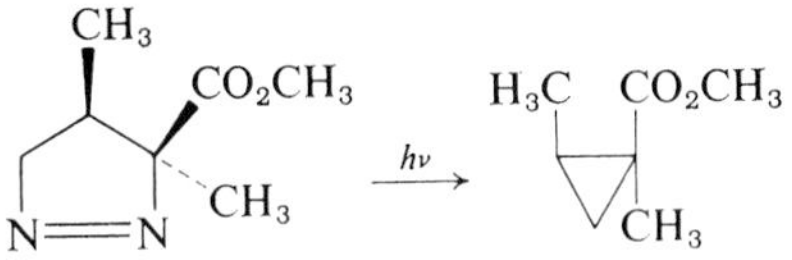

(21) (22)

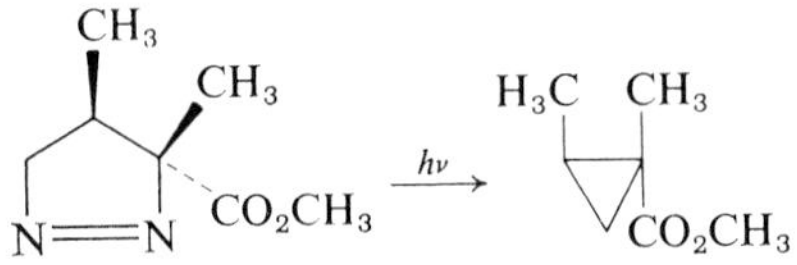

(23) (24)

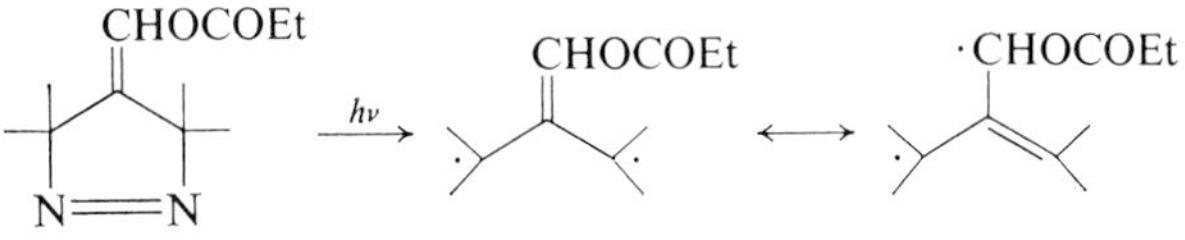

(25) (26) (27)

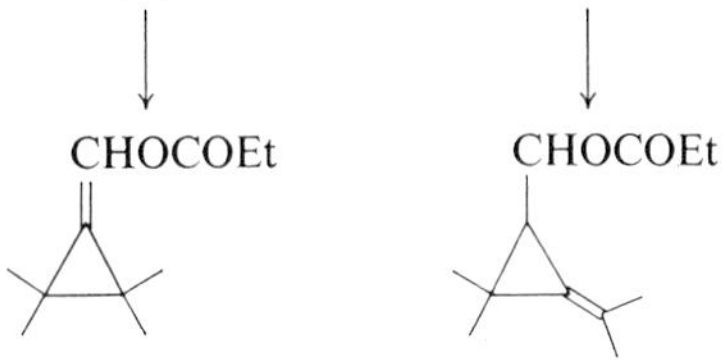

(28), 37% (29), 63%

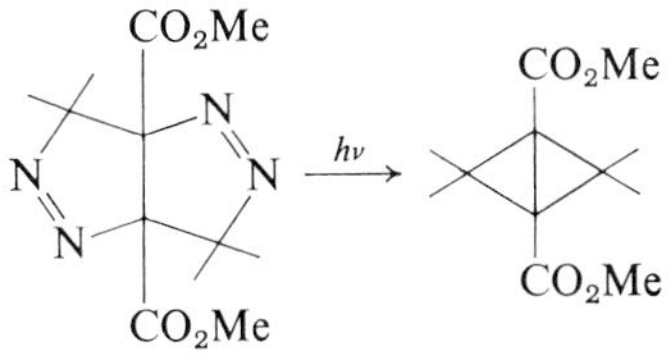

(30) (31), 20%

reaction is stereospecific in some cases. For example, irradiation of the pyrazoline **21** yields the cyclopropane **22**, while the pyrazoline **23** yields **24** (653). Several other examples of small ring formation by azophotolysis are given above (654,655).

An interesting case of azophotolysis is provided by **32** which yields the theoretically important molecule **33**, trimethylene methane; the latter is characterized by its triplet ESR spectrum (656).

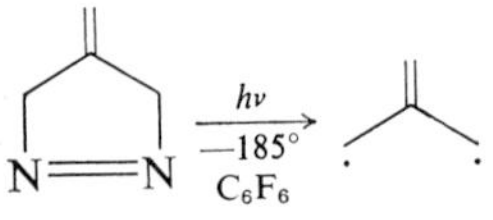

(32)   (33)

Pyrazoles yield cyclopropenes when irradiated. The mechanism appears to be photoring opening to a diazoalkene, which then loses nitrogen. Reversible photoisomerization to diazabicyclo[2.1.0]pentenes competes with nitrogen elimination when the pyrazole is fully alkylated (657).

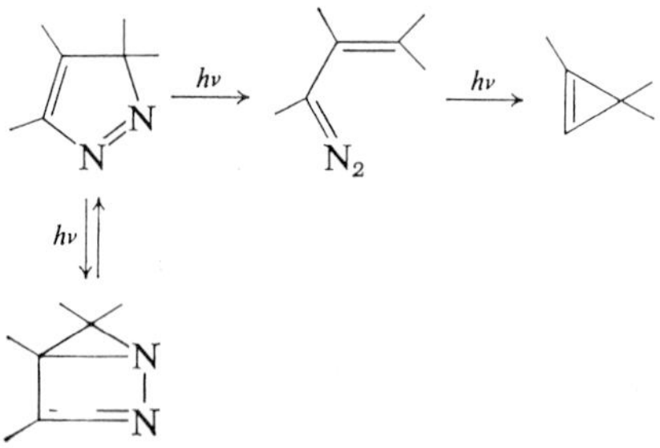

Benzocyclopropenes (658) and cyclopropenes (659) have been prepared by irradiation of appropriate substrates such as **34**.

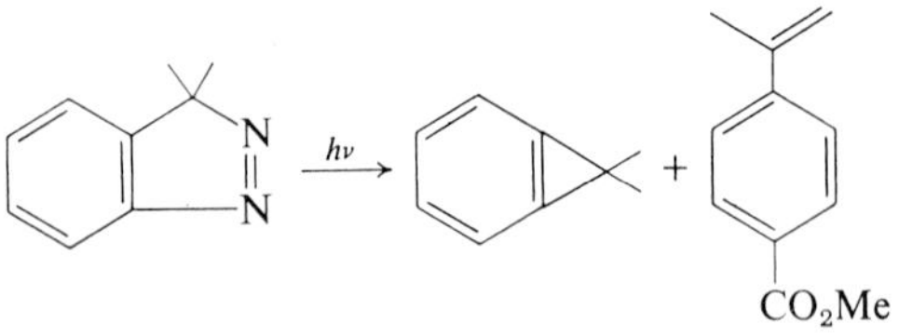

(34)   (35)   (36)

C. AZIDES

Photolyses of various types of azides generally results in evolution of nitrogen and formation of products which are easily rationalized by the intermediacy of a nitrene (660,661). Depending on the spin state of the nitrene and the reaction conditions, a variety of products may result from (a) isomerization by rearrangement of a hydrogen or carbon function to the electron-deficient nitrogen; (b) hydrogen abstraction by the nitrene; or (c) insertion of the nitrene into a saturated or unsaturated bond.

For example, the alkyl azide **37** yields the imine **39** by a hydrogen shift (662). Irradiation of the azide (**40**) in isopropyl alcohol yields benzamide, **42** and **43** (663). Irradiation of **40** in the presence of a photosensitizer results in

$$\text{/\textbackslash/\textbackslash N=\overset{+}{N}=\overset{-}{N}} \xrightarrow{h\nu} \text{/\textbackslash/\textbackslash \ddot{N} + N_2} \longrightarrow \text{/\textbackslash/\textbackslash NH}$$
$$\quad\quad (37) \quad\quad\quad\quad (38) \quad\quad\quad\quad\quad (39)$$

$$\text{PhCON}=\overset{+}{N}=\overset{-}{N} \xrightarrow{h\nu} \text{PhCO\"{N} + N}_2 \xrightarrow{Me_2CHOH}$$
$$\quad (40)$$

$$\text{PhNHCO}_2\text{CHMe}_2 + \text{PhCONH}_2 + \text{PhCONHOCHMe}_2$$
$$\quad\quad (41) \quad\quad\quad\quad (42) \quad\quad\quad\quad (43)$$

quantitative formation of benzamide via a chain sequence. It should be noted for azide photolyses that a nitrene intermediate, while implicated, has not been proven in all cases. One must also consider reactions of the singlet (or triplet) azide which could lead to the same products. In certain low-temperature photolyses of azides, the ESR spectrum of triplet nitrenes may be detected (664).

When a poor migrating group is adjacent to the nitrene, insertion and addition reactions become dominant. For example, ethyl azidoformate undergoes smooth photolysis in isopropyl alcohol to yield **45**. Addition of the nitrene to C—C bonds also occurs.

$$\text{Me}_2\text{CHOH} + \text{EtOCON}_3 \xrightarrow{h\nu} \text{EtOCONH}_2 + \text{Me}_2\text{CO}$$
$$\quad\quad (44) \quad\quad\quad\quad\quad\quad (45), 90\%$$

$$(46)$$

The addition to C—C bonds appears to be stereospecific, implying a singlet nitrene. However, the stereoselectivity drops as the nitrene lifetime increases which implies a triplet nitrene ground state (665–667).

Irradiation of triarylmethyl azides results in formation of anils by an aryl shift. Since the reaction may be sensitized and since the direct and sensitized reactions show similar migratory aptitudes, a triplet azide is implicated (668).

$$\text{Ar}_3\text{CN}_3 \xrightarrow[\text{(sens)}]{h\nu} \text{Ar}_2\text{C}=\text{NAr}$$
$$\quad (47) \quad\quad\quad\quad\quad (48)$$

Irradiation of cyclic triazoles leads to aziridines and azines. These decompositions may be photosensitized and are often cleaner than thermolysis (669).

(49)   (50), *cis*   (52)
                (51), *trans*

Irradiation of 1-phenylbenzotriazole in benzene yields carbazole (670).

(52a)   (52b), 100%

Irradiation of 52c, however, yields the ketenimine 52d and indole 52e (670).

(52c)   (52d)   (52e)

D. DIAZO AND DIAZONIUM COMPOUNDS

The photochemistry of diazocompounds parallels that of azides in many ways. The loss of nitrogen is followed by formation of carbene intermediates in general. Diazo compounds appear to generate singlet carbenes upon direct photolysis and triplet carbenes upon sensitized photolysis.

For example, irradiation of diazomethane in the presence of *cis*- or *trans*-butene results in stereospecific addition to form 1,2-dimethyl cyclopropanes. In addition, C—C and C—H insertion products are formed (671). However, irradiation of diazomethane in the presence of benzophenone as photosensitizer results in nonstereospecific addition (672).

Direct irradiation of α-diazoketones results in formation of rearrangement products. For example, irradiation of the α-diazoketone **53** serves as an entry into the benzocyclobutene series (673).

(53)   (54)

Photolysis of the diazoketone **55** results in an insertion, rather than a rearrangement, and provides a new synthetic approach to penicillins (674).

(55)   (56)

It also appears that, similar to the situation for some azides, photosensitization may induce chain reactions which result in high yields of reduction products. Thus, diazoacetophenone yields both rearrangement and reduction products upon direct photolysis in isopropyl alcohol, but only the reduction product is formed under sensitized photolysis (675).

$$PhCOCHN_2 \xrightarrow[Me_2CHOH]{h\nu} PhCH_2CO_2CHMe_2 + PhCOCH_3$$

$$PhCOCHN_2 \xrightarrow[\substack{Me_2CHOH \\ sens}]{h\nu} PhCOCH_3$$

Photolysis of aromatic diazonium salts generally results in loss of nitrogen by one of two paths: (a) homolytic cleavage of the $C—N_2^+$ bond followed by radical cage coupling (or atom abstraction by the aromatic radical) or (b) heterolytic cleavage of the $C—N_2^+$ bond followed by reaction of the aromatic cation produced. These paths may be strongly solvent dependent. For example, photolysis of 4-nitrobenzene diazonium salts in ethanol leads to nitrobenzene (homolytic cleavage) as the major product, with 4-ethoxynitro-benzene (heterolytic cleavage) as a minor product (676,677).

(57)   (58), 77%   (59), 5%

3. Nitrocompounds and Derivatives

(1) Aliphatic and Aromatic Nitrocompounds

The photochemistry of nitroalkanes has not been extensively studied. Reactions analogous to those of alkyl carbonyl compounds are observed. For example, nitromethane undergoes photorearrangement (678) to methyl nitrite (cf. α-cleavage of ketones) and nitrobenzene undergoes photoreduction (678a).

$$CH_3NO_2 \xrightarrow{h\nu} CH_3ONO$$

$$PhNO_2 + RH \longrightarrow PhNH_2$$

Irradiation of 6-nitrocholesteryl acetate **1** leads to formation of the deconjugated isomer **2** (679). This reaction appears to be analogous to the Type II abstraction by ketones. Another reaction analogous to the addition

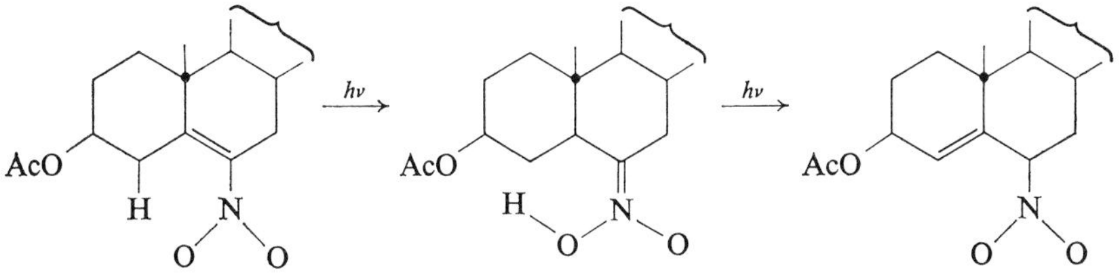

(1)   (2), 30%

of a n,π^* carbonyl-excited state to olefins is found in the rearrangement of **3** to **4** (680).

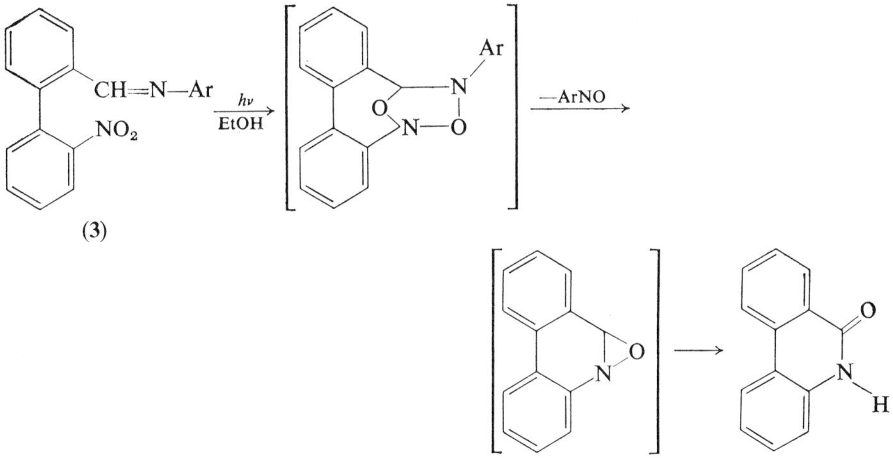

(3)

(4)

A number of light-catalyzed aromatic substitution reactions resulting in displacement of a nitro group are known. The thermal rearrangement reaction of **5**, for example, yields 4-nitrophenol (681).

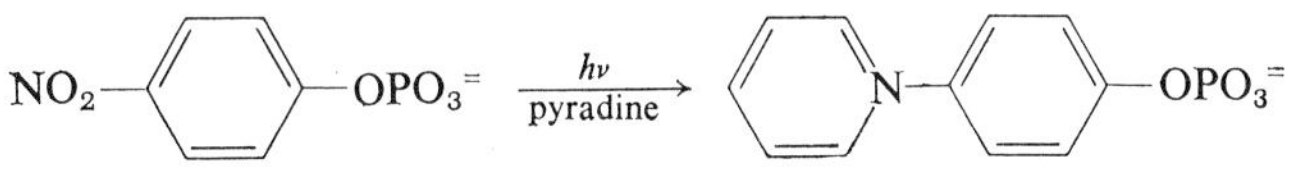

(5)   (6), 25%

(2) N-Oxides

N-oxides undergo several types of rearrangement reactions. Thus, the pyrroline oxide **7** undergoes intramolecular photoaddition of the oxygen atom to the C=C bond (682).

The aryl N-oxide **9** undergoes both oxazirine formation to **10** and *trans–cis* isomerization to **11**. Only the latter reaction is sensitized, and indeed does not

(7)   (8), 28%

occur when **9** is directly excited. Thus, **11** results from the triplet of **9** while **10** results from the singlet of **9** (683,684).

(9)   (10)

(11)

Pyridine *N*-oxides undergo ring contraction in addition to rearrangements. The mechanism of the ring contraction reaction is obscure (684).

(3) Nitrosocompounds

Irradiation of compounds containing the X—NO bond generally causes cleavage of this bond or a bond β to it and formation of products derived from the radicals produced. Some synthetically useful reactions are listed below (685).

$Bu_2NNO \xrightarrow{h\nu}$ $Pr\overset{\|}{C}NHBu + Bu_2NH$
(1)   (2), 66%   (3), 20%

Irradiation of *N*-nitrosodialkylamines in olefins (in the presence of acid) yields oximes, presumably via a cycloaddition (686,687). Irradiation of nitrites generally results in formation of an alkoxy radical and a nitroso radical. This reaction has great synthetic potential in cases where a hydrogen atom exists on a δ-carbon from the nitroso group so that intramolecular hydrogen abstraction may occur and thereby functionalize an otherwise inert carbon atom (687a, 687b).

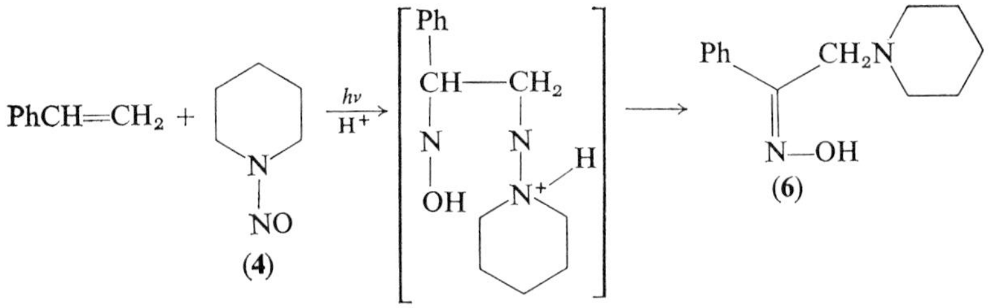

$$PhCH{=}CH_2 + \quad \underset{\underset{NO}{N}}{\bigcirc} \quad \xrightarrow[H^+]{h\nu} \quad \left[\begin{array}{c} Ph \\ | \\ CH{-}CH_2 \\ | \quad\quad | \\ N \quad\quad N{-}H \\ | \quad\quad \overset{+}{N} \\ OH \end{array} \right] \quad \longrightarrow \quad \underset{N{-}OH}{\overset{Ph\quad CH_2N\bigcirc}{|}}$$

$$(4) \quad\quad\quad\quad\quad (5) \quad\quad\quad\quad\quad (6)$$

For example, irradiation of the nitrite **7** yields **8** (688).

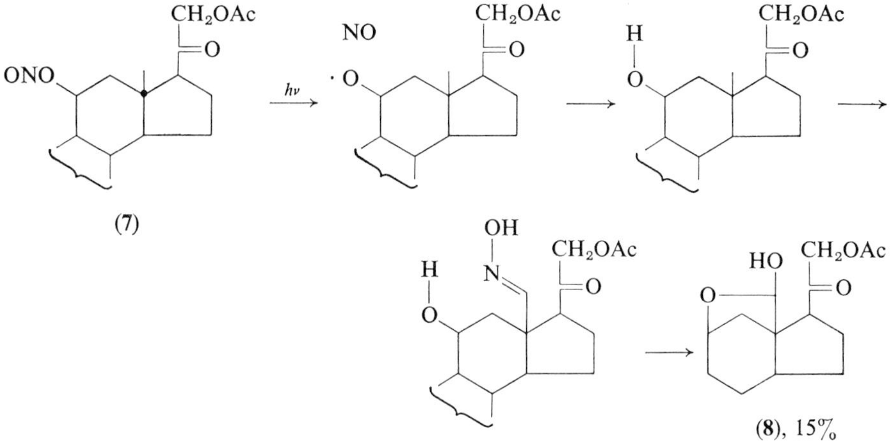

(7)

(8), 15%

4. N-Heterocyclic Compounds

Irradiation of pyridine (**1**) in water yields the amine aldehyde **2** (689).

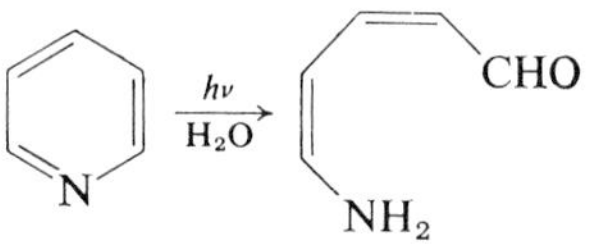

(1)   (2)

The aminopyridine **3** yields a 1,4-1,4-diene **4** (690).

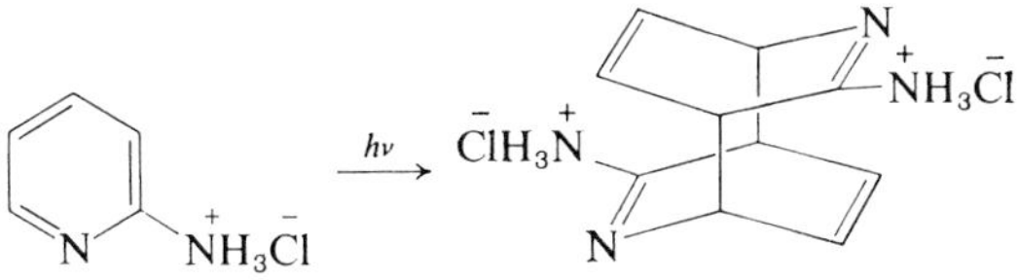

(3)   (4)

Styryl pyridines undergo photocyclization to azaphenanthrenes (692,693) in addition to *cis–trans* isomerization.

Pyrazine and its alkyl derivatives undergo phototransposition of ring atoms, analogous to substituted benzenes (694).

B. QUINOLINE AND ACRIDINE

Quinoline and its derivatives may be photoalkylated by organic acids (695). Irradiation of acridine in alcoholic solvents results in hydrogen abstraction

followed by dimerization or radical coupling (696,697).

References

1. H. H. Jaffe and M. Orchin, *Theory and Applications of Ultraviolet Spectroscopy*, Wiley, New York, 1962, p. 174; L. Salem, *The Molecular Orbital Theory of Conjugated Systems*, Benjamin, New York, 1966.
2. J. Murrell, *Theory of the Electronic Spectra of Organic Molecules*, Wiley, New York, 1963, p. 54.
3. M. R. Robin and N. A. Kubler, *J. Chem. Phys.*, **44**, 2664 (1966).
4. R. S. Mulliken and C. C. J. Roothan, *Chem. Rev.*, **41**, 219 (1947).
5. A. D. Walsh, *J. Chem. Soc.*, **1953**, 2325.
6. R. S. Mulliken, *J. Chem. Phys.*, **7**, 20 (1939).
7. L. Burnell, *J. Chem. Phys.*, **43**, 529 (1965).
8. W. J. Potts, *J. Chem. Phys.*, **23**, 65 (1955).
9. R. B. Woodward and R. Hoffmann, *J. Am. Chem. Soc.*, **87**, 395 (1965).
10. R. Hoffmann and R. B. Woodward, *J. Am. Chem. Soc.*, **87**, 2046 (1965).
11. H. C. Longuet-Higgins and E. W. Abrahamson, *J. Am. Chem. Soc.*, **87**, 2045 (1965).
12. D. F. Evans, *J. Chem. Soc.*, **1960**, 1735.
13. M. R. Robin, R. R. Hart, and N. A. Kuebler, *J. Chem. Phys.*, **44**, 1803 (1966).
14. R. S. Berry, *J. Chem. Phys.*, **38**, 1934 (1963).
15. E. Havinga, *Chimia*, **16**, 145 (1962).
16. D. F. Evans, *J. Chem. Soc.*, **1960**, 1735.
17. R. E. Kellogg and W. T. Simpson, *J. Am. Chem. Soc.*, **87**, 4230 (1965).
18. Reviews of olefin photochemistry: (a) G. J. Fonken, *Advan. Org. Photochem.*, **1**, 197 (1967); (b) R. N. Warrener and J. B. Bremmer, *Rev. Pure Appl. Chem.*, **16**, 117 (1966).
19. N. J. Turro, *Molecular Photochemistry*, Benjamin, New York, 1965, p. 131 ff.
20. J. P. Chesick, *J. Am. Chem. Soc.*, **85**, 3718 (1963).
21. T. Terao, S. Hirokami, S. Sato, and L. J. Cvetanovic, *Can. J. Chem.*, **44**, 2173 (1966).
22. R. B. Mahoney and E. B. Ludlam, *Trans. Faraday Soc.*, **25**, 442 (1929).
23. Review: R. B. Cundall, *Progr. Reaction Kinetics*, **2**, 161 (1964).
24. R. B. Cundall, F. J. Fletcher, and D. G. Milne, *J. Chem. Phys.*, **39**, 3536 (1963).
25. R. B. Cundall and F. J. Fletcher, *J. Am. Chem. Soc.*, **83**, 3902 (1961).
26. G. S. Hammond, N. J. Turro, and P. A. Leermakers, *J. Phys. Chem.*, **66**, 1144 (1962).
27. R. B. Cundall and P. A. Griffiths, *Trans. Faraday Soc.*, **61**, 1698 (1965).
28. R. B. Cundall and P. A. Griffiths, *Trans. Faraday Soc.*, **60**, 1146 (1964).
29. M. Tanaka, M. Kata, and S. Sato, *Bull. Chem. Soc., Japan*, **39**, 1423 (1966).
30. M. A. Golub, C. L. Stephens, and T. L. Brash, *J. Chem. Phys.*, **45**, 1503 (1966).
31. R. J. Cvetanovic and L. C. Doyle, *J. Chem. Phys.*, **37**, 543 (1962).
32. R. Srinivasan, *J. Phys. Chem.*, **67**, 1367 (1963).
33. R. Srinivasan and F. I. Sonntag, *J. Am. Chem. Soc.*, **89**, 407 (1967).
34. R. Srinivasan, *J. Am. Chem. Soc.*, **85**, 819 (1963).
35. D. Elad and R. D. Youssefyeh, *Chem. Commun.*, **1965**, 7.
36. D. R. Arnold and V. Y. Abraitys, *Chem. Commun.*, **1967**, 1053.
36a. H. Yamazaki and R. J. Cvetanovic, *J. Am. Chem. Soc.*, **91** 520 (1969).
37. H. H. Stechl, *Angew. Chem.*, **75**, 1176 (1963).
38. H. H. Stechl, *Ber.*, **97**, 2681 (1964).
39. R. Srinivasan and K. A. Hill, *J. Am. Chem. Soc.*, **88**, 3765 (1966).

40. R. Srinivasan and K. A. Hill, *J. Am. Chem. Soc.*, **87**, 4653 (1965).
41. K. J. Crowley, *Tetrahedron*, **21**, 1001 (1965).
42. D. M. Lemal and J. P. Lokengard, *J. Am. Chem. Soc.*, **88**, 5934 (1966).
43. B. W. Schafer, R. Criegee, R. Askani, and H. Gruner, *Angew. Chem.* (Intern. Ed. Engl.), **6**, 78 (1967).
44. K. E. Wilzback and L. Kaplan, *J. Am. Chem. Soc.*, **87**, 4004 (1965).
45. R. Criegee and R. Askani, *Angew. Chem.* (Intern, Ed. Eng.), **5**, 519 (1966).
46. J. C. Barborak and R. Petit, *J. Am. Chem. Soc.*, **89**, 3080 (1967).
47. W. G. Dauben and D. L. Whalen, *Tetrahedron Letters*, **1966**, 3743.
48. E. E. vanTamelen and D. Carty, *J. Am. Chem. Soc.*, **89**, 3922 (1967).
49. H. D. Scharf and F. Korte, *Ber.*, **97**, 2425 (1964).
50. P. J. Kropp, *J. Am. Chem. Soc.*, **89**, 3650 (1967).
51. P. K. Freeman, D. G. Kuper, and U. N. M. Rao, *Tetrahedron Letters*, **1965**, 3301.
52. Review of related reactions: R. Prinzbach, *Chimia*, **21**, 194 (1967).
53. D. Scharf and F. Korte, *Tetrahedron Letters*, **1963**, 821.
54. W. Reusch, *J. Org. Chem.*, **27**, 1882 (1962).
55. D. J. Trecker, R. S. Foote, J. P. Henry, and J. E. McKeon, *J. Am. Chem. Soc.*, **88**, 3021 (1966).
56. D. R. Arnold, O. J. Trecker, and E. B. Whipple, *J. Am. Chem. Soc.*, **87**, 2597 (1965).
57. D. J. Trecker, J. P. Henry, and J. E. McKeon, *J. Am. Chem. Soc.*, **87**, 3263 (1965).
58. R. L. Cargill and M. R. Willcott, *J. Org. Chem.*, **31**, 3939 (1966).
59. M. Hara, Y. Odaira, and S. Tsutsumi, *Tetrahedron*, **22**, 95 (1966).
60. For related reactions, see A. Cox, P. deMayo, and R. W. Yip, *J. Am. Chem. Soc.*, **88**, 1043 (1966).
61. Review of photochemical intramolecular ring closures: W. Dilling, *Chem. Rev.*, **67**, 373 (1967).
62. G. O. Schenck and R. Ateinmentz, *Chem. Ber.*, **96**, 520 (1963).
63. R. C. Cookson and E. Crundwell, *Chem. Ind.*, **1958**, 1004.
64. G. S. Hammond, N. J. Turro, and A. Fischer, *J. Am. Chem. Soc.*, **83**, 4674 (1961).
65. G. S. Hammond, P. Wyatt, C. D. DeBoer, and N. J. Turro, *J. Am. Chem. Soc.*, **86**, 2533 (1964); S. L. Murov and G. S. Hammond, *J. Phys. Chem.*, **72**, 3797 (1968).
66. W. G. Dauben and R. L. Cargill, *Tetrahedron*, **12**, 186 (1961).
67. P. Gassman, D. H. Ave, and D. S. Patton, *J. Am. Chem. Soc.*, **86**, 441 (1964).
68. H. Tanida et al., *J. Org. Chem.*, **30**, 2259 (1965).
68a. Review: H. Prinzbach, *Pure Applied Chem.*, **16**, 17 (1968).
69. J. R. Edman, *J. Am. Chem. Soc.*, **88**, 3454 (1966).
70. H. Prinzbach, *Chimia*, **21**, 194 (1967).
71. H. D. Scharf and G. Weisgerber, *Tetrahedron Letters*, **1967**, 1567.
72. E. Wiskott and P. Schleyer, *Angew. Chem.* (Intern. Ed. Engl.), **6**, 694 (1967).
73. P. K. Freeman and D. M. Balls, *J. Org. Chem.*, **32**, 3254 (1967).
74. P. DeMayo, J. B. Stothers, and W. Templeton, *Can. J. Chem.*, **39**, 488 (1961).
75. J. S. Bradshaw, *J. Org. Chem.*, **31**, 237 (1966).
76. P. J. Kropp, *J. Am. Chem. Soc.*, **88**, 4091 (1966); P. J. Kropp, *J. Am. Chem. Soc.*, **89**, 1126 (1967); **89**, 5199 (1967).
77. J. A. Marshall and R. D. Carroll, *J. Am. Chem. Soc.*, **88**, 4092 (1966).
78. H. E. Zimmerman and G. L. Grunewals, *J. Am. Chem. Soc.*, **88**, 183 (1966); **89**, 3932 (1967); H. E. Zimmerman, R. S. Givens and R. M. Pagni, *ibid.*, **90**, 4191, 6096 (1968).

79. E. Ciganek, *J. Am. Chem. Soc.*, **88**, 2882 (1966); P. W. Robideau, J. B. Hamilton, and L. Friedman, *ibid.*, **90**, 4465 (1968).

79a. T. D. Walsh, *J. Am. Chem. Soc.*, **91**, 515 (1969); N. J. Turro, M. Tobin, L. Friedman, and J. B. Hamilton, *ibid.*, **91**, 516 (1969).

80. J. Meinwald and B. E. Kaplan, *J. Am. Chem. Soc.*, **89**, 2611 (1967).

81. R. Srinivasan, *J. Am. Chem. Soc.*, **85**, 3048 (1963).

82. R. Srinivasan, *J. Am. Chem. Soc.*, **86**, 3318 (1964).

83. H. Nozaki, Y. Nisikawa, Y. Kamatani, and R. Noyori, *Tetrahedron Letters*, **1965**, 2161; H. Nozaki, Y. Nisikawa, M. Kawanisi, and R. Noyori, *Tetrahedron*, **23**, 2173 (1967).

84. J. K. Crandall and C. F. Meyer, *J. Am. Chem. Soc.*, **89**, 4374 (1967).

85. A. R. Olson and W. Naroney, *J. Am. Chem. Soc.*, **56**, 1320 (1934).

86. R. C. Neuman, Jr., *J. Org. Chem.*, **31**, 1852 (1966); R. C. Neuman, Jr. and R. G. Wolcott, *Tetrahedron Letters*, **1966**, 6267.

87. G. W. Griffin, J. E. Basinski, and L. I. Peterson, *J. Am. Chem. Soc.*, **84**, 1012 (1962).

88. N. J. Turro, P. Wriede, J. C. Dalton, D. Arnold, and A. Glick, *J. Am. Chem. Soc.*, **89**, 3952 (1967).

89. J. Diekman and C. J. Pedersen, *J. Org. Chem.*, **28**, 2879 (1963).

90. R. C. Cookson, V. N. Gogte, J. Hudec, and N. A. Mirza, *Tetrahedron Letters*, **1965**, 3955; *Chem. Commun.*, **1967**, 823.

90a. R. C. Cookson, *Quart. Rev.*, **22**, 423 (1968); *Tetrahedron*, **24**, 3955 (1968).

91. R. C. Cookson, J. Henstock, and J. Hudec, *J. Am. Chem. Soc.*, **88**, 1060 (1966).

92. D. E. McGreer, M. G. Vinje, and R. S. McDaniel, *Can. J. Chem.*, **43**, 1417 (1965).

93. J. Wiemann, N. Thoai, and F. Weisbuch, *Bull. Soc. Chem. France*, **1966**, 575.

94. R. E. Lutz et al., *J. Am. Chem. Soc.*, **85**, 2340 (1963).

95. E. Murad, *J. Am. Chem. Soc.*, **83**, 1327 (1961).

96. W. Kirmse and M. Buschhoff, *Angew. Chem.* (Intern. Ed.), **4**, 692 (1965).

97. J. Saltiel and L. Metts, *J. Am. Chem. Soc.*, **89**, 2232 (1967).

98. R. Srinivasan, in *Advances in Photochemistry*, Vol. 4, W. A. Noyes, Jr., G. S. Hammond, and J. N. Pitts, Jr., Eds., Interscience, New York, 1966, p. 113.

99. M. Mousseron, in *Advances in Photochemistry*, Vol. 4, W. A. Noyes, Jr., G. S. Hammond, and J. N. Pitts, Jr., Eds., Interscience, New York, 1966, p. 195.

100. G. J. Fonken, *Adv. Org. Photochem.*, **1**, 197 (1967).

101. W. G. Dauben, *Chem. Weekblad.*, **60**, 381 (1964).

102. R. Srinivasan and F. I. Sonntag, *J. Am. Chem. Soc.*, **87**, 3778 (1965).

103. I. Haller and R. Srinivasan, *J. Chem. Phys.*, **40**, 1992 (1964).

104. R. Srinivasan, *J. Am. Chem. Soc.*, **85**, 4045 (1963).

105. R. Srinivasan, *J. Am. Chem. Soc.*, **84**, 4141 (1962).

106. R. Srinivasan and F. I. Sonntag, *J. Am. Chem. Soc.*, **87**, 3778 (1965).

107. R. B. Woodward and R. Hoffmann, *J. Am. Chem. Soc.*, **87**, 395 (1965).

108. N. J. Turro, *Molecular Photochemistry*, Benjamin, New York, 1965, p. 216.

109. R. S. H. Liu, N. J. Turro, and G. S. Hammond, *J. Am. Chem. Soc.*, **87**, 3406 (1965).

110. G. S. Hammond, N. J. Turro, and R. S. H. Liu, *J. Org. Chem.*, **28**, 3297 (1963).

111. G. S. Hammond, N. J. Turro, and A. Fischer, *J. Am. Chem. Soc.*, **83**, 4674 (1961).

112. J. Saltiel, R. M. Coates, and W. G. Dauben, *J. Am. Chem. Soc.*, **88**, 2745 (1966).

113. W. G. Dauben, *Chem. Weekblad*, **60**, 381 (1964).

114. G. Sartori, V. Turba, A. Valvassori, and M. Riva, *Tetrahedron Letters*, **211**, 4777 (1966).

115. G. O. Schenck, J. Kuhns, and C. H. Krauch, *Ann. Chem.*, **693**, 20 (1966).
116. G. S. Hammond and P. J. Wagner, in *Advances in Photochemistry*, Vol. 5, W. A. Noyes, Jr., G. S. Hammond, and J. N. Pitts, Jr., Eds., Interscience, New York, 1968, p. 1.
117. N. J. Turro and P. D. Bartlett, *J. Org. Chem.*, **30**, 1849 (1965).
118. W. L. Dilling and J. C. Little, *J. Am. Chem. Soc.*, **89**, 2741, 2742 (1967).
119. W. G. Dauben and W. T. Wipke, *Pure Appl. Chem.*, **9**, 539 (1964).
119a. J. A. Barltrop and H. E. Browning, *Chem. Commun.*, 1481 (1968).
120. K. J. Crowley, *Tetrahedron*, **21**, 1001 (1965).
121. K. J. Crowley, *Proc. Chem. Soc.*, **245**, 334 (1962).
122. H. M. Frey and R. F. Skirmer, *Trans. Faraday Soc.*, **61**, 1918 (1965).
123. W. G. Dauben, R. L. Cargill, R. M. Coates, and J. Saltiel, *J. Am. Chem. Soc.*, **88**, 2742, 1966).
124. G. S Hammond and R. S. H. Liu, *J. Am. Chem. Soc.*, **85**, 477 (1963).
125. D. J.Trecker, R. L. Brandon, and J. P. Henry, *Chem. Ind.*, **1963**, 652.
126. G. S. Hammond, N. J. Turro, and P. A. Leermakers, *J. Phys. Chem.*, **66**, 1144 (1962).
127. G. S. Hammond, J. Saltiel, A. A. Lamola, N. J. Turro, J. S. Bradshaw, D. O. Cowan, R. C. Counsell, V. Vogt, and J. C. Dalton, *J. Am. Chem. Soc.*, **86**, 3197 (1964).
128. A. A. Lamola and G. S. Hammond, *J. Chem. Phys.*, **43**, 2129 (1965).
129. D. A. Ben-Efraim, *Tetrahedron Letters*, **1967**, 957.
130. R. S. H. Liu and G. S. Hammond, *J. Am. Chem. Soc.*, **86**, 1892 (1964).
131. R. S. H. Liu and G. S. Hammond, *J. Am. Chem. Soc.*, **89**, 4937 (1967).
132. R. S. H. Liu, *Tetrahedron Letters*, **1966**, 2159.
133. Other examples of related reactions: J. L. Charlton, P. deMayo, and L. Skattebol, *Tetrahedron Letters*, **1965**, 4679.
134. L. M. Stephenson, D. G. Whitten, G. F. Vesley, and G. S. Hammond, *J. Am. Chem. Soc.*, **88**, 3665, 3893 (1966); L. M. Stephenson and G. S. Hammond, *Pure Applied Chem.*, **16**, 125 (1968).
135. W. J. R. Tyerman, M. Kato, P. Kebarle, S. Masamune, O. P. Strausz, and H. E. Gunning, *Chem. Commun.*, **1967**, 497.
136. L. E. Ellis and E. E. van Tamelen, *J. Am. Chem. Soc.*, **88**, 846 (1966); P. D. Bartlett, R. Helgeson, and O. Wertzer, *Pure Applied Chem.*, **16**, 187 (1968).
137. E. E. van Tamelen and L. E. Ellis, *J. Am. Chem. Soc.*, **89**, 5073 (1967).
138. N. J. Turro and G. S. Hammond, *J. Am. Chem. Soc.*, **84**, 2841 (1962).
139. G. O. Schenck, S. P. Mannsfield, G. Schomberg, and C. H. Krauch, *Z. Naturforsch. Ser. B.*, **19**, 18 (1964); D. H. Scharf, *Tetrahedron Letters*, **1967**, 4231.
140. R. J. DeKock, N. G. Minnard, and E. Havinga, *Rec. Trav. Chim.*, **1967**, **79**, 922 (1960).
141. D. A. Valentine, N. J. Turro, and G. S. Hammond, *J. Am. Chem. Soc.*, **86**, 5202 (1964).
142. N. J. Turro and P. D. Bartlett, *J. Org. Chem.*, **30**, 1849 (1965).
143. E. Babad, D. Ginsburg, and M. B. Rubin, *Tetrahedron Letters*, **1968**, 2361.
143a. S. Masamune, R. T. Seidner, and H. Zenda, *J. Am. Chem. Soc.*, **90**, 5286 (1968).
144. G. Schroeder, *Angew. Chem. (Intern. Ed. Engl.)*, **2**, 481 (1963).
145. For related cleavages see (a) W. R. Roth, *Angew. Chem.* (Intern. Ed. Engl.), **3**, (1964); (b) J. G. Akinson, D. E. Ayer, G. Buchi, and E. W. Robb *J. Am. Chem. Soc.*, **85**, 2257 (1963).

146. For further examples see: H. Prinzbach, R. Kitzing, E. Druckrey, and H. Achenbach, *Tetrahedron Letters*, **1966**, 4265.
147. E. J. Corey and A. G. Hartman, *J. Am. Chem. Soc.*, **85**, 4033 (1963).
148. R. B. Woodward, in *Aromaticity*, Special Publ. No. 21, Chemical Society (London), 1967, p. 222.
149. E. Ciganek, *J. Am. Chem. Soc.*, **89**, 1458 (1967).
150. E. E. Van Tamelen and S. P. Pappas, *J. Am. Chem. Soc.*, **85**, 3297 (1963); R. N. McDonald and C. E. Reinke, *J. Org. Chem.*, **32**, 1878 (1967).
151. For other examples of 1,3-cyclohexadiene bicyclo-2.2.0-hexene reactions see: J. B. Bremmer and R. N. Warrener, *Chem. Commun.*, **1967**, 926.
152. P. G. Gassman and W. E. Hymans, *Tetrahedron*, **24**, 4437 (1968).
153. W. G. Dauben and F. G. Willey, *Tetrahedron Letters*, 893 (1962).
154. G. Just and C. C. Leznoff, *Can. J. Chem.*, **42**, 79 (1964).
155. W. G. Dauben and C. D. Poulter, *Tetrahedron Letters*, **1967**, 3021; *J. Am. Chem. Soc.*, **90**, 802 (1968).
156. O. L. Chapman and D. J. Pasto, *J. Am. Chem. Soc.*, **84**, 1220 (1962); *Chem. Ind.*, **1961**, 53.
157. W. G. Dauben and R. L. Cargill, *Tetrahedron*, **12**, 186 (1961).
158. S. F. Chappell and R. F. Clark, *Chem. Ind.*, **1962**, 1198.
159. W. G. Dauben and R. L. Cargill, *J. Org. Chem.*, **27**, 1910 (1962).
160. G. O. Schenck and R. Steinmetz, *Bull. Soc. Chim. Belges*, **71**, 781 (1962).
161. See K. M. Shumata and G. K. Fonken, *J. Am. Chem. Soc.*, **88**, 1073 (1966) for a related case.
162. R. S. H. Liu, *J. Am. Chem. Soc.*, **89**, 112 (1967).
163. W. G. Dauben, R. L. Cargill, R. M. Coates, and J. Saltiel, *J. Am. Chem. Soc.*, **88**, 2742 (1966).
164. J. Meinwald and P. H. Mazzocchi, *J. Am. Chem. Soc.*, **88**, 2850 (1966).
165. A similar reaction occurs in the vapor phase: R. Srinivasan, *J. Am. Chem. Soc.*, **84**, 3982 (1962).
166. G. J. Fonken, *Tetrahedron Letters*, **1962**, 549.
167. E. N. Marvel et al., *Tetrahedron Letters*, **1965**, 385.
168. R. B. Woodward and R. Hoffmann, *J. Am. Chem. Soc.*, **87**, 2511 (1965).
169. K. J. Crowley, *Tetrahedron Letters*, **1965**, 2863; G. J. Fonken, *Tetrahedron Letters*, **1962**, 549.
170. K. J. Crowley, *Proc. Chem. Soc.*, **1964**, 17.
171. Other examples: J. Meinwald, A. Eckell, and K. L. Erickson, *J. Am. Chem. Soc.*, **87**, 3532 (1965).
172. E. Havinga and J. Schlatmann, *Tetrahedron*, **12**, 146 (1961).
173. E. Havinga, R. J. de Kock, and M. P. Rappolt, *Tetrahedron*, **11**, 276 (1960).
174. G. M. Sanders and E. Havinga, *Rec. Trav. Chim.*, **83**, 665 (1964).
175. D. M. Gale, W. J. Middleton, and C. G. Krespan, *J. Am. Chem. Soc.*, **88**, 3617 (1966).
176. O. L. Chapman and S. L. Smith, *J. Org. Chem.*, **27**, 2271 (1961).
177. W. R. Roth, *Angew. Chem.*, **75**, 921 (1963).
178. O. L. Chapman and G. W. Borden, *Proc. Chem. Soc.*, **1963**, 221; *J. Am. Chem. Soc.*, **89**, 2979 (1967); L. B. Jones and V. K. Jones, *ibid.*, 1540 (1968).
179. O. L. Chapman, G. W. Borden, R. W. King, and B. Winkler, *J. Am. Chem. Soc.*, **86**, 2660 (1964).
180. J. Zirner and S. Winstein, *Proc. Roy. Soc. (London)*, **1964**, 235.
181. W. R. Roth, *Angew. Chem.*, **76**, 378 (1964).

182. G. Schroeder and J. F. Moth, *Tetrahedron Letters*, **1966**, 4083.

183. T. D. Goldfarb and L. Lindquist, *J. Am. Chem. Soc.*, **89**, 458 (1967).

183a. F. A. L. Anet and L. A. Bock, *J. Am. Chem. Soc.*, **90**, 7130 (1968); *ibid.*, **91**, 524 (1969).

184. E. H. White and R. L. Stern, *Tetrahedron Letters*, **1964**, 193.

185. H. Yamazaki and S. Shida, *J. Chem. Phys.*, **24**, 1278 (1956).

185a H. E. Zimmerman and H. Iwamura, *J. Am. Chem. Soc.*, **90**, 4763 (1968).

186. M. Stiles and U. Burckhardt, *J. Am. Chem. Soc.*, **86**, 3396 (1964).

187. See R. M. Kellogg, M. B. Groen, and H. Wynberg, *J. Org. Chem.*, **32**, 3093 (1967) and references therein; H. Hiraoka and R. Srinivasan, *ibid.*, **90**, 2720 (1968).

188. J. M. Patterson and L. T. Burka, Abstracts, 153rd Meeting, American Chemical Society, Miami, April 1967, p. O135.

189. L. A. Paquette, *J. Am. Chem. Soc.*, **86**, 3092 (1964).

190. L. A. Paquette, J. H. Barrett, R. P. Spitz, and R. Piltcher, *J. Am. Chem. Soc.*, **87**, 3417 (1965).

191. J. M. Holovka and P. D. Gardner, *J. Am. Chem. Soc.*, **89**, 6390 (1967).

192. H. H. Jaffe and M. Orchim, *Theory and Applications of Ultraviolet Spectroscopy*, Wiley, New York, 1962; L. Samein, *Molecular Orbital Theory of Conjugated Systems*, Benjamin, New York, 1966.

193. D. Bryce-Smith and H. C. Longuet-Higgins, *Chem. Commun.*, **1966**, 593.

194. E. Farenhorst, *Tetrahedron Letters*, **1966**, 6465.

195. J. Platt et al., *Systematics of the Electronic Spectra of Conjugated Molecules*, Wiley, New York, 1964.

196. R. B. Woodward and R. Hoffmann, *J. Am. Chem. Soc.*, **87**, 2511 (1965).

197. D. S. McClure, *J. Chem. Phys.*, **17**, 905 (1949).

198. G. N. Lewis and M. Kasha, *J. Am. Chem. Soc.*, **66**, 2100 (1944).

199. A. A. Lamola and G. S. Hammond, *J. Chem. Phys.*, **43**, 2129 (1965).

200. T. Midinger and F. Wilkinson, *Trans. Faraday Soc.*, **61**, 620 (1965).

201. I. B. Berlman, *Handbook of Fluorescence Spectra of Aromatic Molecules*, Academic Press, New York, 1965.

202. R. Kellogg, *J. Chem. Phys.*, **44**, 411 (1966).

203. R. G. Bennett and P. J. McCartin, *J. Chem. Phys.*, **44**, 1969 (1966).

204. G. S. Hammond and J. Saltiel, *J. Am. Chem. Soc.*, **85**, 2516 (1963).

204a. D. F. Evans, *J. Chem. Soc.*, **1957**, 1351.

205. I. S. Berlman, *Handbook of Fluorescence Spectra of Aromatic Molecules*, Academic Press, New York, 1965.

206. A. A. Lamola and G. S. Hammond, *J. Chem. Phys.*, **43**, 2129 (1965).

207. D. S. McClure, *J. Chem. Phys.*, **17**, 905 (1949).

208. T. Medinger and F. Wilkinson, *Trans. Faraday Soc.*, **61**, 620 (1965).

209. F. Wilkinson, unpublished results.

210. C. A. Parker and T. A. Joyce, *Trans. Faraday Soc.*, **62**, 2785 (1966).

211. D. F. Evans, *J. Chem. Soc.*, **1957**, 1351.

212. D. F. Evans, *J. Chem. Soc.*, **1959**, 2753.

213. K. E. Wilzbach, T. S. Ritscher, and L. Kaplan, *J. Am. Chem. Soc.*, **89**, 1031 (1967).

214. H. J. F. Angus, J. McDonald, and D. Bryce-Smith, *J. Chem. Soc.*, **1960**, 2003. For a description of Woodward-Hoffman predictions for these isomerizations see I. Haller, *J. Chem. Phys.*, **47**, 1117 (1967).

215. H. R. Ward and J. S. Wishnok, *J. Am. Chem. Soc.*, **90**, 1085 (1968).

216. R. Steinmetz, *Fortschr. Chem. Forschung*, **7**, 445 (1967).

217. O. L. Chapman and G. Lenz, *Org. Photochem.*, **1**, 283 (1967).
218. H. J. F. Angus and D. Bryce-Smith, *J. Chem. Soc.*, **1960**, 4791.
219. E. Grovenstein, Jr., D. V. Rao, and T. W. Taylor, *J. Am. Chem. Soc.*, **83**, 1705 (1961).
220. D. Bryce-Smith and J. E. Lodge, *J. Chem. Soc.*, **1963**, 695; *Chem. Commun.*, **1968**, 19; Review: D. Bryce-Smith, *Pure Applied Chemistry*, **16**, 47 (1968).
221. G. O. Schenck and R. Steinmetz, *Tetrahedron Letters*, **1960**, 21.
222. W. M. Hardham and G. S. Hammond, *J. Am. Chem. Soc.*, **87**, 3200 (1967).
223. J. S. Bradshaw, *J. Org. Chem.*, **31**, 3974 (1966).
224. G. Kolzenburg, P. G. Fruss, S. P. Mannsfeld, and G. O. Schenck, *Tetrahedron Letters*, **1966**, 1861.
225. D. Bryce-Smith and J. E. Lodge, *J. Chem. Soc.*, **1963**, 695.
226. E. Grovenstein, Jr. and D. V. Rao, *Tetrahedron Letters*, **1964**, 193.
227. E. Farenhorst and H. F. Bickel, *Tetrahedron Letters*, **1966**, 5911.
228. L. Kaplan, J. S. Ritscher, and K. E. Wilzbach, *J. Am. Chem. Soc.*, **88**, 2881 (1966), footnote 10a.
229. D. Bryce-Smith, A. Gilbert, and H. C. Longuet-Higgins, *Chem. Commun.*, **1967**, 240.
230. K. E. Wilzbach and L. Kaplan, *J. Am. Chem. Soc.*, **88**, 2066 (1966).
231. D. Bryce-Smith, A. Gilbert, and B. H. Orger, *Chem. Commun.*, **1966**, 512.
232. M. Bellas, D. Bryce-Smith, and A. Gilbert, *Chem. Commun.*, **1967**, 862; **1967**, 263.
233. G. Koltzenburg and K. Kraft, *Tetrahedron Letters*, **1966**, 389.
234. K. Kraft and G. Koltzenburg, *Tetrahedron Letters*, **1967**, 4357; **1967**, 4723.
235. E. E. van Tamelen and S. P. Pappas, *J. Am. Chem. Soc.*, **84**, 3789 (1962).
236. K. E. Wilzbach and L. Kaplan, *J. Am. Chem. Soc.*, **86**, 2307 (1964).
237. E. M. Arnett and J. M. Bollinger, *Tetrahedron Letters*, **1964**, 3803.
238. L. Kaplan, E. E. Wilzbach, W. G. Brown, and S. S. Yang, *J. Am. Chem. Soc.*, **87**, 675 (1965).
239. K. E. Wilzbach and L. Kaplan, *J. Am. Chem. Soc.*, **87**, 4004 (1965); **90**, 1116, 5868 (1968).
240. H. Kristinsson and G. S. Hammond, *J. Am. Chem. Soc.*, **89**, 5968 (1967).
241. D. Kumari and S. K. Mukerju, *Tetrahedron Letters*, **1967**, 4169.
242. See also: G. W. Griffin et al., *J. Am. Chem. Soc.*, **87**, 1410 (1965); *Tetrahedron Letters*, **1965**, 2951.
243. C. D. DeBoer, Ph.D. thesis, California Institute of Technology, Pasadena, California, 1965.
244. G. S. Hammond, P. Wyatt, C. D. DeBoer, and N. J. Turro, *J. Am. Chem. Soc.*, **86**, 2532 (1964).
245. G. S. Hammond and R. S. Cole, *J. Am. Chem. Soc.*, **87**, 3256 (1965).
246. H. Kristinsson and G. W. Griffin, *Tetrahedron Letters*, **1966**, 3259 .
247. H. Kristinsson and G. W. Griffin, *J. Am. Chem. Soc.*, **88**, 37 (1966).
248. See however, D. B. Richardson et al., *J. Am. Chem. Soc.*, **87**, 2763 (1965).
249. G. W. Griffin, R. C. Petterson, and C. S. Irving, *Chem. Ind.*, **1966**, 1562.
250. G. W. Griffin, J. Covell, R. C. Petterson, R. M. Dodson, and G. Klose, *J. Am. Chem. Soc.*, **87**, 1410 (1965).
251. C. S. Irving, R. C. Petterson, I. Sarkar, H. Kristinsson, C. S. Aaron, G. W. Griffin, and G. J. Bondereaux, *J. Am. Chem. Soc.*, **88**, 5675 (1966).
252. H. Kristinsson, *Tetrahedron Letters*, **1966**, 2343.
253. H. Kristinsson and G. W. Griffin, *J. Am. Chem. Soc.*, **88**, 1579 (1966).
254. Related preparation of CCl_2, M. Jones et al., *J. Am. Chem. Soc.*, **88**, 3167 (1966).

255. A. M. Trozzolo, N. A. Yager, G. W. Griffin, H. Kristinsson, and I. Serkar, *J. Am. Chem. Soc.*, **89**, 3357 (1967).
256. E. Meyer and G. W. Griffin, *Angew. Chem.* (Intern. Ed. Engl.), **6**, 634 (1967).
257. W. G. Brown, *J. Am. Chem. Soc.*, **90**, 1916 (1968).
258. H. Stegemeyer, *Angew. Chem.*, **75**, 922 (1963).
259. J. R. Edman, *J. Am. Chem. Soc.*, **88**, 3454 (1966).
260. E. Ciganek, *J. Am. Chem. Soc.*, **88**, 2882 (1966).
261. D. P. Kelly, J. T. Pinkey, and R. D. G. Rigby, *Tetrahedron Letters*, **1966**, 5953.
262. See for example E. L. Wehry and L. B. Rogers, *J. Am. Chem. Soc.*, **87**, 4234 (1965) and references therein.
263. N. Kharasch et al., *Science*, **116**, 309 (1952).
264. Review: V. I. Stenberg, *Org. Photochem.*, **1**, 129 (1967).
265. H. E. Zimmerman and V. R. Sandel, *J. Am. Chem. Soc.*, **85**, 915 (1963).
266. Review: E. Havinga, in *Reactivity of the Photoexcited Organic Molecule*, Wiley, New York, 1967, p. 201.
267. See E. L. Wehry, *J. Am. Chem. Soc.*, **89**, 41 (1967) and references therein.
268. W. M. Horspool and P. L. Paulson, *Chem. Commun.*, **1967**, 195.
269. G. Frater and H. Schmid, *Helv. Chem. Acta*, **50**, 255 (1967).
270. K. H. Grellman, G. M. Sherman, and H. Linschitz, *J. Am. Chem. Soc.*, **85**, 1881 (1963); **86**, 303 (1964).
271. E. J. Bowen and J. H. D. Eland, *Proc. Chem. Soc.*, **1963**, 202.
272. W. Carruthers, *Chem. Commun.*, **1966**, 272.
273. Review: R. K. Sharma and N. Kharasch, *Angew. Chem.* (Intern. Ed. Engl.), **7**, 36 (1968).
274. N. Kharasch et al., *Chem. Ind.*, **1962**, 1720.
275. W. Wolf and N. Kharasch, *J. Org. Chem.*, **30**, 2493 (1965); **26**, 283 (1961).
276. P. W. Jeffs and J. F. Hansen, *J. Am. Chem. Soc.*, **89**, 2798 (1967).
277. N. Kharasch and R. K. Sharma, *Chem. Commun.*, **1967**, 492.
278. Y. Odaira, K. Yamaj, and S. Tsutsumi, *Bull. Chem. Soc. Japan*, **37**, 1410 (1964).
279. M. P. Cava, R. H. Schlessinger, and J. P. Van Meter, *J. Am. Chem. Soc.*, **86**, 3173 (1964).
280. W. H. F. Sasse, P. J. Collin, and G. Sugowdz, *Tetrahedron Letters*, **1967**, 3373; **1968**, 1689.
281. P. J. Collin and W. H. F. Sasse, *Tetrahedron Letters*, 1689 (1968); R. J. McDonald and B. K. Selinger, *ibid.*, 4791 (1968).
282. G. O. Schenck, J. Kuhls, S. P. Mannsfeld, and C. H. Krauch, *Chem. Ber.*, **96**, 813 (1963).
283. V. I. Stenberg and R. J. Perkins, *J. Org. Chem.*, **27**, 4111 (1962).
284. J. S. Bradshaw and G. S. Hammond, *J. Am. Chem. Soc.*, **85**, 3953 (1963); *Australian J. Chem.*, **21**, 733 (1968).
284a. The correct structure of the dimer of **61** is in dispute: M. Sterns and B. K. Selinger, *Aus. J. Chem.*, **21**, 2131 (1968); *J. Am. Chem. Soc.*, **91**, 621 (1969).
285. H. H. Wasserman and P. M. Keehn, *J. Am. Chem. Soc.*, **89**, 2770 (1967).
286. D. Bryce-Smith and B. Vickery, *Chem. Ind.*, **1961**, 429.
287. M. V. Sargent and C. J. Timmons, *J. Chem. Soc.*, **1964**, 5544.
288. Review: F. D. Greene, *Bull. Soc. Chim. France*, **1960**, 1356.
289. D. Applequist et al., *Chem. Ind.*, **1959**, 850.
290. D. C. Neckers, *Mechanistic Organic Photochemistry*, Reinhold, 1967, p. 98 ff.
291. E. J. Bowen, in *Advances in Photochemistry*, Vol. 1, W. A. Noyes, Jr., G. S. Hammond, and J. N. Pitts, Jr., Eds., Interscience, New York, 1963, p. 37.

292. R. Livingston and K. S. Wei, *J. Am. Chem. Soc.*, **89**, 3098 (1967).
293. J. B. Birks, J. H. Appleyard, and R. Pope, *Photochem. Photobiol.*, **2**, 493 (1963).
294. H. S. Taylor and A. A. Vernon, *J. Am. Chem. Soc.*, **53**, 2527 (1931).
295. G. W. Griffin et al., *Tetrahedron Letters*, **1965**, 2951.
296. H. Kristinsson and G. W. Griffin, *J. Am. Chem. Soc.*, **88**, 378 (1966).
297. H. Kristinsson and G. W. Griffin, *Tetrahedron Letters*, **1966**, 3259.
298. G. O. Schenck et al., *Chem. Ber.*, **95**, 1642 (1962).
299. J. Bowyer and Q. N. Porter, *Australian J. Chem.*, **19**, 1455 (1965).
300. C. H. Krauch and W. Metzner, *Chem. Ber.*, **98**, 2762 (1965); J. J. McCullough and C. W. Huang, *Chem. Commun.*, **1967**, 815; I. W. Haitmann and G. O. Schenck, *Chem. Ber.*, **100**, 3156 (1967).
301. Review: R. Exelby and R. Grinter, *Chem. Rev.*, **65**, 247 (1965); E. Fischer, *Fortschr. Chem. Forsch.*, **7**, 605 (1967).
302. J. Kole and R. S. Becker, *J. Phys. Chem.*, **71**, 4045 (1967); **72**, 997 (1968).
303. M. Pomerantz, *J. Am. Chem. Soc.*, **89**, 694 (1967).
304. J. Meinwald and P. H. Mazzocchi, *J. Am. Chem. Soc.*, **1967**, 696.
305. G. P. Schenck and R. Wolgast, *Naturwiss.*, **48**, 737 (1961).
306. I. M. Hartmann, W. Hartmann, and G. P. Schenck, *Chem. Ber.*, **100**, 3146 (1967).
307. D. O. Cowan and R. L. Drisko, *Tetrahedron Letters*, **1967**, 1255; *J. Am. Chem. Soc.*, **89**, 3068 (1967).
308. H. Wynberg, R. M. Kellogg, H. van Driel, and G. E. Beekhuis, *J. Am. Chem. Soc.*, **89**, 3501 (1967) and previous papers in this series.
309. Review of stilbene photochemistry: F. R. Stermitz, *Org. Photochem.*, **1**, 197 (1967); M. Scholz, F. Dietz, and M. Muehlstaedt, *Z. Chem.*, **7**, 329 (1967).
310. C. S. Wood and F. B. Mallory, *J. Org. Chem.*, **29**, 3373 (1964).
311. F. B. Mallory, C. S. Wood, and J. T. Gordon, *J. Am. Chem. Soc.*, **86**, 3904 (1964).
312. F. B. Mallory et al., *J. Am. Chem. Soc.*, **84**, 4361 (1962).
313. F. B. Mallory, J. T. Gordon, and C. S. Wood, *J. Am. Chem. Soc.*, **85**, 828 (1963).
314. K. A. Maszkat and E. Fischer, *J. Chem. Soc.*, *Ser. B.*, **1967**, 662.
315. W. R. Moore et al., *J. Am. Chem. Soc.*, **85**, 829 (1963).
316. K. A. Muszkat, D. Gegiore, and E. Fischer, *Chem. Commun.*, **1965**, 447.
317. O. L. Chapman and W. R. Adams, *J. Am. Chem. Soc.*, **89**, 4243 (1967); **90**, 2333 (1968).
318. R. Breslow, P. Gal, H. W. Chang, and L. J. Altman, *J. Am. Chem. Soc.*, **87**, 5139 (1965).
319. C. DeBoer and R. Breslow, *Tetrahedron Letters*, **1967**, 1033.
320. E. H. White and J. P. Anholt, *Tetrahedron Letters*, **1965**, 3937.
321. C. D. DeBoer and R. H. Schlessinger, *J. Am. Chem. Soc.*, **90**, 803 (1968).
322. M. Kasha, in *Light and Life*, W. B. McElroy and B. Glass, Eds., Johns Hopkins University Press, Baltimore, Md., 1961, p. 31.
323. H. E. Zimmerman, in *Advances in Photochemistry*, Vol. 1, W. A. Noyes, Jr., G. S. Hammond, and J. N. Pitts, Jr., Eds., Interscience, New York, 1963, p. 183.
324. D. E. Freeman and W. Klemperer, *J. Chem. Phys.*, **45**, 52 (1966).
325. H. L. McMurray, *J. Chem. Phys.*, **9**, 231, 241 (1941).
326. R. S. Mulliken, *J. Chem. Phys.*, **3**, 564 (1935).
327. J. C. D. Brand, *J. Chem. Soc.*, **1956**, 856.
328. G. W. Robinson, *Can. J. Phys.*, **34**, 699 (1956).
329. J. C. D. Brand and D. G. Williamson, *Advan. Phys. Org. Chem.*, **1**, 365 (1963).
330. E. W. Abrahamson, J. G. F. Littler, and K. P. Vo, *J. Chem. Phys.*, **44**, 4082 (1966).
331. R. M. Hochstrasser, *J. Chem. Phys.*, **39**, 3153 (1963).

332. T. Godfrey and J. N. Murell, *Proc. Roy. Soc. (London)*, *Ser. A*, **278**, 71 (1964).
333. A. N. Terenin and V. L. Ermolaev, *Trans. Faraday Soc.*, **52**, 1042 (1956).
334. V. L. Ermaolaev and A. Terenin, *J. Chem. Phys.*, **55**, 698 (1958).
335. W G. Herkstroeter, A. A. Lamola, and G. S. Hammond, *J. Am. Chem. Soc.*, **86**, 4537 (1964).
336. S. P. McGlynn, F. J. Smith, and G. Cilento, *Photochem. Photobiol.*, **3**, 269 (1964).
337. W. G. Herkstroeter, A. A. Lamola, and G. S. Hammond, *J. Am. Chem. Soc.*, **86**, 4537 (1964).
338. D. R. Arnold, Abstracts, 149th Meeting, American Chemical Society, Detroit, April 1965, p. 50P.
339. W. G. Herkstroater, Ph.D. thesis, California Institute of Technology, Pasadena, California, 1965.
340. N. C. Yang, D. S. McClure, S. L. Murov, J. J. Houser, and R. Dusenberg, *J. Am. Chem. Soc.*, **89**, 5466 (1967).
341. E. J. Baum, J. R. S. Wan, and J. N. Pitts, Jr., *J. Am. Chem. Soc.*, **88**, 2652 (1966).
342. D. R. Kearns and W. A. Case, *J. Am. Chem. Soc.*, **88**, 5087 (1966).
343. W. G. Kerkstroeter, A. A. Lamola, and G. S. Hammond, *J. Am. Chem. Soc.*, **86**, 4537 (1964).
344. D. R. Arnold, Abstracts, 149th Meeting, American Chemical Society, Detroit, Michigan, April 1965, p. 50P.
345. G. N. Lewis and M. Kasha, *J. Am. Chem. Soc.*, **66**, 2100 (1944).
346. G. Porter and P. Suppan, *Trans. Faraday Soc.*, **61**, 1664 (1965).
347. V. L. Ermolaev and A. Terenin, *J. Chim. Phys.*, **55**, 698 (1958).
348. K. Yoshihara and D. R. Kearns, *J. Chem. Phys.*, **45**, 1991 (1966).
349. J. W. Sidman, *Chem. Rev.*, **58**, 689 (1958).
350. H. H. Jaffee and M. Orchin, *Theory and Applications of Ultraviolet Spectroscopy*, Wiley, New York, 1962.
351. G. N. Lewis and M. Kasha, *J. Am. Chem. Soc.*, **66**, 2100 (1944).
352. G. Porter and P. Suppan, *Trans. Faraday Soc.*, **62**, 3375 (1966).
353. M. S. Kharasch, W. H. Urry, and B. M. Kuderna, *J. Org. Chem.*, **14**, 248 (1949).
354. H. Sakurai, K. Shima, and I. Aono, *Bull. Chem. Soc. Japan*, **38**, 760, 1227 (1965).
355. G. Buchi, C. G. Inman, and E. S. Lipinsky, *J. Am. Chem. Soc.*, **76**, 4327 (1954).
356. For reviews see J. Calvert and J. N. Pitts, Jr., *Photochemistry*, Wiley, New York, 1966, p. 371; J. N. Pitts, Jr. and J. K. S. Wan, in *The Chemistry of the Carbonyl Group*, S. Patai, Ed., Interscience, New York, 1966, p. 823.
357. P. deMayo, *Advan. Org. Chem.*, **2**, 367 (1960).
358. K. Schaffner, *Chimia*, **19**, 575 (1965).
359. I. Orban, K. Schaffner, and O. Jeger, *J. Am. Chem. Soc.*, **85**, 3034 (1963).
360. K. H. Schulte-Elte and G. Ohloff, *Tetrahedron Letters*, **1964**, 1143.
361. D. Elad and R. D. Youssefych, *J. Org. Chem.*, **29**, 2031 (1964).
362. Review: D. Elad, in *Chemistry of the Ether Linkage*, S. Patai, Ed., Wiley, New York, 1967, p. 353; *Fortschr. Chem. Forsch.*, **7**, 528 (1967).
363. N. J. Turro and P. A. Wriede, *J. Am. Chem. Soc.*, **90**, 6863 (1968); M. Tomioka, Y. Izawa and Y. Ogata, *Tetrahedron*, **24**, 5734 (1968).
364. N. J. Turro, P. Wriede, J. C. Dalton, D. R. Arnold, and A. H. Glick, *J. Am. Chem. Soc.*, **89**, 3950 (1967).
365. P. J. Wagner and G. S. Hammond, *J. Am. Chem. Soc.*, **88**, 1245 (1966); **87**, 4009 (1965).
366. D. R. Coulson and N. C. Yang, *J. Am. Chem. Soc.*, **88**, 4511 (1966).
367. J. Hill, *Chem. Commun.*, **1966**, 260.

368. H. Morrison, *Tetrahedron Letters*, **1964**, 3653.
369. N. C. Yang, M. Nussim, and D. R. Coulson, *Tetrahedron Letters*, **1965**, 1525.
370. H. Morrison, *J. Am. Chem. Soc.*, **87**, 932 (1965).
371. For related radical closures to five-membered rings see C. Walling et al., *J. Am. Chem. Soc.*, **88**, 5361 (1966).
372. G. Quinkert et al., *Tetrahedron Letters*, **1963**, 1863.
373. For a review of the photochemistry of haloketones see J. R. Mayer and J. P. Simons, in *Advances in Photochemistry*, Vol. 2, W. A. Noyes, Jr., G. S. Hammond, and J. N. Pitts, Jr., Eds., Interscience, New York, 1964, p. 137.
373a. J. A. Barltrop and A. Thomson, *J. Chem. Soc.*, *Ser. C*, 155 (1968).
374. R. Srinivasan, *Advances in Photochemistry*, Vol. 1, W. A. Noyes, Jr., G. S. Hammond, and J. N. Pitts, Jr., Eds., Interscience, New York, 1963, p. 83.
375. N. J. Turro, W. B. Hammond, and S. S. Edelson, unpublished results.
376. N. J. Turro and R. S. Southam, *Tetrahedron Letters*, **1967**, 545 and references therein.
377. N. J. Turro et al., *J. Am. Chem. Soc.*, **87**, 5843 (1965).
378. N. J. Turro, W. B. Hammond, and P. A. Leermakers, *J. Am. Chem. Soc.*, **87**, 2774 (1965).
379. P. Dunion and C. N. Trumbore, *J. Am. Chem. Soc.*, **87**, 4211 (1965).
380. J. E. Starr and R. H. Eastman, *J. Org. Chem.*, **31**, 1393 (1966).
381. For a review of the photochemistry of steroidal cyclopentanones see K. Schaffner, *Fortschr. Chem. Org. Naturstoffe*, **22**, 1 (1964).
382. G. Quinkert, W. Wiersdorf, M. Finke, and K. Opitz, *Tetrahedron Letters*, **1966**, 2193.
383. G. Quinkert, K. Opitz, W. Wiersdorf, and M. Finke, *Ann. Chem.*, **693**, 44 (1966).
384. R. Srinivasan, in *Advances in Photochemistry*, Vol. 1, W. A. Noyes, Jr., G. S. Hammond, and J. N. Pitts, Jr., Eds., Interscience, New York, 1963, p. 83.
385. R. Srinivasan and S. E. Cremer, *J. Am. Chem. Soc.*, **87**, 1647 (1965).
386. T. Masui, A. Komatsu, and T. Moroe, *Bull. Chem. Soc. Japan*, **40**, 2204 (1967); R. C. Cookson, J. Undec, A. Szabo, and G. E. Usher, *Tetrahedron*, **24**, 4353 (1968).
387. N. C. Yang, M. Nussim, M. J. Jorgenson, and S. Murov, *Tetrahedron Letters*, **1964**, 3657.
388. N. C. Yang, *Pure Appl. Chem.*, **9**, 591 (1964).
389. J. S. Bradshaw, *J. Org. Chem.*, **31**, 237 (1966).
390. F. Bergmann and Y. Hirschberg, *J. Am. Chem. Soc.*, **65**, 1429 (1943).
391. J. A. Bell and H. Linschitz, *J. Am. Chem. Soc.*, **85**, 528 (1963).
392. G. S. Hammond and P. A. Leermakers, *J. Am. Chem. Soc.*, **84**, 207 (1962).
393. V. L. Ermolaev and A. N. Terenin, *Sov. Phys. Uspek.*, **3**, 423 (1960).
394. N. C. Yang, R. Loeschen, and D. Michel, *J. Am. Chem. Soc.*, **89**, 5465 (1967); N. C. Yang and R. L. Loeschen, *Tetrahedron Letters*, 2571 (1968).
395. See, however, G. Porter and P. Suppan, *Trans. Faraday Soc.*, **62**, 3375 (1966).
396. D. E. Applequist, T. L. Brown, J. R. Kleiman, and S. T. Young, *Chem. Ind.*, **1959**, 850.
397. C. Weizmann, E. Bergmann, and Y. Hirshberg, *J. Am. Chem. Soc.*, **60**, 1530 (1938).
398. G. S. Hammond, W. P. Baker, and W. M. Moore, *J. Am. Chem. Soc.*, **83**, 2795 (1961); S. G. Cohen, D. A. Laufer, and W. V. Sherman, *J. Am. Chem. Soc.*, **86**, 3060 (1964).
399. H. -D. Becker, *J. Org. Chem.*, **32**, 2140 (1967).
400. J. Petrushka, *J. Chem. Phys.*, **34**, 1120 (1961).

401. H. Skull, *J. Chem. Phys.*, **27**, 1388 (1957).
402. D. R. Kearns and W. A. Case, *J. Am. Chem. Soc.*, **88**, 5087 (1967).
403. A. A. Lamola, *J. Chem. Phys.*, **47**, 4810 (1967).
404. N. C. Yang, D. S. McClure, S. L. Murov, J. J. Houser, and R. Dusenbery, *J. Am. Chem. Soc.*, **89**, 5466 (1967). N. C. Yang and R. L. Dusenbery, *ibid.*, **90**, 5899 (1968).
405. J. S. Bradshaw, *J. Org. Chem.*, **31**, 237 (1966).
406. G. Buchi, J. T. Kofron, E. Koller, and D. J. Rosenthal, *J. Am. Chem. Soc.*, **78**, 876 (1956).
407. G. Wetterman, *Photochem. Photobiol.*, **4**, 621 (1965).
408. M. Pfau, N. D. Heindel, and T. F. Lemke, *Compt. Rend.*, **261**, 1017 (1965).
409. D. R. Arnold, R. L. Hinman, and A. H. Glick, *Tetrahedron Letters*, **1964**, 1424.
410. P. J. Wagner and G. S. Hammond, *J. Am. Chem. Soc.*, **88**, 1245 (1966). J. A. Barltrop and J. D. Coyle, *ibid.*, **90**, 6584 (1968); P. J. Wagner and A. E. Kemppainer, *ibid.*, **90**, 5896, 5898 (1968); J. N. Pitts, Jr., D. R. Burley, J. C. Mani, and A. D. Broadbent, *ibid.*, **90**, 5902 (1968).
411. P. Yates and A. G. Szabo, *Tetrahedron Letters*, **1965**, 485; N. J. Turro and F. D. Lewis, *Tetrahedron Letters*, 5845 (1968).
412. R. B. LaCount and C. E. Griffin, *Tetrahedron Letters*, **1965**, 1549.
413. A. C. Weiss, Jr. and J. Course, *J. Am. Chem. Soc.*, **87**, 2068 (1965).
414. R. A. Clasen and S. Searles, Jr., *Chem. Commun.*, **1966**, 289.
415. E. J. Baum and J. N. Pitts, Jr., *J. Phys. Chem.*, **70**, 2066 (1966).
416. Review: A. Padwa, *Org. Photochem.*, **1**, 91 (1967).
417. G. W. Griffin, E. J. O'Connell, and H. A. Hammond, *J. Am. Chem. Soc.*, **85**, 1001 (1963).
418. H. E. Zimmerman, B. R. Cowly, C. Y. Tseng, and J. W. Wilson, *J. Am. Chem. Soc.*, **86**, 947 (1964).
419. B. Singh and E. F. Ullman, *J. Am. Chem. Soc.*, **89**, 6911 (1967).
420. For a review see N. J. Turro, *Molecular Photochemistry*, Benjamin, New York, 1965, p. 137.
421. G. S. Hammond, W. P. Baker, and W. M. Moore, *J. Am. Chem. Soc.*, **83**, 2795 (1961).
422. M. J. Cziesla, K. F. Mueller, and O. Jones, *Tetrahedron Letters*, **1966**, 813.
423. J. N. Pitts, Jr. et al., *J. Am. Chem. Soc.*, **81**, 1068 (1959).
424. A. Beckett and G. Porter, *Trans. Faraday Soc.*, **59**, 2038 (1963).
425. R. S. Davidson, *Chem. Commun.*, **1968**, 575; S. G. Cohen and R. J. Baumgarten, *J. Am. Chem. Soc.*, **89**, 3471 (1967) and references therein.
426. D. Scharf and F. Korte, *Tetrahedron Letters*, **1963**, 821.
427. N. C. Yang, J. I. Cohen, and A. Shani, *J. Am. Chem. Soc.*, **90**, 3264 (1968).
428. J. Saltiel, R. M. Coates, and W. G. Dauben, *J. Am. Chem. Soc.*, **88**, 2745 (1965).
429. A. Beckett and G. Porter, *Trans. Faraday Soc.*, **59**, 2051 (1963).
430. N. C. Yang and C. Rivas, *J. Am. Chem. Soc.*, **83**, 2213 (1961).
431. G. Porter and P. Suppan, *Trans. Faraday Soc.*, **61**, 1664 (1965).
432. G. Porter and P. Suppan, *Pure Appl. Chem.*, **9**, 499 (1964).
433. S. G. Cohen and M. Nasim Saddiqui, *J. Am. Chem. Soc.*, **86**, 5047 (1964); S. G. Cohen and J. I. Cohen, *J. Phys. Chem.*, **72**, 3782 (1968).
434. L. A. Singer and P. D. Bartlett, *Tetrahedron Letters*, **1964**, 1887; L. A. Singer, G. A. David, and V. P. Muralidhoran, *J. Am. Chem. Soc.*, **91**, 897 (1969).
435. C. H. Krauch, W. Metzner, and G. P. Schenck, *Chem. Ber.*, **99**, 1723 (1966).
436. W. E. Bachman, *J. Am. Chem. Soc.*, **55**, 391 (1933).
437. C. Weizmann, E. Bergmann, and Y. Hirschberg, *J. Am. Chem. Soc.*, **60**, 1530 (1938).

438. A. Schonberg and A. Mustafa, *J. Chem. Soc.*, **1944**, 67.

439. K. R. Hoffman, M. Loy, and E. F. Ullman, *J. Am. Chem. Soc.*, **87**, 5417 (1965).

440. E. F. Zwickler, L. I. Grossweiner, and N. C. Yang, *J. Am. Chem. Soc.*, **85**, 2671 (1963); *Chem. Ber.*, **101**, 1398 (1968).

441. A. Beckett and G. Porter, *Trans. Faraday Soc.*, **59**, 2051 (1963).

442. E. F. Ullman and K. R. Hoffman, *Tetrahedron Letters*, **1965**, 1863.

443. J. R. Merrill and R. G. Bennett, *J. Chem. Phys.*, **43**, 1410 (1965).

444. A. A. Lamola and L. F. Sharp, *J. Phys. Chem.*, **70**, 2634 (1966).

445. K. R. Huffman and E. F. Ullman, *J. Am. Chem. Soc.*, **89**, 5629 (1967).

446. F. Bergmann and Y. Hirschberg, *J. Am. Chem. Soc.*, **65**, 1429 (1943).

447. N. C. Yang, M. Nussim, M. J. Jorgenson, and S. Murov, *Tetrahedron Letters*, **1964**, 3657.

448. W. C. Agosta, *J. Am. Chem. Soc.*, **89**, 3505 (1967); **89**, 3926 (1967).

449. G. Oster, L. Citarel, and M. Goodman, *J. Am. Chem. Soc.*, **84**, 703 (1962).

450. E. T. Kaiser and T. F. Wulfers, *J. Am. Chem. Soc.*, **86**, 1897 (1964).

451. M. Inatone and L. P. Kuhn, *Tetrahedron Letters*, **1965**, 73.

452. A. Schonberg and A. Mustafa, *J. Chem. Soc.*, **1943**, 275.

453. A. Mustafa, in *Advances in Photochemistry*, Vol. 2, W. A. Noyes, Jr., G. S. Hammond, and J. N. Pitts, Jr., Eds., Interscience, New York, 1964, p. 63.

454. A. Schonberg, *Preparative Organic Photochemistry*, Springer-Verlag, New York, 1968.

455. A. Yogev, M. Gorodetsky, and Y. Mazur, *J. Am. Chem. Soc.*, **86**, 5208 (1964).

456. M. Feldkimel and Y. Mazur, *Tetrahedron Letters*, **1963**, 369.

457. A. Yogev, M. Gorodetsky, and Y. Mazur, *J. Am. Chem. Soc.*, **86**, 5213 (1964).

458. M. Goradetsky and Y. Mazur, *Tetrahedron*, **22**, 3607 (1966).

459. A. Yogev and Y. Mazur, *J. Am. Chem. Soc.*, **87**, 3520 (1965).

460. For a review of the photo-Fries reaction see D. Bellus and P. Hrdlovis, *Chem. Rev.*, **67**, 599 (1967), and V. I. Stenberg, *Org. Photochem.*, **1**, 127 (1967); For recent work on the mechanism, see M. R. Sandner and D. J. Trecker, *J. Am. Chem. Soc.*, **89**, 5725 (1967).

461. J. C. Anderson and C. B. Reese, *J. Chem. Soc.*, **1963**, 1781.

461a. M. R. Sandner, E. Hedaya, and D. J. Tucker, *J. Am. Chem. Soc.*, **90**, 7249 (1968).

462. D. Taub, C. H. Kuo, N. L. States, and N. L. Wendler, *Tetrahedron*, **19**, 1 (1963).

463. R. C. Cookson, J. Hudec, and N. A. Mirza, *Chem. Commun.*, **1967**, 824.

464. R. A. Finnegan and D. Knutson, *J. Am. Chem. Soc.*, **89**, 1970 (1967).

465. For a review see D. Elad, in *Chemistry of the Ether Linkage*, S. Patai, Ed., Wiley, New York, 1967, p. 353.

466. D. Elad, *Tetrahedron Letters*, **1963**, 77.

467. D. Elad and J. Rakach, *J. Chem. Soc.*, **1965**, 800.

468. D. Elad, D. V. Rao, and V. I. Stenberg, *J. Org. Chem.*, **30**, 3252 (1965).

469. U. Schmidt, *Angew. Chem.* (Intern. Ed. Engl.), **4**, 146 (1965).

470. U. Schmidt, *Angew. Chem.* (Intern. Ed. Engl.), **4**, 239 (1965); **3**, 641 (1964).

471. Y. Shigemitsu, Y. Odaira, and S. Tsutsumi, *Tetrahedron Letters*, **1967**, 55.

472. A. G. Brook and J. M. Duff, *J. Am. Chem. Soc.*, **89**, 454 (1967).

473. See, for example, R. Cundall and A. S. Davies, *J. Am. Chem. Soc.*, **88**, 1329 (1966) and references therein.

474. G. D. Gutsche and J. W. Baum, *Tetrahedron Letters*, **1965**, 2301.

475. C. Willis and K. D. Bayes, *J. Am. Chem. Soc.*, **88**, 3203 (1966).

476. A. Wolf, personal communication.

477. H. Nozaki, M. Nakano, and K. Kando, *Tetrahedron*, **22**, 447 (1966).

478. H. E. Zimmerman and D. H. Paskovich, *J. Am. Chem. Soc.*, **86**, 2149 (1964).
479. J. C. D. Brand and D. G. Williamson, *Discussions Faraday Soc.*, **35**, 184 (1963).
480. J. C. D. Brand and D. G. Williamson, *Discussions Faraday Soc.*, **35**, 18 (1963).
481. H. E. Zimmerman et al., *J. Am. Chem. Soc.*, **88**, 159 (1966).
482. H. E. Zimmerman and J. S. Swenton, *J. Am. Chem. Soc.*, **86**, 1436 (1964).
483. G. S. Hammond, P. A. Stout, and A. A. Lamola, *J. Am. Chem. Soc.*, **86**, 3103 (1964).
484. W. G. Herkstroeter, Ph.D. thesis, California Institute of Technology, Pasadena, California, 1965.
485. H. E. Zimmerman et al., *J. Am. Chem. Soc.*, **89**, 6589 (1967).
486. J. W. Sidman and D. S. McClure, *J. Am. Chem. Soc.*, **77**, 6461, 6471 (1955).
487. N. A. Shcheglova et al., *Zh. Fiz. Khim.*, **39**, 893 (1965).
488. P. A. Leermakers, P. C. Warren, and G. F. Vesley, *J. Am. Chem. Soc.*, **86**, 1768 (1964).
489. P. A. Leermakers and G. F. Vesley, *J. Am. Chem. Soc.*, **85**, 3776 (1963).
490. W. G. Herkstroeter, J. Saltiel, and G. S. Hammond, *J. Am. Chem. Soc.*, **85**, 382 (1963).
491. W. G. Herkstroeter and G. S. Hammond, *J. Am. Chem. Soc.*
492. R. A. Ford and F. Parry, *Spectrochim. Acta*, **12**, 78 (1958).
493. L. Forster, *J. Chem. Phys.*, **26**, 1761 (1957).
494. J. W. Sidman and D. S. McClure, *J. Am. Chem. Soc.*, **77**, 6461, 6471 (1955).
495. J. C. D. Brand, *Trans. Faraday Soc.*, **50**, 431 (1954).
496. A. A. Lamola and G. S. Hammond, *J. Chem. Phys.*, **43**, 2129 (1965).
497. H. Berg and K. Kramarczyk, *Ber. Bunsen, Phys. Chem.*, **68**, 296 (1964).
498. J. M. Hollas and L. Goodman, *J. Chem. Phys.*, **42**, 760 (1965).
499. J. Saltiel, Ph.D. dissertation, California Institute of Technology, Pasadena, California, 1964.
500. M. Kasha, *Radiation Res.*, **2**, 243 (1960).
501. N. C. Yang, *Pure Appl. Chem.*, **9**, 591 (1964); *J. Org. Chem.*, **32**, 2462 (1967).
502. R. C. Cookson, J. Hudec, S. A. Knight, and B. R. D. Whitear, *Tetrahedron*, **19**, 1995 (1963).
503. R. Srinivasan and K. H. Carbough, *J. Am. Chem. Soc.*, **89**, 4933 (1967).
504. N. C. Yang and M. J. Jorgenson, *Tetrahedron Letters*, **1964**, 1203.
505. O. L. Chapman and T. J. Murphy, *J. Am. Chem. Soc.*, **89**, 3476 (1967).
506. M. J. Jorgenson and N. C. Yang, *J. Am. Chem. Soc.*, **85**, 1698 (1963).
507. I. A. Williams and P. Bladon, *Tetrahedron Letters*, **1964**, 257; *J. Chem. Soc., Ser. C.*, **1967**, 2032.
508. R. A. Schneider and J. Meinwald, *J. Am. Chem. Soc.*, **89**, 2023 (1963).
509. G. Quinkert et al., *Tetrahedron Letters*, **1963**, 1863.
510. C. W. Bird and J. Hudec, *Chem. Ind.*, **1959**, 570.
511. D. H. R. Barton, *Helv. Chim. Acta*, **42**, 2604 (1959).
512. J. E. Baldwin and M. C. McDaniel, *J. Am. Chem. Soc.*, **89**, 1537 (1967); *ibid.*, **90**, 6118 (1968).
513. P. E. Eaton, *Acc. Chem. Res.*, **1**, 50 (1968).
514. P. E. Eaton, *J. Am. Chem. Soc.*, **84**, 2344 (1962); P. E. Eaton, *J. Am. Chem. Soc.*, **84**, 2454 (1962).
515. P. E. Eaton, *Tetrahedron Letters*, **1964**, 3695.
516. J. D. White and D. N. Gupta, *J. Am. Chem. Soc.*, **88**, 5364 (1966).
517. R. Criegee and H. Furrer, *Chem. Ber.*, **97**, 2949 (1964).
518. R. L. Cargill, M. E. Beckham, A. E. Siebert, and J. Dorn, *J. Org. Chem.*, **30**, 3647 (1965).

519. Review P. E. Eaton, *Advan. Chem. Res.*, **1**, 50 (1968).
520. P. E. Eaton and W. S. Hurt, *J. Am. Chem. Soc.*, **88**, 5038 (1966).
521. J. L. Ruhlen and P. A. Leermakers, *J. Am. Chem. Soc.*, **88**, 5671 (1966); J. L. Ruhlen and P. A. Leermakers, *J. Am. Chem. Soc.*, **89**, 4944 (1967).
522. P. DeMayo, J. P. Pete, and M. Tchir, *J. Am. Chem. Soc.*, **89**, 5782 (1967); P. deMayo, J. P. Pete and M. Tchir, *Can. J. Chem.*, **46**, 2535 (1968).
523. P. E. Eaton and T. W. Cole, Jr., *J. Am. Chem. Soc.*, **86**, 3157 (1964).
524. W. L. Dilling, *Chem. Rev.*, **66**, 373 (1966).
525. T. Matsura and K. Ogura, *J. Am. Chem. Soc.*, **89**, 3850 (1967); *Chem. Commun.*, **1967**, 1247.
526. J. H. Wheeler and R. H. Eastman, *J. Am. Chem. Soc.*, **81**, 236 (1959).
527. O. L. Chapman and L. F. Englert, *J. Am. Chem. Soc.*, **85**, 3028 (1963).
528. H. Hart and D. W. Swatton, *J. Am. Chem. Soc.*, **89**, 1874 (1967).
529. H. E. Zimmerman and J. O. Grunewald, *J. Am. Chem. Soc.*, **89**, 3354 (1967).
530. E. J. Corey, R. B. Mitra, and H. Uda, *J. Am. Chem. Soc.*, **86**, 485 (1964); E. J. Corey, J. D. Boss, R. Le Mehieu, and R. B. Mitra, *J. Am. Chem. Soc.*, **86**, 5570 (1964).
531. Y. Yamada, H. Uda, and K. Nakanishi, *Chem. Commun.*, **1966**, 423.
532. E. Y. Lam, D. H. Valentine, and G. S. Hammond, *J. Am. Soc.*, **89**, 3482 (1967).
533. O. L. Chapman, T. A. Rettig, A. A. Griswald, A. I. Dutton, and P. Fitton, *Tetrahedron Letters*, **1963**, 2049; *Rec. Chem. Prog.*, **28**, 167 (1967).
534. H. E. Zimmerman, R. D. Ricke, and J. R. Scheffer, *J. Am. Chem. Soc.*, **89**, 2033 (1967).
535. H. E. Zimmerman et al., *J. Am. Chem. Soc.*, **88**, 159 (1966).
536. O. L. Chapman, J. B. Sieja, and W. J. Welstead, *J. Am. Chem. Soc.*, **88**, 161 (1966).
537. H. E. Zimmerman and D. J. Sam, *J. Am. Chem. Soc.*, **88**, 4114 (1966); H. E. Zimmerman and D. J. Sam, *J. Am. Chem. Soc.*, **88**, 4905 (1966).
538. G. Buchi and I. M. Goldman, *J. Am. Chem. Soc.*, **79**, 4741 (1957).
539. J. J. Hurst and G. H. Whitham, *J. Chem. Soc.*, **1960**, 2864.
540. W. F. Erman, *J. Am. Chem. Soc.*, **89**, 3828 (1967).
541. W. F. Erman and H. C. Kretschmar, *J. Am. Chem. Soc.*, **89**, 3842 (1967).
542. P. Eaton and K. Lin, *J. Am. Chem. Soc.*, **87**, 2052 (1965).
543. E. J. Corey, M. Tada, R. A. LeMahieu, and L. Libit, *J. Am. Chem. Soc.*, **87**, 2054 (1965).
544. P. Eaton and K. Lin, *J. Am. Chem. Soc.*, **86**, 2087 (1964).
545. H. Nozaki, M. Kurita, and R. Noyori, *Tetrahedron Letters*, 2025 (1968).
546. M. D. Cohen and G. M. J. Schmidt, *J. Chem. Soc.*, **1964**, 1966 and following papers.
547. J. Bergmann, K. Osaki, G. M. J. Schmidt, and F. I. Sonntag, *J. Chem. Soc.*, **1964**, 2021.
548. C. H. Krauch, S. Farid, and G. O. Schenck, *Chem. Ber.*, **99**, 625 (1966).
549. G. S. Hammond, C. A. Stout, and A. A. Lamola, *J. Am. Chem. Soc.*, **86**, 3103 (1964).
550. J. W. Hanifin and E. Cohen, *Tetrahedron Letters*, **1966**, 1419.
551. O. L. Chapman and W. R. Adams, *J. Am. Chem. Soc.*, **89**, 4243 (1967); **90**, 2333 (1968).
552. P. Praetorius and F. Korn, *Chem. Ber.*, **43**, 2744 (1910).
553. G. W. Recktenwald, J. N. Pitts, Jr., and R. L. Letsinger, *J. Am. Chem. Soc.*, **75**, 3028 (1953).
554. K. J. Crowley, R. A. Schneider, and J. Meinwald, *J. Chem. Soc.*, **1966**, 571.

555. G. O. Schenck and M. Huke, *Arch. Pharm.*, **297**, 703 (1964).
556. K. Schaffner, *Advances in Photochemistry*, Vol. 4, W. A. Noyes, Jr., G. S. Hammond, and J. N. Pitts, Jr., Eds., Interscience, New York, 1966, p. 81.
557. H. E. Zimmerman, *Pure Appl. Chem.*, **9**, 493 (1964).
558. P. J. Kropp, *Org. Photochem.*, **1**, 1 (1967).
559. O. L. Chapman, *Advances in Photochemistry*, Vol. 1, W. A. Noyes, Jr., G. S. Hammond, and J. N. Pitts, Jr., Eds., Interscience, New York, 1963, p. 323.
560. K. S. Schaffner, *Fortschr. Chem. Org. Naturstoffe*, **22**, 1 (1964).
561. H. E. Zimmerman and D. I. Schuster, *J. Am. Chem. Soc.*, **84**, 4527 (1962).
562. H. E. Zimmerman and J. S. Swenton, *J. Am. Chem. Soc.*, **89**, 906 (1967).
563. D. J. Patel and D. I. Schuster, *J. Am. Chem. Soc.*, **89**, 184 (1967).
564. J. King and D. Leaver, *Chem. Commun.*, **1965**, 539.
565. D. I. Schuster and D. J. Patel, *J. Am. Chem. Soc.*, **87**, 2514 (1965).
566. D. I. Schuster and D. J. Patel, *J. Am. Chem. Soc.*, **88**, 1825 (1966).
567. Review: M. Mousseron, *Advances in Photochemistry*, Vol. 4, W. A. Noyes, Jr., G. S. Hammond, and J. N. Pitts, Jr., Eds., Interscience, New York, 1966, p. 195.
568. M. B. Rubin, G. E. Hipps, and D. Glover, *J. Org. Chem.*, **29**, 68 (1964).
569. M. Mousseron-Canet et al., *Bull. Soc. Chim. France*, **1964**, 50.
570. M. Mousseron-Canet, M. Mousseron, P. Legendre, and J. Wylde, *Bull. Soc. Chim. France*, **1963**, 379.
571. K. H. Crosley, *J. Am. Chem. Soc.*, **85**, 1210 (1963).
572. D. H. R. Barton, *J. Chem. Soc.*, **1960**, 1.
573. H. Hart and A. J. Waring, *Tetrahedron Letters*, **1965**, 325.
574. P. M. Collins and H. Hart, *J. Chem. Soc.*, *Ser. C*, **1967**, 1197.
575. P. M. Collins and H. Hart, *J. Chem. Soc. Ser. C*, **1967**, 895.
576. H. Hart and R. K. Murray, Jr., *J. Org. Chem.*, **32**, 2448 (1967); J. Griffiths and H. Hart, *J. Am. Chem. Soc.*, **90**, 5296 (1968); O. L. Chapman and J. D. Lassila, *ibid.*, **90**, 2449 (1968).
577. Review: K. F. Koch, in *Alicyclic Chemistry*, Vol. 1, H. Hart and G. J. Karabatsos, Eds., Academic, New York, 1966, p. 257.
578. T. Tezuka, Y. Akasaki, and T. Mukai, *Tetrahedron Letters*, **1967**, 1397.
579. A. S. Kende and J. E. Lancaster, *J. Am. Chem. Soc.*, **89**, 5283 (1967).
580. T. Mukai et al., *Tetrahedron Letters*, **1967**, 433.
581. T. Mukai and T. Miyashi, *Tetrahedron*, **23**, 1613 (1967).
582. G. W. Griffin and E. J. O'Connell, *J. Am. Chem. Soc.*, **84**, 4148 (1962).
583. H. E. Zimmerman, H. G. C. Durr, R. G. Lewis, and S. Bram, *J. Am. Chem. Soc.*, **84**, 4149 (1962); **89**, 1863 (1967).
584. Review: W. Dilling, *Chem. Rev.*, **67**, 373 (1967).
585. R. C. Cookson, E. Crundwell, R. R. Hill, and J. Hudec, *J. Chem. Soc.*, **1964**, 3062.
586. P. de Mayo, S. T. Reid, and R. W. Yip, *Can. J. Chem.*, **42**, 2828 (1964).
587. A. Cox, P. deMayo, and R. W. Yip, *J. Am. Chem. Soc.*, **88**, 1043 (1966).
588. R. Robson, P. W. Grubb, and J. A. Barltrop, *J. Chem. Soc.*, **1964**, 2153.
589. G. W. Griffin, A. F. Vellturo, and K. Furukawa, *J. Am. Chem. Soc.*, **83**, 2725 (1961).
590. Review: R. Steinmetz, *Fortschr. Chem. Forsch.*, **7**, 445 (1967).
591. R. Steinmetz, W. Hartmann, and G. O. Schenck, *Chem. Ber.*, **98**, 3854 (1965).
591a. Review: D. Bryce-Smith, *Pure Applied Chem.*, **16**, 47 (1968).
592. G. O. Schenck, J. Kuhls, and C. H. Krauch, *Z. Naturforschung*, **206**, 635 (1965).
593. G. O. Schenck, J. Kukls, and C. H. Krauch, *Ann. Chem.*, **693**, 20 (1966).
594. G O. Schenck et al., *Chem. Ber.*, **96**, 498 (1963).

595. R. Criegee et al., *Chem. Ber.*, **97**, 2942 (1964).

596. H. D. Scharf and F. Korte, *Chem. Ber.*, **98**, 764 (1965).

597. H. D. Scharf and F. Korte, *Chem. Ber.*, **98**, 3672 (1965).

598. W. H. Urry and D. J. Trecker, *J. Am. Chem. Soc.*, **84**, 118 (1962).

599. E. S. Huyser and D. C. Neckers, *J. Org. Chem.*, **29**, 276 (1964).

600. P. A. Leermakers and F. G. Vesley, *J. Am. Chem. Soc.*, **85**, 3776 (1963).

601. H. A. Staab and J. I. Baktschi, *Tetrahedron Letters*, **1966**, 583; *Chem. Ber.*, **101**, 1457 (1968).

602. R. F. C. Brown and R. K. Solly, *Tetrahedron Letters*, **1966**, 169.

603. For an exhaustive review, see G. P. Fundt and G. O. Schenck, in *1,4-Cycloadditions*, J. Hamer, Ed., Academic, New York, 1967, p. 345.

604. C. H. Krauch, S. Farid, and G. O. Schenck, *Chem. Ber.*, **98**, 3102 (1965).

605. C. H. Krauch, S. Farid, and D. Hess, *Cham. Ber.*, **99**, 1881 (1966).

606. Review: J. M. Bruce, *Quart. Rev.*, **21**, 405 (1967).

607. J. Petranek and O. Ryba, *Chem. Ind.*, **1965**, 225; J. M. Brunce, D. Creed, and J. N. Ellis, *J. Chem. Soc.*, *Ser. C*, **1967**, 1486.

608. D. Bryce-Smith and A. Gilbert, *Proc. Chem. Soc.*, **1964**, 87; *J. Chem. Soc.*, *Ser. C*, **1967**, 383.

609. D. Bryce-Smith, G. I. Frey, and A. Gilbert, *Tetrahedron Letters*, **1964**, 2137.

610. H. E. Zimmerman and L. Craft, *Tetrahedron Letters*, **1964**, 2131.

611. J. A. Barltrop and B. Hesp, *Proc. Chem. Soc.*, **1964**, 195.

612. J. A. Barltrop and B. Hesp, *J. Chem. Soc.*, **1965**, 5182.

613. R. C. Cookson, D. A. Cox, and J. Hudec, *J. Chem. Soc.*, **1961**, 449.

614. G. O. Schenck, I. Hartmann, and W. Metzner, *Tetrahedron Letters*, **1965**, 347.

615. C. M. Orlando, Jr., H. Mark, A. K. Bose, and M. S. Manhas, *Tetrahedron Letters*, **1966**, 3003; *J. Am. Chem. Soc.*, **89**, 6527 (1967).

616. A. T. Shulgin and H. O. Kerlinger, *Tetrahedron Letters*, **1965**, 3355.

617. J. Rennert, S. Japar, and M. Guttman, *Photochem. Photobiol.*, **6**, 485 (1967); *J. Am. Chem. Soc.*, **90**, 464 (1968).

618. D. Schulte-Frohlinde and C. V. Sonntag, *Z. Phys. Chem.*, **44**, 314 (1965).

619. C. Krauch and S. Farid, *Tetrahedron Letters*, **1966**, 4783.

620. K. Tickle and F. Wilkenson, *Trans. Faraday Soc.*, **61**, 1981 (1965).

621. H. H. Dearman and A. Chan, *J. Chem. Phys.*, **44**, 416 (1966).

622. D. Bryce-Smith, A. Gilbert, and M. G. Johnson, *Tetrahedron Letters*, **1968**, 2863.

623. J. W. Sidman, *Chem. Rev.*, **58**, 689 (1958).

624. C. Steel and T. F. Thomas, *Chem. Commun.*, **1966**, 900.

625. M. B. Robin, R. R. Hart, and N. A. Huebler, *J. Am. Chem. Soc.*, **89**, 1564 (1967).

626. L. B. Jones and G. S. Hammond, *J. Am. Chem. Soc.* **87**, 4219 (1965).

627. P. S. Engel, *J. Am. Chem. Soc.*, **89**, 5731 (1967).

628. T. Thomas and C. Steel, *J. Am. Chem. Soc.*, **87**, 5290 (1965).

629. R. K. Brinton and D. H. Volman, *J. Chem. Phys.*, **19**, 1394 (1951).

630. F. D. Lewis and W. H. Saunders, Jr., *J. Am. Chem. Soc.*, **89**, 645 (1967).

631. G. N. Lewis and M. Kasha, *J. Am. Chem. Soc.*, **66**, 2100 (1944).

632. H. H. Joffe, S. J. Yeh, and R. W. Gardner, *J. Mol. Spectry.*, **2**, 120 (1958).

633. J. Calvert and J. N. Pitts, Jr., *Photochemistry*, Wiley, New York, 1966, p. 455.

634. D. F. Evans, *J. Chem. Soc.*, **1959**, 2753.

635. G. Wettermark et al., *J. Chem. Phys.*, **40**, 1486 (1964); *J. Phys. Chem.*, **69**, 1584 (1964); *J. Am. Chem. Soc.*, **87**, 1433 (1965).

636. M. Fischer, *Chem. Ber.*, **100**, 3599 (1967).

637. A. Padwa and L. Hamilton, *J. Am. Chem. Soc.*, **89**, 102 (1967).

638. H. Tiefenthaler, W. Dorscheln, A. Goth, and H. Schmidt, *Helv. Chem. Acta*, **50**, 2244 (1967).
639. P. Beak, J. L. Miesel, and W. R. Messer, *Tetrahedron Letters*, **1967**, 5317.
640. R. S. Becker and W. F. Richey, *J. Am. Chem. Soc.*, **89**, 1298 (1967).
641. J. Amin and P. deMayo, *Tetrahedron Letters*, **1963**, 1585.
642. R. O. Kan and R. L. Furey, *J. Am. Chem. Soc.*, **90**, 1666 (1968).
642a. A. Padwa, W. Bergmark, and D. Pashayan, *J. Am. Chem. Soc.*, **90**, 4458 (1968).
643. R. F. Hutton and C. Steel, *J. Am. Chem. Soc.*, **86**, 745 (1964).
644. P. Smith, J. E. Sheats, and P. E. Miller, *J. Org. Chem.*, **27**, 4053 (1962).
645. G. S. Hammond and J. R. Fox, *J. Am. Chem. Soc.*, **86**, 1918 (1964); **86**, 4031 (1964).
646. R. C. Cookson, I. D. R. Stevens, and C. T. Watts, *Chem. Commun.*, **1965**, 259.
647. G. O. Schenck, H-R. Kopp, B. Kim, and E. K. von Gustorf, *Z. Naturforsch.*, **20b**, 637 (1965).
648. L. B. Jones and G. S. Hammond, *J. Am. Chem. Soc.*, **87**, 4219 (1965).
649. G. Zimmerman, L. Chow, and U. Paik, *J. Am. Chem. Soc.*, **80**, 3528 (1958).
650. D. R. Kearns, *J. Phys. Chem.*, **69**, 1062 (1965).
651. G. M. Badger R. J. Drewer, and G. E. Lewis, *Australian J. Chem.*, **17**, 1036 (1964); **18**, 190 (1965).
652. P. Hugelshofer, J. Kalvoda, and K. Schaffner, *Helv. Chim. Acta*, **43**, 1322 (1960).
653. T. V. Van Auken and K. L. Reinhart, *J. Am. Chem. Soc.*, **84**, 3736 (1962).
654. A. C. Day and M. C. Whiting, *J. Chem. Soc.*, *Ser. C*, **1966**, 467; *J. Am. Chem. Soc. Ser. B*, **1967**, 991.
655. M. Franck-Neuman, *Angew. Chem.* (Intern. Ed. Engl.), **6**, 79 (1967).
656. P. Dowd, *J. Am. Chem. Soc.*, **88**, 2587 (1966); see also R. J. Crawford and D. M. Cameron, *J. Am. Chem. Soc.*, **88**, 2589 (1966).
657. G. L. Closs, W. A. Boll, H. Heyn, and V. Dev, *J. Am. Chem. Soc.*, **90**, 173 (1968).
658. R. Anet and F. A. L. Anet, *J. Am. Chem. Soc.*, **86**, 525 (1964); G. L. Closs, L. R. Kaplan, and V. I. Bindall, *J. Am. Chem. Soc.*, **89**, 3376 (1967).
659. G. L. Closs and W. Boll, *J. Am. Chem. Soc.*, **85**, 3905 (1963).
660. Reviews: R. A. Abramovitch and B. A. Davies, *Chem. Rev.*, **64**, 149 (1964); W. Lwoski, *Angew. Chem.* (Intern. Ed. Engl.), **6**, 897 (1967).
661. L. Horner and A. Christmann, *Angew. Chem.* (Intern. Ed. Engl.), **2**, 599 (1963).
662. D. H. R. Barton and A. N. Starratt, *J. Chem. Soc.*, **1965**, 2444.
663. L. Horner, G. Bauer, and J. Dorges, *Chem. Ber.*, **98**, 2631 (1965).
664. E. Wasserman, G. Smolinsky, and W. A. Yager, *J. Am. Chem. Soc.*, **86**, 3166 (1964).
665. R. Kreher and G. H. Bockhorn, *Angew. Chem.*, **76**, 681 (1964).
666. R. Ruttner and K. Hafner, *Tetrahedron Letters*, **1964**, 3119.
667. K. Hafner et al., *Tetrahedron Letters*, **1964**, 3953.
668. F. D. Lewis and W. H. Sanders, *J. Am. Chem. Soc.*, **89**, 645 (1967).
669. P. Scheiner, *J. Am. Chem. Soc.*, **88**, 4759 (1966); *Tetrahedron*, **24**, 2757 (1968).
670. E. M. Burgess, R. Carithers, and L. McCullagh, *J. Am. Chem. Soc.*, **90**, 1923 (1968).
671. Review: W. Kirmse, *Carbene Chemistry*, Academic, New York, 1964.
672. K. R. Kopecky, G. S. Hammond, and P. A. Leermakers, *J. Am. Chem. Soc.*, **84**, 1015 (1962).
673. L. Horner, K. Muth, and H. G. Schmelzer, *Chem. Ber.*, **92**, 2953 (1959).
674. E. J. Corey and A. M. Felix, *J. Am. Chem. Soc.*, **87**, 2518 (1965).
675. A. Padwa and R. Layton, *Tetrahedron Letters*, **1967**, 2167.
676. W. E. Lee, J. C. Calvert, and E. W. Malmberg, *J. Am. Chem. Soc.*, **83**, 1928 (1961).
677. J. deJonge, R. Dijkstra, and G. L. Wiggerink, *Rec. Trav. Chim.*, **71**, 846 (1952).

678. R. E. Rebbert and N. Slagg, *Bull. Soc. Chim. Belges*, **71**, 709 (1962).
678a. J. A. Barltrop and N. J. Bunce, *J. Chem. Soc.*, *Ser. C*, 1467 (1968).
679. J. T. Pinkey and E. Rizzado, *Chem. Commun.*, **1965**, 362.
680. E. C. Taylor, B. Farth, and M. Pfau, *J. Am. Chem. Soc.*, **87**, 1400 (1965).
681. R. L. Letsinger and O. B. Ramsay, *J. Am. Chem. Soc.*, **87**, 2945 (1965).
682. L. Kaminsky and M. Lamchen, *Chem. Commun.*, **1965**, 130.
683. K. Shinzawa and I. Tanaka, *J. Phys. Chem.*, **68**, 1205 (1964); K. Kogano and I. Tanaka, *J. Phys. Chem.*, **69**, 2545 (1965).
684. For example, see J. Streith, *Tetrahedron Letters*, **1966**, 1347.
685. E. M. Muller, *Chem. Ber.*, **87**, 1449 (1954).
686. Y. L. Chow, *Tetrahedron Letters*, **1964**, 2333.
687. Y. L. Chow, *J. Am. Chem. Soc.*, **87**, 4642 (1965); *Can. J. Chem.*, **43**, 2711 (1965).
688. D. H. R. Barton and J. M. Beaton, *J. Am. Chem. Soc.*, **82**, 2641 (1960); **83**, 4083 (1963).
689. J. Joussot-Dublin and J. Houdard, *Tetrahedron Letters*, **1967**, 4389.
690. E. C. Taylor, R. O. Kan, and W. W. Paudler, *J. Am. Chem. Soc.*, **83**, 4484 (1961).
691. L. A. Paquette and G. Slomp, *J. Am. Chem. Soc.*, **85**, 765 (1963).
692. H. H. Perkampres and G. Kassebeer, *Ann. Chem.*, **696**, 1 (1966); *Ber. Bunsen. Phys. Chem.*, **71**, 40 (1967).
693. H. H. Perkampres and G. Kassebeer, *J. Chem. Soc.*, *Ser. C*, **1967**, 1343.
694. F. Lahmani and N. Ivanoff, *Tetrahedron Letters*, **1967**, 3913.
695. H. Nozaki, M. Kato, R. Noyori, and M. Kawaniski, *Tetrahedron Letters*, **1967**, 4259.
696. E. Vander Donckt and G. Porter, *J. Chem. Phys.*, **46**, 1173 (1967).
697. A. Goeth et al., *Helv. Chem. Acta*, **48**, 1395 (1965).
698. S. Niizuma et al., *Bull. Chem. Soc. Japan*, **40**, 2249 (1967); *J. Chem. Phys.*, **48**, 1868 (1968).
699. F. D. Lewis and N. J. Turro, unpublished results.
700. E. H. Gilmore, G. E. Gibson, and D. S. McClure, *J. Chem. Phys.*, **20**, 829 (1952); **23**, 1772 (1955).
701. J. A. Bell and H. Lipschitz, *J. Am. Chem. Soc.*, **85**, 528 (1963).
702. W. G. Herkstroeter, Ph.D. thesis, California Institute of Technology, Pasadena, California, 1965.
703. V. Ermolaev and A. Terenin, *J. Chem. Phys.*, **59**, 698 (1958).

General References

1. N. J. Turro, *Molecular Photochemistry*, W. A. Benjamin Co., New York, 1965.
2. R. O. Kan, *Organic Photochemistry*, McGraw-Hill, New York, 1966.
3. J. G. Calvert and J. N. Pitts, Jr., *Photochemistry*, Wiley, New York, 1966.
4. D. C. Neckers, *Mechanistic Organic Photochemistry*, Reinhold, New York, 1967.
5. W. A. Noyes, Jr., G. S. Hammond, and J. N. Pitts, Jr., *Advances in Photochemistry*, Vols. 1–5, Wiley, New York, 1963–68.
6. R. Steinmetz, "Cycloadditions," in *Fortschr. Chem. Forsch.*, **7**, 445 (1967).
7. D. Elad, "Photoalkylations," in *Fortschr., Chem. Forsch.*, **7**, 428 (1967).
8. M. Pape, "Photooximation," in *Fortschr. Chem. Forsch.*, **7**, 559 (1967).
9. E. Fischer, "Photochromism and Reversible Photoisomerizations," in *Fortschr. Chem. Forsch.*, **7**, 605 (1967).
10. O. L. Chapman, *Organic Photochemistry*, Vol. 1, M. Decker, New York, 1967.

11. J. M. Bruce, "Quinone Photochemistry," in *Quart. Rev.*, **21**, 405 (1967).
12. D. Bellus and P. Hrdlovic, "Photo Fries," in *Chem. Rev.*, **67**, 599 (1967).
13. "Reactivity of the Photoexcited Organic Molecule," Solvay Conference, Interscience, New York, 1967.
14. B. Capon, M. J. Perkins, and C. W. Rees, "Photochemical Reaction Mechanisms," in *Organic Reaction Mechanisms-1966*, Interscience, New York, 1967; *ibid.*, 1968.
15. D. Elad, "Photochemistry of Ethers," in *Chemistry of the Ether Linkage*, S. Patai, Ed., Wiley, New York, 1967, p. 335.
16. K. F. Koch, "Tropolones," in *Advances in Alicyclic Chemistry*, H. Hart and G. J. Karabatson, Eds., Academic, New York, 1966, p. 258.
17. R. N. Warrener and J. B. Bremmer, "Photochemistry of Unsaturated Systems," in *Rev. Pure Appl. Chem.*, **16**, 117 (1966).
18. A. Schonberg, *Preparative Organic Photochemistry*, Verlag Chemie, New York, 1968.
19. J. N. Pitts, Jr. and J. K. S. Wan, "Photochemistry of Carbonyl Compounds," in *The Chemistry of the Carbonyl Group*, S. Patai, Ed., Interscience, New York, 1966, p. 823.

CHAPTER IV

PHOTOCHEMICAL METHODS

Ted R. Evans

*Department of Chemistry, Science Center, Wesleyan University,
Middletown, Connecticut*

This chapter will be concerned with both preparative and mechanistic photochemistry. The general experimental procedure has been discussed emphasizing commercially available apparatus and techniques which require only a minimum of special equipment. The effect of such variables as solvent, temperature, and exciting wavelength have been discussed using available literature examples to illustrate their importance.

The techniques discussed in the section on mechanistic studies have been chosen because their application requires little special equipment and yet allows a great amount of information to be obtained about photochemical reactions.

I. SYNTHETIC PHOTOCHEMISTRY

1. Survey

No attempt has been made to catalog types of photochemical reactions which have been used synthetically since this would involve far too much duplication of previous chapters. There are, however, a number of reactions that have been used synthetically that should be mentioned. These should serve to illustrate the utility of photochemical methods to preparative chemistry.

Promising methods of photoreduction have been found using lithium aluminum hydride, sodium borohydride, or sulfites. It has been observed that intermittent irradiation of 3-methoxyphenanthro[4,5-*bcd*]furan in the presence of lithium aluminum hydride–cobalt chloride allows ether cleavage, whereas other methods of reduction give 9,10-dihydro products Eq. (1).

$$\text{(1)}$$

$$80\text{–}90\%$$

Witkop and co-workers have recently investigated photoreductions in the presence of sodium borohydride (2–6) or sodium sulfites (5,6). These reductions have also been applied to uridine, tryptophan (3) and thymidine (4). (See equations (2) and (3).) At present, there is no evidence concerning the reactive species in these reductions.

The photolysis of olefinic metal complexes has proved to be of great utility in the past few years. In most cases, the exact function of the metal is not known, but the synthetic advantages are appreciable. The cuprous chloride-catalyzed photoreaction of norborene gave **1** and **2** in a 97:3 ratio (5,6). Acetophenone-sensitized reaction of norbornene gave the same two isomers, **1** and **2**, but in a 12:88 isomer ratio (5). Direct photolysis did not give dimers (6) (Eqs. (4) and (5)). Direct photolysis of 1,5-cyclooctadiene gave low yields of the tricyclooctane **3** (7), but the irradiation of the cuprous–chloride complex gave yields of **3** up to 50% along with other products (7–9) (Eq. (6)). While the mechanism of this reaction is not clear, the radical reactions that have been observed (10) have been shown to arise from photoinitiated reactions of the cuprous chloride–ether complex and not from photolysis of

$$+ \text{ polymeric materials } 76\% \qquad (2)$$

$$(3)$$

the cuprous chloride–olefin complex (11). Using a partially deuterated olefin, Srinivasan has shown that when the exciting light is filtered so as to irradiate only the olefin–copper complex, no deuterium scrambling is observed (11).

$$1 + 2 = 26\% \qquad (4)$$

$$1 + 2 = 23\% \qquad (5)$$

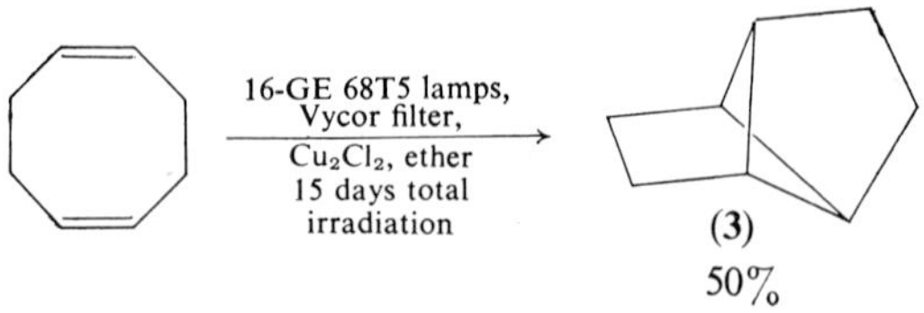

$$(6)$$

(3)

50%

However, when unfiltered light is used, the ether–metal complex is irradiated as well as the olefin–metal complex, deuterium scrambling is observed in accordance with the earlier observations (10,11).

Purine derivatives have been alkylated by irradiating an acid–methanol solution of the base with a low-pressure mercury lamp (12) (Eq. (7)).

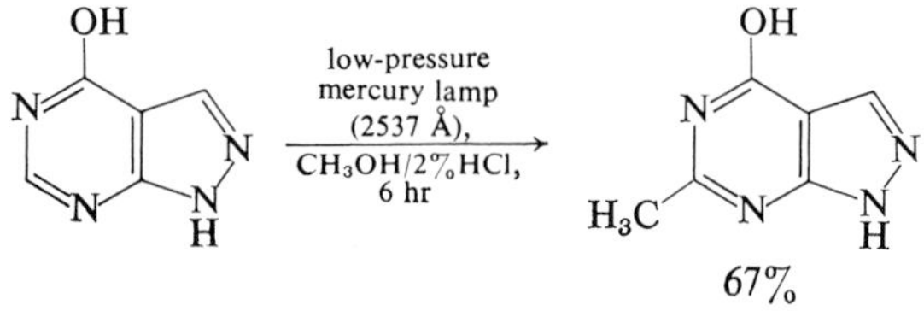

$$(7)$$

67%

Several photolabile protective groups have been developed (13–16). They allow removal under very mild conditions:

For acids (13):

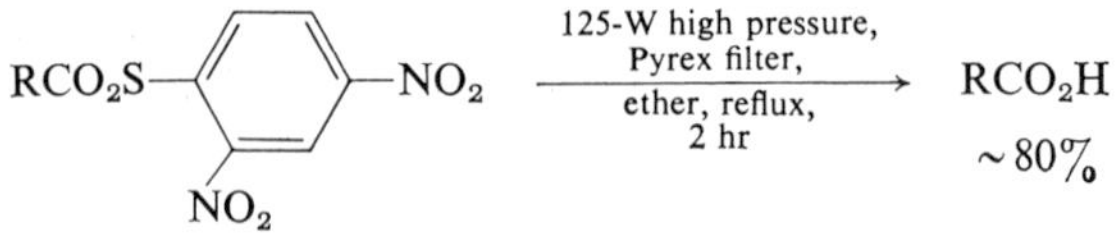

$$RCO_2H \quad (8)$$

$\sim 80\%$

For phenols (13):

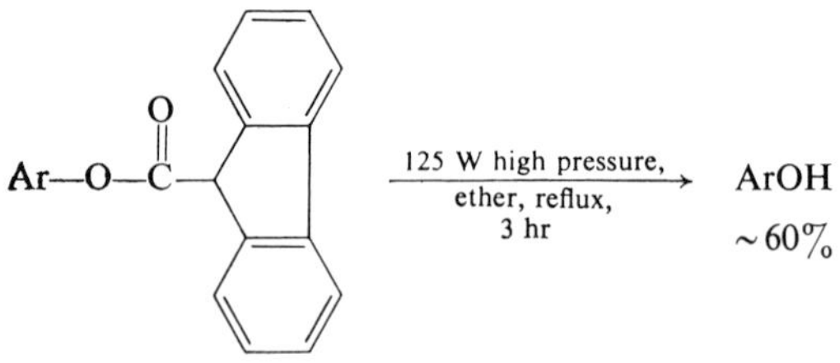

$$ArOH \quad (9)$$

$\sim 60\%$

For amino acids (14,15):

$$HO_2CCH_2NH-\overset{O}{\underset{||}{C}}O-CH_2C_6H_6 \xrightarrow[\text{aq. EtOH}]{\text{500-W Hanovia,}} NH_2CH_2CO_2H \quad (10)$$
$$\sim 70\%$$

For phosphates (16):

$$(RO)_3PO \cdot \xrightarrow[\substack{\text{aq. pyridine,} \\ \text{5 hr}}]{h\nu \text{ Pyrex filter}} (RO)_3POH \qquad (11)$$

We should also like to note the increasing application of photochemical techniques to the synthesis of natural products (17–22).

(12) 50%

(13) 75%

(14) 60%

(15) 60%

Synthesis leading to aporphins and protoberberine alkaloids is illustrated in Eqs. (12)–(15).

Synthesis leading to berberine alkaloids (19) is shown by Eq. (16) and

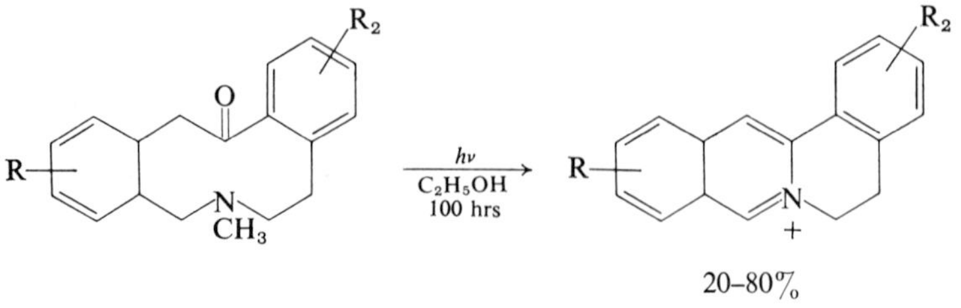

$$\xrightarrow[\substack{C_2H_5OH \\ 100 \text{ hrs}}]{h\nu} \qquad (16)$$

20–80%

synthesis leading to lycopodium alkaloids (22) by Eq. (17).

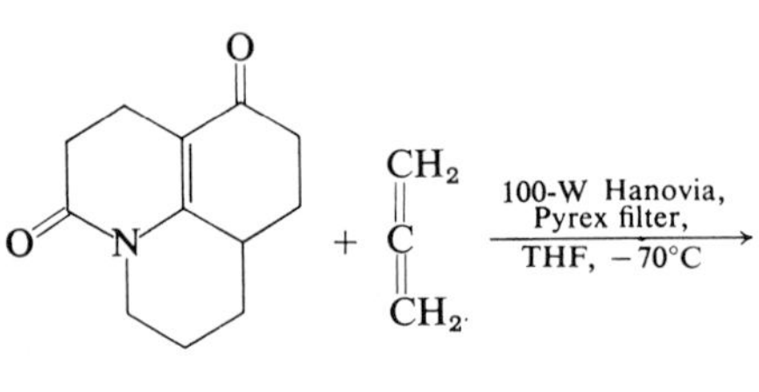

$$\xrightarrow[\substack{\text{Pyrex filter,} \\ \text{THF, } -70°C}]{\text{100-W Hanovia,}} \qquad (17)$$

100%

A photo-Fries rearrangement has been used for a commercial preparation of griseofulvin (23) (Eq. (18)).

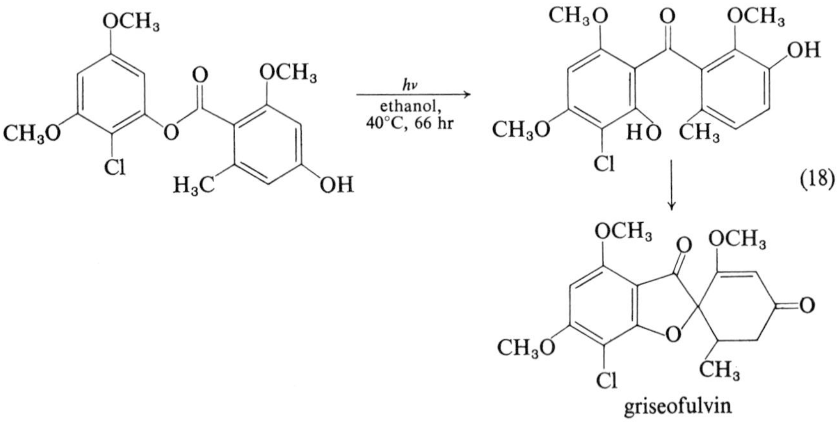

$$\xrightarrow[\substack{\text{ethanol,} \\ 40°C, 66 \text{ hr}}]{h\nu} \qquad (18)$$

griseofulvin

Mixed additions of α,β-unsaturated ketones to olefins have been used in the synthesis of a number of terpenes and steroids. DeMayo and co-workers have recently synthesized stipitotamic acid (24) and β-himachalene (25) starting with derivatives of cyclopentenone and appropriate olefins (Eqs. (19) and (20)).

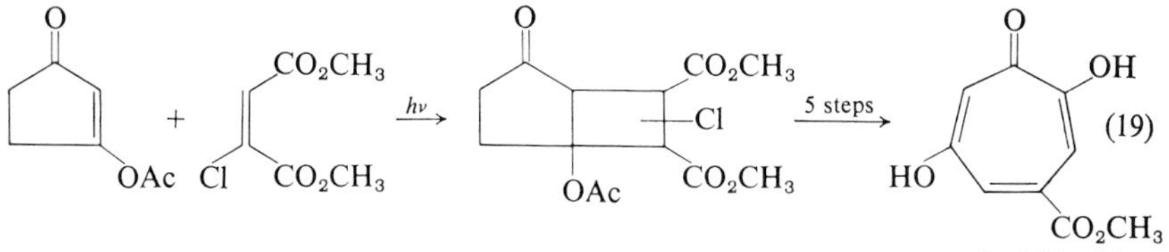

$$\text{(19)}$$

overall yield, 4%
stipitotamic acid

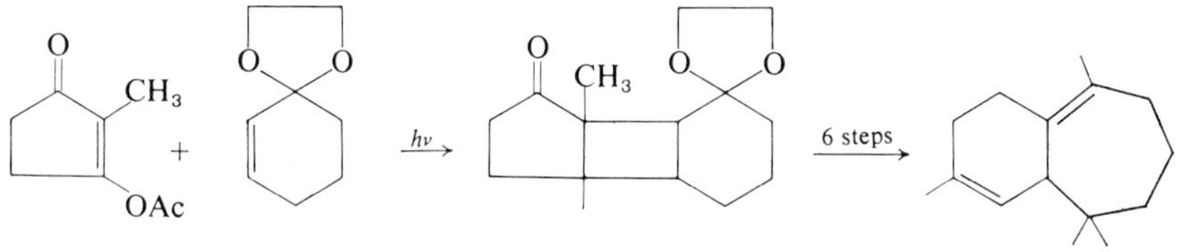

β-himachalene (20)

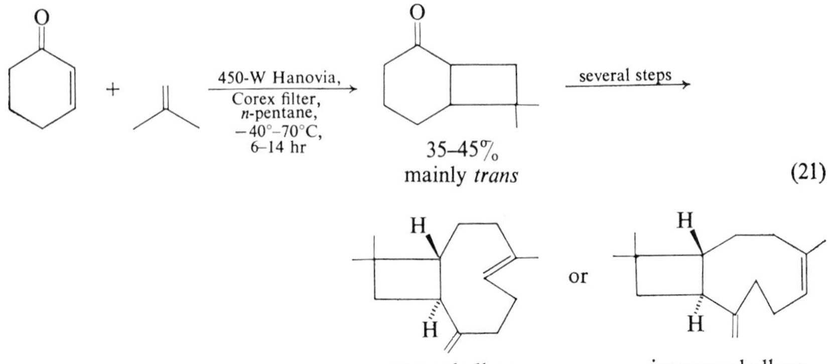

450-W Hanovia,
Corex filter,
n-pentane,
−40°–70°C,
6–14 hr

35–45%
mainly *trans*

$$\text{(21)}$$

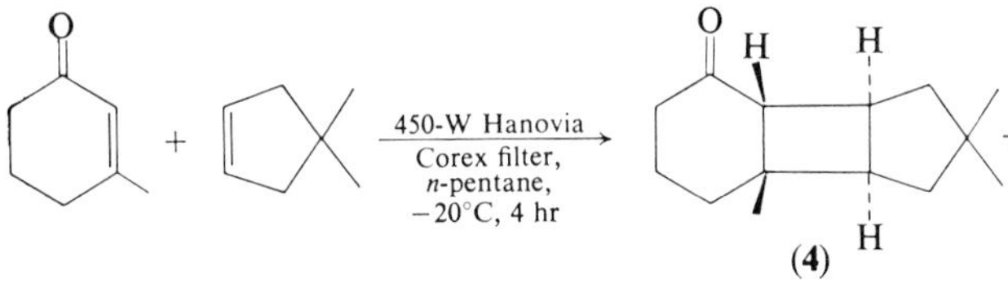

or

caryophyllene   isocaryophyllene

450-W Hanovia
Corex filter,
n-pentane,
−20°C, 4 hr

(4)

+ 2 other isomers (22)

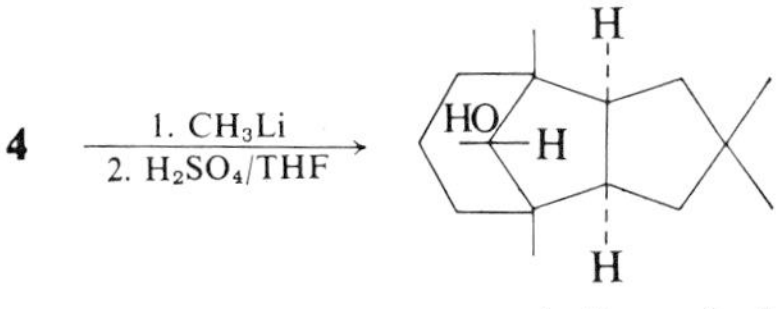

4   1. CH₃Li
     2. H₂SO₄/THF

$$\text{(23)}$$

α-caryophyllene alcohol

Photoadditions of enones have also been used in a multistep synthesis of caryophyllene (26), isocaryophyllene (26) and in an elegant three-step synthesis of α-caryophyllene alcohol (27) (Eqs. (21)–(23)).

Fried and co-workers have used a mixed enone dimerization to prepare steroid derivatives (28). This is apparently the first example of a cycloaddition of two different α,β-unsaturated ketones (Eq. (24)).

Corey and Hortmann have utilized a conrotatory (4 + 2) (29) photo-chemical ring opening reaction in the synthesis of dihydrocostunolide (30) (Eq. (25)). The ratio of **5** to **6** at the photostationary state is about 1:1.

Appropriately substituted keto steroids have been found to give cyclo-butanol derivatives in good yields (31,32) (Eq. (26)). Since cyclobutanol products normally comprise only 10–15% of the products from the photolysis of straight-chain aliphatic ketones, the high yields for the relatively rigid systems are perhaps surprising. This may indicate that the singlet state of the keto steroid can abstract a hydrogen atom from the γ-methyl before intersystem crossing occurs.

A simple synthesis of heptahelicene has been developed on the basis of a stilbene cyclization (33) (Eq. (27)).

(27)

12%

Photochemical techniques provide an entry into a large number of highly strained systems that are otherwise inaccessible or difficult to prepare by other methods. Well-known examples include cubane (34), prismane (35), benzvalene (36), and dewar benzene (37). Hexamethyl-dewar benzene is now commercially available. Other small-ring systems prepared by photolytic routes are basketene (38), bicyclo[2.2.0]hexane (39), bicyclo[2.1.1]hexane (40), tricyclo[2.1.0.0.^{2,5}]pentane (41), and tricyclo[2.2.0.0.^{2,6}]hexane (42).

2. Experimental Procedure

The primary objective of the synthetic organic photochemist is to get enough light of the appropriate wavelength into the starting material in order to convert it to the desired photoproduct. Although careful control of such variables as wavelength and temperature are usually not critical, it is extremely important that the starting material absorb a significant portion of the incident light. It is often also desirable that the photoproducts do *not* absorb in the same region as the substrate, as they will act as an internal filter and thus make irradiation of the substrate increasingly inefficient as the reaction proceeds. The photoproducts may also undergo photoreactions, thereby making the chemical analysis of the reaction quite complex. If the photochemical reaction is being performed for the first time, and the photoproducts are not known, it is suggested that the reaction only be allowed to proceed to 10–20% completion. The products obtained in this way are most likely primary products and can be further tested for photostability.

If an energy-transfer donor or *sensitizer* is to be used, then care must be taken that it absorb a major amount of the incident light. The decision of whether to use a sensitizer and the choice of which sensitizer must be made within the framework of the preceding chapter.

In general, for preparative purposes one must be concerned with the spectral distribution and intensity of the lamp and the optical properties of the reaction vessel, solvent, and substrate (or sensitizer, or both). The following discussion will be concerned with laboratory-scale reactions only and will not consider industrial-scale reactions.

A. DIRECT PHOTOREACTIONS

For a great many operations, nothing more elegant than a commercial sun lamp and a Pyrex flask are sufficient to carry out a laboratory-scale preparation. The chief precaution in this case is to insure that the compound absorbs at wavelengths greater than 300 nm, which is the transmittance cutoff for Pyrex.

However, slightly more exotic lamps and reaction vessels are available, which in combination allow higher intensity and greater efficiency. These units will generally be desirable for the chemist who makes more than occasional use of photochemistry. Two basic designs are most commonly used: one in which the lamp is immersed in the solution, enabling the complete absorption of all useful radiation, and the other in which the reaction vessel is surrounded by one or several lamps.

The immersion unit has the advantage that since the light does not have to pass through the reaction vessel, Pyrex vessels can be used for irradiations at all wavelengths.

TABLE 1

Energy Distribution for Hanovia 679A Lamp

Mercury line, Å	Radiated watts
2482	2.3
2537	5.8
2652	4.0
2804	2.4
2967	4.3
3025	7.2
3130	13.2
3341	2.4
3660	25.6
4045	11.0
4358	20.2
5461	24.5
5780	20.0

Hanovia Lamp Division of Englehard Industries manufactures immersion wells made of Vycor or fused quartz, cooled by a water jacket, and into which is placed a medium- to high-pressure mercury lamp (Fig. 1). Filter sleeves which fit around the lamp and cut off light of wavelengths shorter than 2200 Å (Vycor), 2800 Å (Corex), and 3000 Å (Pyrex), may be obtained from the same company. The immersion well is placed in a cylindrical flask containing the solution. Several lamps are available that fit into the well; a typical and very useful one is the Hanovia Type L, 679A, 450-W lamp with the spectral distribution given in Table 1. As is characteristic of medium- and high-pressure mercury lamps, the strongest line (and very often the most useful) is at 3660 Å, with some radiation also being emitted at 3130 Å.

Ultraviolet Products Inc. and Nester/Faust Mfg. Corp. make smaller immersion lamps which have the advantage of fitting into standard laboratory

Fig. 1. Hanovia medium-pressure mercury lamp with power supply.

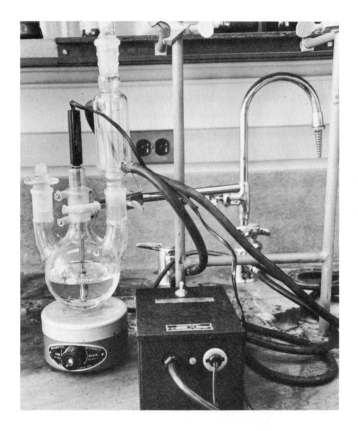

Fig. 2. Ultraviolet Products low-pressure immersion lamp.

glassware (Figs. 2 and 3). The lamp manufactured by Ultraviolet Products is available in several lengths with taper joints, sizes ranging from 10/30 up to 71/60. Both companies make power supplies designed for their lamps.

An alternative to the immersion unit is the system in which the light source surrounds the reaction vessel. This may be done by a single helical lamp or by several parallel lamps surrounding the reaction vessel. Units of the former type are being manufactured by Nuclear Supplies Inc. and Hanovia Inc. A unit of the latter type is manufactured by the Southern New England Ultraviolet Co. and consists of a fan-cooled chamber surrounded by 16 lamps. The chamber is large enough to hold a 6-liter reaction vessel. There are several types of interchangeable lamps available, all utilizing the mercury 2537-Å resonance line. The emitting wavelength region depends upon the type of phosphor coated onto the interior of the lamp. The manufacturer

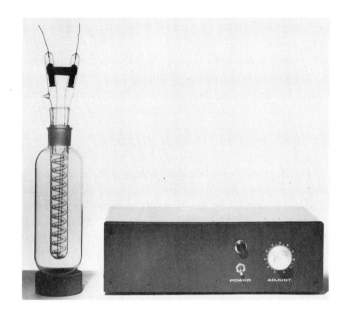

Fig. 3. Nester/Faust low-pressure immersion lamp. Courtesy of Nester/Faust Mfg. Corporation.

TABLE 2

Approximate Wavelength Limits for Some Common Optical Materials[a]

Material	Thickness, mm	50%	30%	10%
Pyrex (Corning 774)	1	3060	2970	2800
	2	3170	3090	2970
	4	3300	3190	3100
Corex D	1	2780	2670	2500
(Pyrex, Corning 9-53 9700)	2	2880	2800	2670
	4	3040	2920	2810
Corex A	2.9	2480	2430	2400
Vycor 790	2			> 2540
Vycor 791	1	2150	2130	2120
	2	2230	2170	2130
	4	2360	2250	2170
Quartz, crystal	5	1850		
	10	1930	1920	1860
Quartz, clear fused	1	1850		
(General Electric)	10	1940	1810	1720

[a] See ref. 93, p. 748.

supplies lamps emitting at 2537 Å, 3000 Å, and 3500 Å. Two larger photo-chemical reactors (RPR-204, Fig. 4, and RPR-208) are also available with interchangeable lamps.

Although the commercial light sources described above should be adequate for most purposes, special projects often require specially designed lamps. Hanovia Lamp Division and Thermal American Fused Quartz Co. will fabricate special lamps upon receipt of a scale drawing or accurate description of the lamp.

For external irradiations below 3000 Å, glassware other than Pyrex must be used. The optical properties of a number of different fabricating materials are given in Table 2. Because of its transmittance properties, quartz is often the preferred material for glassware construction. However, quartz does pass the 1849-Å line, which is emitted by low-pressure mercury lamps, and absorption of this light by the solvent can occasionally cause side reactions. Yang and Thap (43) have found that irradiation of mesityl oxide in alcohols gives only products derived from alcohol photodecomposition and subsequent radical reactions. No photoreaction was observed when Vycor apparatus was used.

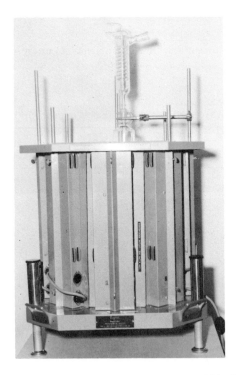

Fig. 4. The Southern New England Rayonet reactor, type RPR-204. Courtesy of the Southern New England Ultraviolet Co.

Since air strongly absorbs light below 2000 Å, the 1849-Å line will not impinge upon the sample if the source and the sample are separated by a small air space.

3. Effects and Choice of Solvent

The selection of a solvent may be very crucial or very unimportant depending upon the reaction in question. There are probably very few photochemical reactions which are totally unaffected by the solvent. Too often the effect of the solvent is ignored when a photochemical reaction is under investigation.

The first requirement for any solvent used for a photochemical reaction is that the solvent should not absorb the incident light. The cutoff wavelengths for a number of solvents are listed in Table 3.

TABLE 3

Solvent	Cutoff wavelengths[a]		
	A	B	C
Water	< 200		
Hydrocarbons	~ 240	~ 220	< 200
Alcohols	~ 240	~ 235	~ 220
Acetonitrile	240	223	210
Acetic acid	266	255	246
Chloroform	268	256	243
Carbon tetrachloride	285	275	262
Benzene	308	284	276
Dimethyl sulfoxide	310	278	262
Acetone	344	337	328

[a] All solvents were run in a 0.5-cm cell versus air; column A is the point at which there is no absorption by the solvent; column B, O.D. = 0.1; and column C, O.D. = 1.0.

Other than the rather obvious danger of using a solvent which can act as a "physical quencher," solvents often interfere through "chemical quenching" mechanisms.* Naturally, the chemical quenching reactions can often be put to use to synthesize compounds incorporating the solvent, but we shall consider the ideal solvent as one which simply acts to solubilize the substrate and is inert to the photochemical reaction.

Alkyl- and arylketones have been shown to abstract hydrogen atoms from many solvents. Hydrogen-abstraction from solvent can compete even with

* The term "physical quenching" is meant to imply quenching by energy transfer whereas "chemical quenching" implies quenching by atom or electron transfer to a photoexcited molecule.

intramolecular processes (44,45). Photolysis of cyclooctanone gives two major products in solvents capable of hydrogen donation (Eq. (28)). Presumably

$$\text{(28)}$$

only product **7** would be formed if the photolysis were conducted in a solvent which could not donate hydrogen atoms (e.g., benzene).

It is very difficult to predict the reactivity of a series of solvents except with reference to a given hydrogen-abstracting agent. Triplet benzophenone is the only compound for which the relative rates of abstraction from a large number of hydrogen donors are known. These relative rates are given in Table 4. The values have been changed to $k_{rel/ml}$ so as to reflect solvent reactivities rather than molecular reactivities. Table 5 lists some relative solvent reactivities reported for several ethers. The values in Table 4 have been adjusted to fit on a common scale. Cyclohexane and 2-propanol were common to both Walling's and Cohen's studies and the agreement between the two studies is very good. Unfortunately the values listed for the ethers in Table 5 cannot be accurately compared with the values in Table 4 since none of these ethers were studied by any of the other workers. However, $k_{rel/mole}$ for methyl-

TABLE 4

Solvent	k rel/ml
2-Propanol	12.7 [a]
2-Butyl amine	12.5 [b]
2-Octanol	6.5 [a]
Cumene	2.4 [a]
Cyclohexane	2.0 [a,b]
Cyclohexene	2.0 [b]
2,2,4-Trimethylpentane	1.9 [b]
n-Hexane	1.8 [b]
2,3-Dimethylbutane	1.5 [b]
t-Butyl amine	1.5 [b]
Triethylamine	1.3 [b]
t-Butanol	1.1 [c]
Toluene	0.94 [a]
Anisole	0.49 [a]

[a] Ref. 150.
[b] Ref. 151.
[c] Ref. 152.

TABLE 5[a]

Solvent	k rel/ml
Diethyl ether	3.1
Dioxane	2.2
Tetrahydrofuran	1.7
Diisopropyl ether	0.8

[a] Ref. 153.

2-octyl ether has been found to be about the same as that for t-butyl amine (46). For a good discussion concerning hydrogen abstraction by free radicals the reader is referred to the text by Pryor (47).

Benzene, acetonitrile, and acetic acid are all normally considered to be inert solvents. If an alcohol solvent is desired, t-butanol, while still reactive, is much less likely to chemically quench a photochemical reaction than most other alcohols. There are no unreactive aliphatic hydrocarbons. Dimethyl butane appears to be somewhat less reactive than the other aliphatic solvents.

There is a second danger in using a solvent that is reactive toward hydrogen abstraction. The solvent radical formed can react with the substrate or with the photoproducts and increase the complexity of the product analysis (48–55).

Loader and Timmons have found that solvent incorporation occurs when the stilbazole **8** is photolyzed in cyclohexane or n-hexane (48) (Eq. (29)). Kumler has found a similar reaction in the irradiation of the stilbazole **9** (Eq. (30)). It is not clear exactly how the alkyl radical is generated in these reactions but it has been suggested (49) that it derives from the alkyl hydro-peroxide, formed by photosensitized autooxidation, which then decomposes to the alkyl radical.

Solvent addition to quinizarin **10** has been observed when benzopenone is used as a sensitizer (50) (Eq. (31)).

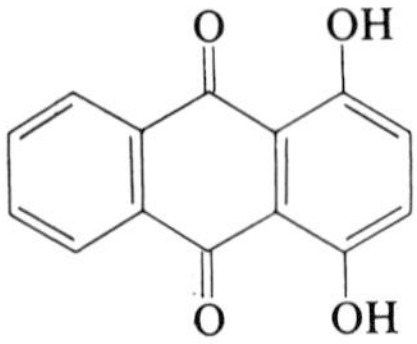

(10)

The photosensitized radical addition of alcohols to steroids has been used synthetically (51) (Eq. (32)).

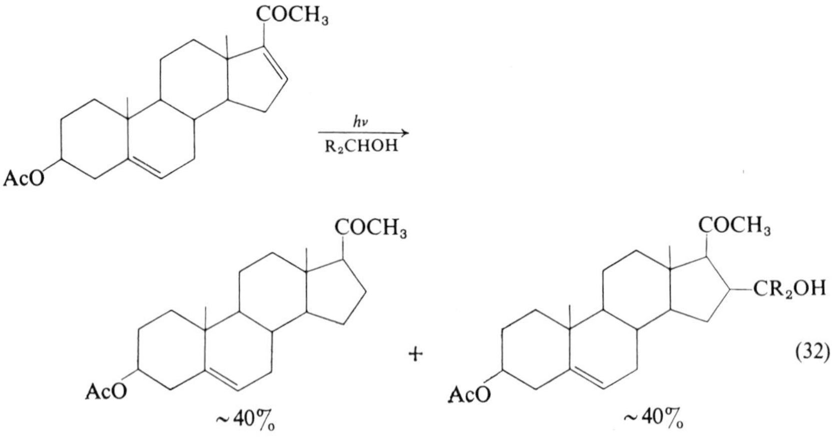

(32)

~40%   ~40%

Ethyl oxalate, hydrazine, ethyl chloroformate, and ethyl cyanoformate all give alkylated products when photolyzed in cyclohexane (52,53). Shuster has observed a number of products from the irradiation of **11** in ether, some of which probably arise from solvent radicals attacking the starting material (54) (Eq. (33)).

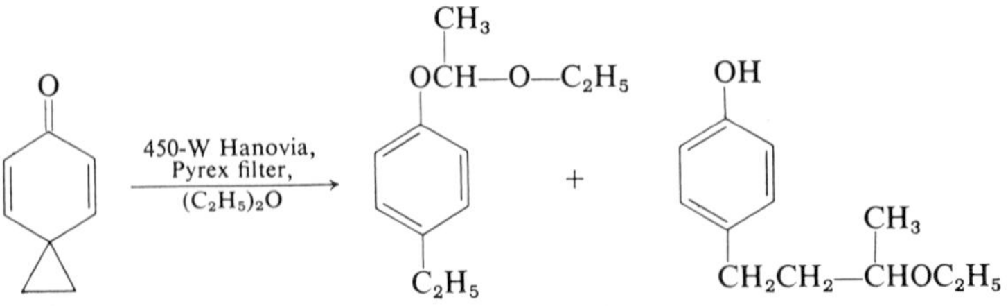

(33)

(11)

+ other products

Solvent addition to the iminium salt **12** has been observed (55). Tetra-hydrofuran addition to tetraphenyl cyclopentadienone occurs when the latter is photolyzed in the presence of hydrochloric acid (56) (Eqs. (34) and (35)).

$$\tag{34}$$

$$\tag{35}$$

A fundamentally different type of solvent-addition reaction has recently been reported (57,58). Marshall and Kropp have found that cycloalkenes react with alcohols upon irradiation (Eq. (36)). The reactive intermediate

$$\tag{36}$$

appears to be the transoid olefin rather than an electronically excited state, although this is not conclusive at present.

An old report that crotonic acid photochemically adds alcohol (59) has been refuted (60). However, intramolecular phenol addition has been observed for acyclic olefins (61) so the presence of a high-energy transoid olefin is not absolutely required for alcohol addition (Eqs. (37) and (38)).

Dauben has also reported ether formation from the photolysis of several alicyclic dienes (62). The possible extension of Marshall and Kropp's findings to this work is obvious. Products related to **13** and **14** have recently been shown to arise from a photoallylic rearrangement of the ether **15** (63) (Eqs. (39) and (40)).

Aside from chemical and physical quenching effects, large variations in both efficiency of product formation (quantum yield) and chemical yields are found by changing the solvent system.

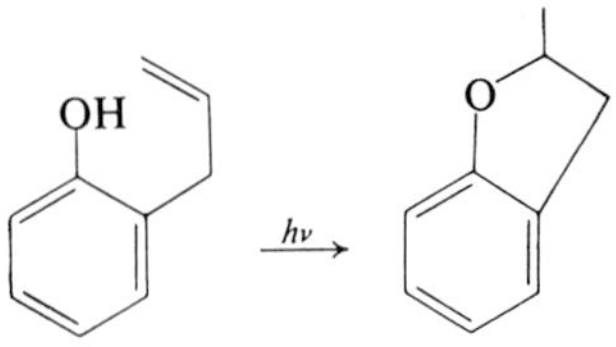

(37)

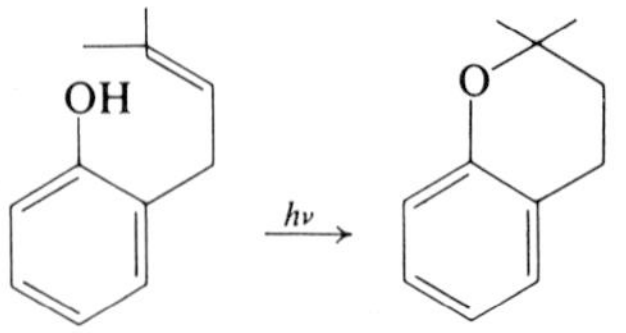

(38)

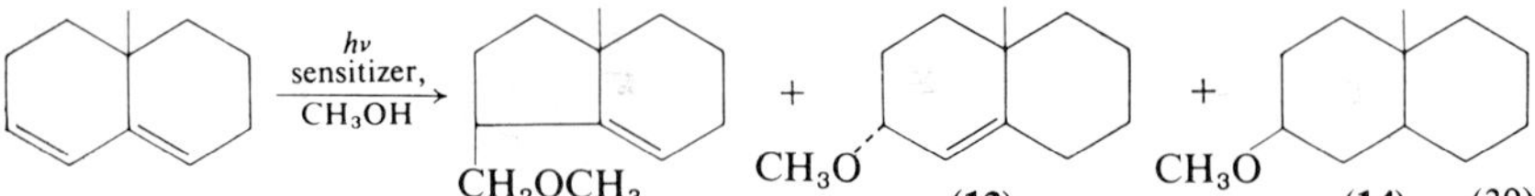

(39)

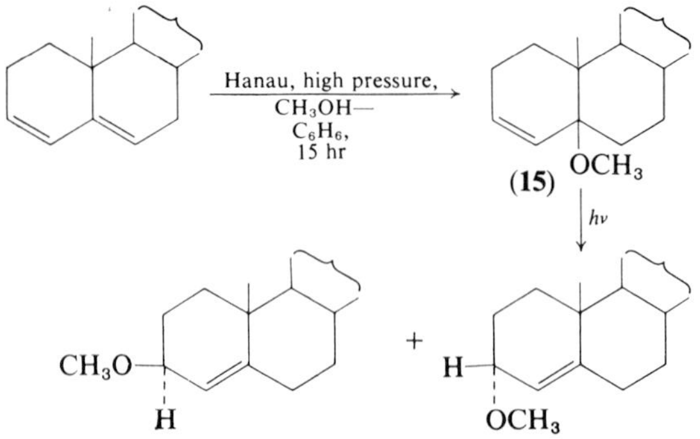

(40)

Wagner (45,64) has found that the quantum yield of the Norrish Type II process can double when the solvent is changed from a nonpolar to a polar solvent. Wagner believes that this increase in quantum yield is due to hydrogen bonding with the diradical **16**, which is then prevented from returning to starting material (Eq. (41)).

$$[R\overset{O}{\overset{\|}{C}}CH_2CH_2CH_2R']^* \underset{\nleftarrow}{\overset{S-H-O}{\rightleftarrows}} R\overset{}{C}CH_2CH_2CHR' \longrightarrow R\overset{OH}{\overset{\|}{C}} = CH_2 + CH_2 = CHR' \quad (41)$$

$$(16)$$

The chemical and quantum yields of the photoproducts from the photo-Fries reaction are drastically affected by hydrogen bonding (65) and viscosity

(66) (Eqs. (42) and (43)). In nonpolar solvents the salicylates are internally hydrogen bonded (Eqs. (44)). This intramolecular hydrogen bond allows a

rapid decay of the photo-excited state via a six-membered transition state. External hydrogen bonding prevents this rapid decay pathway allowing slower reactions to be observed (67). The viscosity dependence on the photo-Fries reaction is interpreted in terms of two competing reactions, tightly bound unimolecular rearrangement giving the *ortho*-substituted product (**19**) and a radical fragmentation reaction leading to the disubstituted product (**20**)

(Eq. (45). Thus the quantum yield for the formation of **19** is independent of viscosity but the quantum yield for the formation of **20** decreases with increasing viscosity since **20** is formed by a radical pair escape and is subject to "cage effects."

Other photoreactions which appear to be influenced by hydrogen bonding are those of the nitrones (68) and amine oxides (69).

Pappas and co-workers have found that the stereochemistry of the dihydro-benzofurans, produced by the photolysis of the keto ester **21** (Eq. (46)), can

TABLE 6

Solvent	Temp., °C	22a/22b
Acetonitrile	0	2.0/1
Heptane	0	> 20/1
Heptane	100	3/1
Benzene	15	> 20/1
t-Butanol	80	1/1

be controlled by the solvent system or the temperature of the reaction medium (Table 6) (70). At present it is not clear whether hydrogen bonding, polarity, or some other factor is most important.

It has been known for several years that the products arising from enone dimerizations are solvent dependent (71–74). The dimer ratio, **23a/23b**, changes with solvent polarity and with cyclopentenone concentration. Although there may be two reactive intermediates involved in this reaction (71) (Eq. (47)), there is a correlation of the log of the dimer ratio **23a/23b** with the Kirkwood-Onsager solvent parameter (Fig. 5) (75,76) and so the syn/anti variation is apparently just a reflection of the polarity differences in the transition states leading to **23a** and **23b**. There is some scatter in Figure 5 due to the large amounts of cyclopentenone dissolved in the solvents.

When a molecule has two nearby states (n,π and π^*,π^*) interaction of these states with the solvent can often cause inversion of these states (77,78). In nonpolar media the reactive n,π^* triplet of unsubstituted aryl ketones is lower than the relatively unreactive π,π^* triplet state, but in very polar media (e.g., phosphoric acid, ethylene glycol–water, silica gel) the states are inverted (77) and the photoreactivity decreases drastically (78). Spectroscopic studies on acridone (79) and xanthone (80) indicate that n,π^*, π,π^* inversion also

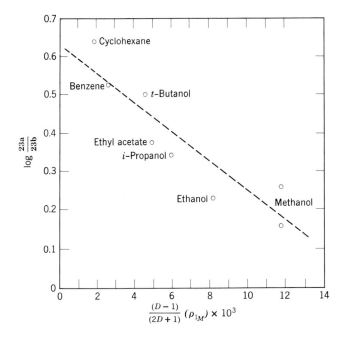

Fig. 5. Plot of the dimer ratio **23a/23** ^{c} vs. the Kirkwood-Onsager polarity parameter (75).

occurs with these molecules when the solvent is changed from nonpolar to polar.

The singlet–triplet transition probability can be influenced by the presence, internal or external, of heavy atoms (81). Reactions which give both singlet and triplet products would be expected to be influenced by using a heavy atom solvent (e.g., n-propyl bromide). The singlet–triplet transition probability is not affected when the photoreactive state is n,π^* (82,83), but when the products are formed from a π,π^* state a heavy atom effect is observed (84). Acenaphthylene photodimerizes to give a *cis* and a *trans* dimer. The *trans* dimer is apparently formed from the triplet state whereas the *cis* dimer is formed in a singlet-state reaction. The *cis–trans* ratio is somewhat dependent upon the polarity of the solvent (85) (Table 7). The absolute yield of the *cis* dimer is not affected by the heavy atom solvent, but the yield of the *trans* dimer is greatly increased.

Changing the media from liquid to a surface or a pressed alkali halide disk can produce interesting effects. Leermakers and co-workers have shown that silica gel induces electronic perturbations of various types of molecules (86), exerts a strong polar effect, and can act as a matrix surface which holds the first formed photoproducts in their original position (88). Thus the photolysis

TABLE 7[a]

Solvent	cis–trans	Per cent conversion
Methanol	5.7	43
Cyclohexane	4.2	71
Benzene	2.4	41
n-Propyl bromide	0.41	92

[a] Ref. 85.

of azo-bis-isobutyronitrile **24** in benzene gives two products, the major one being the ketenimine **25**. In a benzene–silica gel slurry, only the dinitrile **26** is formed (88) (Eqs. (48) and (49)).

$$
\begin{array}{c}
\overset{\text{CN}}{\underset{|}{}}\quad\overset{\text{CN}}{\underset{|}{}} \\
(\text{CH}_3)_2\text{C--N}\!=\!\text{N--C}(\text{CH}_3)_2 \xrightarrow[\text{C}_6\text{H}_6]{h\nu\ (366\ \text{nm})} (\text{CH}_3)_2\overset{\text{CN}}{\underset{|}{\text{C}}}\text{--N}\!=\!\text{C}\!=\!\text{C}(\text{CH}_3)_2 \\
(\textbf{24}) \qquad\qquad (\textbf{25}),\ 60\%
\end{array}
$$

$$+ (\text{CH}_3)_2\overset{\text{CN}}{\underset{|}{\text{C}}}\!\!-\!\!-\!\!\overset{\text{CN}}{\underset{|}{\text{C}}}(\text{CH}_3)_2 \quad (48)$$
$$(\textbf{26}),\ 40\%$$

$$(\textbf{24}) \xrightarrow[\substack{\text{benzene--}\\ \text{silica gel}}]{h\nu\ (366\ \text{nm})} (\textbf{26}),\ 100\% \qquad\qquad (49)$$

Several groups have used potassium bromide pellets as a supporting medium for photochemical reactions (89–92). There is some question as to the physical state of the substrate in the KBr matrix. Pitts considers the substrate–KBr mixture to be a solid solution under high pressure (89,90), but Bernas and co-workers have found that anthracene exists as a micro crystal with photodimerization occurring only at crystal surface (91).

4. Effect of Temperature

Primary photochemical processes are generally found to be temperature independent (93a) in spite of the fact that appreciable activation energies (~ 5 kcal) are often associated with these processes (94). Since solvent properties vary with temperature, care must be taken to isolate temperature dependence from solvent dependence in condensed phases. It is difficult to evaluate the temperature effect on photoreactions in solution because few studies have been performed; indeed, many authors do not even specify the temperature of the reaction media. A few examples will serve to illustrate the synthetic and mechanistic importance of the temperature of the system.

In accord with the thesis that only small activation energies are found for photoreactions in solution, Pitts and co-workers have found that the apparent activation energy for the Norrish Type II reaction of butyrophenone in benzene solution is about 2 kcal (95). This "activation energy" is not readily equated with E_a, the activation energy, since it is derived from the temperature effect on the quantum yield, a ratio of rate constants, and not from the temperature effect on any single reaction rate. Fischer and co-workers have found that the quantum yield for photoisomerization of stilbenes depends upon both temperature and viscosity. The temperature dependence was ascribed to a temperature-dependent intersystem crossing yield (with an apparent activation energy of 1.2 kcal), while the viscosity dependence resulted from volume increase in the *trans* to *cis* isomerization (96).

Small *differences* in activation energies for the formation of two or more products are of great synthetic importance. Consider Eq. (50), where B and C

$$A \overset{\displaystyle \nearrow B}{\underset{\displaystyle \searrow C}{}} \tag{50}$$

are formed from A by two separate paths. If B and C are formed at equal rates then $\Delta\Delta G^{\ddagger} = \Delta G_{B}^{\ddagger} - \Delta G_{C}^{\ddagger} = 0 = \Delta\Delta H^{\ddagger} - T\Delta\Delta S^{\ddagger}$ where $\Delta\Delta G^{\ddagger}$, $\Delta\Delta H^{\ddagger}$, and $\Delta\Delta S^{\ddagger}$ are the differences in the activation parameters for the formation of the products B and C. The temperature at which $\Delta\Delta G^{\ddagger} = 0$ is defined as the isokinetic temperature (97), $T\beta$, and is equal to $\Delta\Delta H^{\ddagger}/\Delta\Delta S^{\ddagger}$. Assuming kinetic control, product C will predominate above the isokinetic temperature while below the isokinetic temperature product B will predominate.

Below the isokinetic temperature the ratio of the products will be controlled mainly by the enthalpy differences for the two transition states while above the isokinetic temperature the products will be determined by the differences in the entropies of activation. The products of a reaction can often be dramatically controlled by slight changes in temperature if the isokinetic temperature is near room temperature.

The photoreactions of α-keto esters would appear to be temperature dependent (70,98) with an isokinetic temperature between 0 and 100°C. Huyser and Neckers have found that the decomposition of benzoyl formic esters is temperature dependent (98). At room temperature, in alcohol, the esters undergo normal reductive dimerization while at 80°C an intramolecular rearrangement occurs (Eqs. (51) and (52)).

$$\tag{51}$$

$$(52)$$

The products of the reaction of maleic anhydride with substituted benzenes are also influenced by the temperature of media (99). With *p*-xylene the isomers **29** and **30** are formed in a 20:1 ratio at 20°C and in a 1:10 ratio at 100°C. The equilibrium, **27** $\rightleftarrows$ **28**, of the charge-transfer complexes is apparently the thermal-dependent factor in this reaction. The isokinetic temperature for this reaction should be approximately 60°C.

$$(53)$$

If one of the steps leading to product formation is really a thermal reaction, then a temperature dependence is to be expected. Liu has found that the photochemical conversion of *cis,cis*-1,3-cyclooctadiene, **31**, to the bicyclooctene, **33**, is temperature dependent (100). At 20°C the bicyclooctene, **33**, was not formed and temperatures of 80–90°C were required for its production. The bicyclooctene is formed by a thermal cyclization of *cis,trans*-cyclooctadiene **32**, which is photochemically produced from the *trans,trans*-isomer **31** (Eq. (54)). The reaction which is influenced by temperature is only the second reaction.

(54)

(31)   (32)   (33)

5. Effect of Wavelength

Photoreactions in solution are normally not wavelength dependent. Higher vibrational states are normally quenched by the nearby solvent molecules, and internal conversion is usually rapid with respect to photo-chemical conversion. In certain cases, however, a wavelength dependence is observed. Zimmerman et al. have found that the quantum yield for azobenzene isomerization depends upon the wavelength of the exciting light (101). The quantum yield is constant within a particular band but is somewhat lower at shorter wavelengths. Malkin and Fischer have unconventionally proposed that the lower quantum yield for higher energy exciting light may mean that the higher singlet states have greater probability for radiationless transitions (102).

The products from the photolysis of thiobenzophenone are dependent upon the wavelength of the exciting light (103,104). When thiobenzophenone is irradiated with visible light (at 588 mμ, in the n–π^* band) in ethanol in the presence of oxygen, benzophenone is produced. No reaction is observed when the exciting light is changed to ultraviolet (365 mμ). In the absence of oxygen, photoreduction is observed but only when ultraviolet light is employed (103). Kaiser and Wulfers have reported that thiobenzophenone reacts with olefins only when the wavelength of the exciting light is shorter than 280 mμ (104). It would therefore appear that there are two or perhaps three states which can react before internal conversion occurs.

An epoxy–enone rearrangement has been found to occur only when the π,π^* band is irradiated. The n,π^* state is unreactive toward this *rearrangement*, but both states *photoreduce* to give the same products (105) (Eq. (55)).

A few other reactions have been found to be wavelength dependent, but some of these may be trivial in the sense that the photoproducts are absorbing light as well as the substrate. This type of wavelength dependence has been postulated for the anthracene photodimerizations (106,107). Shorter wave-length light gave dimerization products but the yield was less than that

$$\text{(55)}$$

obtained for longer wavelength irradiations. Since the anthracene photo-dimers can cleave photolytically to give the starting materials, the wave-length dependence may be simply due to competitive absorption by the photodimer at the shorter wavelengths.

II. MECHANISTIC STUDIES—EXPERIMENTAL METHODS

The previous sections have been concerned with synthetic procedures which differ from those required for mechanistic studies in several respects.

Fig. 6. A PEK high-pressure lamp enclosed in a protective shield.

For mechanistic studies the wavelength of the exciting light must be more carefully controlled and a high-intensity light source is not as necessary since only small amounts of photoproducts are required. Although monochromators are occasionally used by photochemists to isolate certain regions of the mercury spectrum, chemical filters have found wider use because of the greater amount of light passed. An excellent compilation of chemical filter systems can be found in the monograph by Calvert and Pitts (93b). An apparatus that has been found useful is shown in Figure 6 consisting of a PEK lamp enclosed in a protective shield and mounted on an optical bench with holders for both sample and filters. The light from the 500-W PEK lamp is collimated by means of a lens, passed through a set of filters, and then through the samples, which are held in the Beckman cell holders. Since the light is not homogeneous across the face of the cell holder, the samples have to be interchanged several times during the irradiation period.

Another piece of apparatus that has been found useful by us is the "merry-go-round" apparatus originally designed by Moses at The California Institute

Fig. 7. The Southern New England Ultraviolet "merry-go-round," MGR-100 in a RPR-100 Rayonet reactor. Courtesy of The Southern New England Ultraviolet Co.

Fig. 8. The Southern New England Ultraviolet "merry-go-round," MGR-500. Courtesy
of The Southern New England Ultraviolet Co.

of Technology. The commercial models manufactured by Southern New
England Ultraviolet Co. are shown in Figures 7 and 8. The MGR-100
(Fig. 7) is convenient for use either in the Rayonet Reactors or in front of the
PEK lamp in place of the Beckman cell holders. This eliminates the need for
interchanging the cells during irradiation and allows simultaneous irradiation
of up to eight samples. The MGR-500 (Fig. 8) is designed for use with a lamp
positioned in the well of the merry-go-round. The advantage of the merry-
go-round is that the position of the light source and lamp fluctuations do not
prevent equal irradiation of all samples. Nearly all of the experiments that we
shall describe later require that two or more samples be irradiated simultaneously and that each sample absorb an equal number of photons over the
given time period.

Although spectroscopic techniques (absorption, emission, electron spin
resonance, flash photolysis) have contributed a great deal and are essential
for understanding photochemical mechanisms, we shall only be concerned
with nonspectroscopic techniques within this chapter.

1. Quantum Yields

The concept of a quantum yield was introduced in Chapter I of this volume, but its meaning and uses should be further explored. The expression for the quantum yield is usually written as

$$\phi = \frac{\text{number of molecules formed (reacted)}}{\text{number of photons absorbed}} \tag{56}$$

however, the kinetic expression is perhaps more meaningful. For any given photoreaction the kinetic form of the quantum yield is:

$$\phi = k_p/(k_p + \sum k_i) \tag{57}$$

where k_p is the rate of product formation or substrate disappearance and $\sum k_i$ is the sum of the rates for *all* other deactivation processes. A low quantum yield implies that one or several deactivation processes are able to compete effectively with the product-forming reaction, i.e., $\sum k_i > k_p$. A high quantum yield requires that the rate constants for the product-forming reaction be greater than for any deactivation step.

The photodecomposition of butyrophenone in solution has been widely studied (45,64,78,95,108), and the important steps appear to be Eqs. (58)–(65):

$$\underset{\substack{\| \\ O}}{C_6H_5C}-CH_2CH_2CH_3 \xrightarrow{h\nu} [C_6H_5\overset{O}{\overset{\|}{C}}CH_2CH_2CH_3]^{S_1} \tag{58}$$

$$[C_6H_5\overset{O}{\overset{\|}{C}}CH_2CH_2CH_3]^{S_1} \xrightarrow{k_{isc}} [C_6H_5\overset{O}{\overset{\|}{C}}CH_2CH_2CH_3]^{T_1} \tag{59}$$

$$[C_6H_5\overset{O}{\overset{\|}{C}}CH_2CH_2CH_3]^{S_1} \xrightarrow{k_s} C_6H_5\overset{O}{\overset{\|}{C}}CH_2CH_2CH_3 \tag{60}$$

$$[C_6H_5\overset{O}{\overset{\|}{C}}CH_2CH_2CH_3]^{T_1} \xrightarrow{k_r} C_6H_5\overset{OH}{\overset{|}{C}}CH_2CH_2\dot{C}H_2 \tag{61}$$

$$C_6H_5\overset{OH}{\overset{|}{C}}CH_2CH_2\dot{C}H_2 \xrightarrow{k'_r} C_6H_5\overset{O}{\overset{\|}{C}}CH_2CH_2CH_3 \tag{62}$$

$$C_6H_5\overset{OH}{\overset{|}{C}}CH_2CH_2\dot{C}H_2 \xrightarrow{k_e} C_6H_5\overset{OH}{C}=CH_2 + CH_2=CH_2 \tag{63}$$

$$[C_6H_5\overset{O}{\overset{\|}{C}}CH_2CH_2CH_3]^{T_1} \xrightarrow{k_d} C_6H_5\overset{O}{\overset{\|}{C}}CH_2CH_2CH_3 \tag{64}$$

$$C_6H_5\overset{OH}{\overset{|}{\underset{.}{C}}}CH_2CH_2\dot{C}H_2 \xrightarrow{k_c} C_6H_5 \begin{array}{c} \square \\ \text{OH} \end{array} \tag{65}$$

The kinetic expression for the production of enol or ethylene from butyrophenone [Norrish type II reaction] is:

$$\phi = \phi_{\text{isc}} \, [k_r/(k_r + k_d)][k_e/(k_e + k'_r)] \tag{66}$$

where $\phi_{\text{isc}} = k_{\text{isc}}/(k_{\text{isc}} + k_s)$ and is unity for aryl ketones. Notice that the
quantum yield for this reaction is composed of two components, one measur-
ing the efficiency of the photochemical process and the other being a measure
of the efficiency of the processes deriving from the diradical intermediate. In
benzene solution the quantum yield for Norrish Type II process is 0.42 for
butyrophenone (95,108), but it increases to 0.86 when t-butanol is used as the
solvent (45,64). Assuming that the quantum yield for intersystem crossing is
the same in the two solvents, the low quantum yield in benzene can be due to
either a low value of $k_r/k_r + k_d$ or a low value for $k_e/k_e + k'_r$. Since the value
of k_r is not greatly influenced by solvent, Wagner has inferred that the change
to a more polar solvent influences the rate of butyrophenone regeneration, k'_r.

An important point here is that a change in the quantum yield does not
necessarily imply any change in the reactivity of the photoreactive molecule
since there is often no direct relationship between reactivity and quantum
yields, since the latter are a measure of a number of competing processes.

As mentioned in Chapter I, the quantum yield for reactant disappearance
and that for formation of a given product are not necessarily identical. If
they are identical, then there is only one photoproduct. If they are not
identical then more than one product must be present. As noted, the quantum
yield for olefin formation from butyrophenone in t-butanol is 0.86. However,
the quantum yield for butyrophenone disappearance is 1.0, indicating the
presence of at least one other photoproduct. The 1-phenyl-1-cyclobutanol
comprising 10–15% of the photoproducts nicely accounts for the remaining
products. Thus the measurement of both quantum yields can aid in the
product analysis of the photoreaction.

Since the *chemical* yield does not depend upon the number of photons
absorbed, there is no relationship between a chemical yield and a quantum
yield for a given product (109). Thus the chemical yield of ethylene from
butyrophenone is the same for photolysis in either benzene or t-butanol,
although the quantum yield differs by a factor of 2. A low quantum yield
does not imply a low chemical yield, although a high quantum yield does
require a high net chemical yield. The quantum yield sets a lower limit to the
chemical yield. If the quantum yield for product formation is 0.1, then the net
chemical yield can be from 10% up to 100% depending upon the number
of other photoproducts. However, for a photoreaction which gives only
A and B, there is a relationship between the *ratio* of the chemical yields of A
and B and the *ratio* of the quantum yields of A and B.

$$\%A/\%B = \phi A/\phi B \tag{67}$$

2. Determination of Chemical Quantum Yields

The most accurate method for quantum yield determinations involves the use of chemical actinometers and other methods will not be discussed here. There are three requirements for the determination of a quantum yield: (a) a suitable light source; (b) a photon counter (actinometer); and (c) a means of insuring equal irradiation of sample and actinometer.

The light sources have been previously described, but in general this requirement is best fulfilled by using a medium- or high-pressure mercury lamp coupled with suitable chemical and glass filters or a monochromator. When the 2537 Å mercury line is desired, a low-pressure lamp is best since $> 90\%$ of its output is in this region.

The basic requirement that must be met for an accurate quantum yield is that the actinometer and the sample under investigation must absorb a known amount of light. If the sample and the actinometer have different absorption ranges, which is the usual case, then care must be exercised to insure that all of the light absorbed by the actinometer is also absorbed by the sample and vice versa. This problem is most easily circumvented by having both actinometer and sample optically opaque at the irradiation wavelength range (as determined by the filter system).

In order for two samples to absorb equal amounts of light, an equal number of photons must impinge on each sample in the given time period. This requirement is most easily fulfilled by using a "merry-go-round" apparatus as previously described. In all future discussions where two or more samples are being simultaneously irradiated the condition of equal light absorption can be presumed to be met by having the solutions optically dense and by using a merry-go-round or some similar device.

A. THE FERRIOXALATE ACTINOMETER (110)

This is the most accurate and widely used chemical actinometer. Its useful range is wide, 250–509 nm, and is relatively simple to use. For a 1.0–1.5 cm path length and $0.15M$ $K_3Fe(C_2O_4)_3$, the actinometer solution does not absorb all of the light at wavelengths longer than 340 nm and so corrections must be applied. Its wide range can be a hinderance however, because it is sensitive to visible light it must be handled in the dark and used in the presence of only the light source to be measured.

The photochemical reaction of ferrioxalate is (111,112):

$$[Fe^{III}(C_2O_4)_3]^{-3} \xrightarrow{h\nu} C_2O_4^{-} + [Fe^{II}(C_2O_4)_2]^{-2} \qquad (68)$$
$$\text{oxalate}$$
$$\text{radical}$$

$$C_2O_4^{-} + [Fe^{III}(C_2O_4)_3]^{-3} \longrightarrow (C_2O_4)^{-2} + [Fe^{III}(C_2O_4)_3]^{-2} \qquad (69)$$

$$[Fe^{III}(C_2O_4)_3]^{-2} \longrightarrow [Fe^{II}(C_2O_4)_2]^{-2} + 2CO_2 \qquad (70)$$

Thus, due to the dark reaction of the oxalate radical, the observed quantum yield is twice that of the primary quantum yield. The quantum yield for ferrous ion production is nearly constant at short wavelengths but decreases at longer wavelengths. It has been suggested that at long wavelengths collisional degradation and/or primary recombination may lower the extent of dissociation (113). The observed quantum yields for ferrous ion production are given in Table 8.

TABLE 8

Wavelength, nm	$K_3Fe(C_2O_4)_3$, M	$\Phi_{Fe^{2+}}$ 22°C
Φ		
253.7	0.006	1.25 [a]
297	0.006	1.24 [a]
302		
313	0.006	1.24 [a]
334	0.006	1.23 [a]
358	0.006	1.25 [c]
366	0.006	1.21,[a] 1.26 [b]
	0.15	1.15,[a] 1.20 [b]
392	0.006	1.13 [c]
405	0.006	1.14 [a]
416	0.006	1.12 [c]
	0.006	1.11 [a]
436	0.15	1.01 [a]
468	0.15	0.93 [a]
480	0.15	0.94 [a]
509	0.15	0.86 [a]
546	0.15	0.15 [a]
577	0.15	0.013 [c]

[a] Data taken from Hatchard and Parker (110).
[b] Data taken from Lee and Seliger (113).
[c] Data taken from Wagner and Adamson (114).

B. REINECKE'S SALT ACTINOMETER (114)

This is a very recently developed actinometer which should find its greatest application for irradiations in the visible region. The useful range extends from 316 to >600 nm. The quantum yield for thiocyanate release is nearly constant over this range. The photoreaction is simply one of aquation, releasing a free thiocyanate ion. The quantum yields for photolysis at various

$$Cr(NH_3)_2(NCS)_4^- \xrightarrow[\text{H}_2\text{O}]{h\nu} Cr(NH_3)_2(NCS)_3(H_2O) + NCS^- \tag{71}$$

wavelengths are given in Table 9. The concentrations have been made up to absorb all of the light at the wavelengths below 600 nm. Above 600 nm transmission corrections will have to be applied.

TABLE 9

Wavelength, nm	Extinction coeff., ϵ	KCr(NH$_3$)$_2$(NCS)$_4$, M	Φ_{NCS^-}, 23°
360	11,000	0.0011	0.291
350	> 100	0.003	0.388
392	93.5	0.005	0.316
416	67.5	0.008	0.310
452	31.2	0.010	0.311
504	97.5	0.005	0.299
520	106.5	0.004	0.286
545	90.5	0.005	0.282
585	43.8	0.010	0.270
600	29.0	0.025	0.276
676	0.75	0.045	0.271
713	0.35	0.046	0.284
735	0.27	0.045	0.302
750	0.15	0.048	0.273

C. BENZOPHENONE–BENZHYDROL ACTINOMETER (115,116)

Moore has developed a unique system of actinometry which does not depend upon any previously determined quantum yield for the actinometer. The actinometer employs the photoreduction of benzophenone by benzhydrol, for which the following mechanism has been proposed:

$$(C_6H_5)_2C{=}O \xrightarrow{h\nu} [(C_6H_5)_2C{=}O]^{S_1} \qquad (72)$$

$$[(C_6H_5)_2C{=}O]^{S_1} \xrightarrow{\Phi_{ics}} [(C_6H_5)_2C{=}O]^{T_1} \qquad (73)$$

$$[(C_6H_5)_2C{=}O]^{T_1} + (C_6H_5)_2CHOH \xrightarrow{k_r} 2(C_6H_5)_2\dot{C}OH \qquad (74)$$

$$[(C_6H_5)_2C{=}O]^{T_1} \xrightarrow{k_d} (C_6H_5)_2C{=}O \qquad (75)$$

$$2(C_6H_5)_2\dot{C}OH \xrightarrow{k_c} (C_6H_5)_2C\underset{OH}{\overset{}{\rule{0pt}{0pt}}}{-}\!\!{-}C(C_6H_5)_2 \qquad (76)$$
$$\qquad\qquad\qquad\qquad\qquad OH \quad\ OH$$

For the benzophenone–benzhydrol system the following rate law is obeyed:

$$1/\phi_B = 1 + (k_d/k_r[BH_2]) \qquad (77)$$

where ϕ_B is the quantum yield for disappearance of benzophenone and [BH$_2$] is the concentration of benzhydrol. If several benzophenone–benzhydrol samples, with constant concentrations of benzophenone and varying amounts of benzhydrol, are irradiated simultaneously and if one of these samples is chosen as the actinometer, the multiplication of the above equation by ϕ_{act} gives

$$\phi_{act}/\phi_B = \phi_{act} + (k_d\phi_{act}/k_r[BH_2]). \tag{78}$$

When ϕ_{act}/ϕ_B is plotted* against $1/[BH_2]$, the intercept is ϕ_{act} and the slope is $k_d\phi_{act}/k_r$. Thus the value of the intercept gives the quantum yield for the actinometer. The benzophenone–benzhydrol system has the advantage that the quantum yield for the actinometer is redetermined each time and therefore the presence of impurities does not affect the accuracy of the measured quantum yields.

In principle, this technique can be applied to any system. However, the general equation for ketone photoreduction is

$$1/\phi = 1/a + k_d/ak_r[BH_2] \tag{79}$$

where a is the quantum yield for the production of photoreactive molecules and the other terms have their usual meanings. In the limiting case when there are no pathways for regeneration of starting material (e.g., $2R_2\dot{C}OH \rightarrow R_2C{=}O + R_2CHOH$), $a = \phi_{isc}$. In order to extend this method to other systems, the value of a must be experimentally determined.

Many other actinometers have been used (93c) including the uranyl oxalate (117–120) actinometer and the o-nitrobenzaldehyde actinometer (121), but the three previously described actinometers should fulfill most general needs.

Obviously any photochemical reaction whose quantum yield has been determined with reference to any of the above systems can itself be used as a standard. This is often desirable if a series of compounds are being investigated, all of which have similar absorption spectra. An accurate quantum-yield determination for one of these compounds will serve as a standard for quantum-yield determinations for the remaining compounds. The advantage of this procedure is that light filtering will be much less important for the remaining quantum-yield determinations.

3. Determination of Rates of Reaction

The kinetic expression for the quantum yield for olefin formation from the Norrish Type II reaction of butyrophenone was given on page 328. In the

$$\phi_0 = \phi_{isc}[k_r/(k_r + k_d)][k_e/(k_e + k'_r)] \tag{80}$$

---

* The determination of this ratio does not require absolute knowledge of ϕ_{act} or ϕ; this ratio is simply the relative amount of actinometer benzophenone consumed per amount of sample benzophenone (at a given BH_2 concentration) consumed.

presence of added quencher, an additional reaction has to be considered:

$$[C_6H_5 \overset{\overset{O}{\|}}{C} CH_2CH_2CH_3]^{T_1} + Q \xrightarrow{k_q} C_6H_5 \overset{\overset{O}{\|}}{C} CH_2CH_2CH_3 + Q^* \qquad (81)$$

and the quantum yield in the presence of quencher becomes

$$\phi = \phi_{\mathrm{isc}}[k_r/(k_r + k_d + k_q[Q])][k_e/(k_e + k'_r)]. \qquad (82)$$

If Eq. (80) is divided by Eq. (82), one obtains the familiar Stern-Volmer Eq. (83).

$$\phi_0/\phi = 1 + [k_q[Q]/(k_r + k_d)] \qquad (83)$$

In general the Stern-Volmer equation can be written,

$$\phi_0/\phi = 1 + [k_q[Q]/\sum k_i) \qquad (84)$$

where $\sum k_i$ is the sum of all rates for deactivation of the *quenchable* excited states. The lifetime of the photoexcited molecule is the inverse of the sum of all of the rates of deactivation,

$$\tau_0 = 1/\sum k_i \qquad (85)$$

and Eq. (84) often is written

$$\phi_0/\phi = 1 + k_q[Q]\tau_0. \qquad (86)$$

A plot of ϕ_0/ϕ vs. [Q] should give a straight line with slope equal to $k_q/k_r + k_d$ and an intercept of unity. For reactions proceeding with a high quantum yield (> 0.5) the value of k_r must be greater than any other deactivation rate and so $k_q/k_r + k_d$ can, and often is, approximated as k_q/k_r. Furthermore, the main contributor to a low quantum yield can often be regeneration of starting material from radical intermediates, not rapid radiationless processes; since this reaction does not proceed from a photoexcited state, its rate does not appear in the Stern-Volmer equation. However, this must be tested for each individual case.

Some representative values of k_q/k_r are given in Table 10. The entries (a), (b), and (c), (d) (Table 10) show the effect of changing the H-abstraction from I^0 to II^0. The entries also show the greater selectivity of the aromatic ketones as compared to the aliphatic ketones. For aryl–alkyl ketones the reactivity ratios of $1:18:50:60$ are observed for primary:secondary:secondary benzylic:tert-C—H abstractions in the Norrish Type II reaction (108,124). Entry (e) shows that keto acid reactivities are comparable to those for aliphatic ketones and so the —CO_2H group has little effect on the H-abstracting ability of the keto group.

TABLE 10

For Norrish Type II Reactions in Benzene Substrate

Substrate	k_q/k_r	Ref.
(a) 2-Pentanone	50	108
(b) 2-Hexanone	10	108
(c) n-Butyrophenone	1,850	108
(d) n-Valerophenone	100	45, 108
(e) α-Ketodecanoic acid	9.1	122

Since comparison of k_q/k_r values is valid only when the studies have been performed in the same solvent, a knowledge of the absolute value of k_q for a number of solvents would be desirable.

In general, the rate of a diffusion-controlled reaction can be calculated from Eq. (87):

$$k_q = [4\pi N\alpha(D_A + D_B)(r_A + r_B)]/1,000 \tag{87}$$

where D_A and D_B are the diffusion coefficients, r_A and r_B are the encounter radii of A and B, and α is the probability that a collision will result in energy transfer. The diffusion coefficient can usually be expressed by the Stokes-Einstein equation

$$D = kT/6\pi\kappa r \tag{88}$$

where κ is the solvent viscosity, and r is the molecular radius which is normally assumed to be identical to the encounter radius. Substitution of Eq. (88) into Eq. (87) gives

$$k_q = (2RT\alpha/3000\kappa)[(r_A + r_B)^2/r_A r_B] \text{ liter mole}^{-1} \text{ sec}^{-1}. \tag{89}$$

If the encounter radii are assumed to be equal, then the above equation reduces to the familiar form

$$k_q = 8RT\alpha/3000\kappa. \tag{90}$$

It is normally assumed that $\alpha = 1$ and that all quenchers will react at the same rate in a given solvent. In fact, using Eq. (90), α is often found to be less than unity and may vary with the structure of the donor, the acceptor, and with the nature of the solvent. The value of k_q for exothermic processes has been found in benzene to vary from 8.2×10^9 to 1.3×10^9 liter mole^{-1} sec^{-1} depending upon the quencher (Table 11). The calculated value for k_q in benzene is 9.5×10^9 liter mole^{-1} sec^{-1}. The observed rates of diffusion are consistently lower than the calculated rates in nonviscous solvents. In benzene, the rate found for azulene quenching of anthracene triplets is 80% of the

TABLE 11

Rate Constants for Quenching Various Triplets in Benzene

Quencher [a]	k_q, liter mole^{-1} sec^{-1}	Ref.
Isoprene	6.4×10^9	127
Tetramethylbutadiene	4.6×10^9	127
Myrcene	2.6×10^9	127
1,3-Cyclohexadiene	1.3×10^9	127
Azulene	7.5×10^9	125
Biacetyl	$8.2–7.0 \times 10^9$	128

[a] In all cases, energy transfer is exothermic by at least 4 kcal.

calculated value (125) and in hexane, the measured value is 60% of the calculated value (126).

As the viscosity of the solvent increases the efficiency of quenching also increases, as estimated using Eq. (90) (129,130). In going from high molecular weight solvents to smaller, less viscous hydrocarbons, the increase in the rates of diffusion do not parallel the decrease in the viscosities. Wagner has suggested (129) in analogy with the classical work by Noyes (131), that in viscous solvents, once the encounter diameter for energy transfer between the donor and acceptor is reached, a solvent cage is formed preventing the two molecules from diffusing apart. In nonviscous solvents the acceptor and the donor can diffuse apart before energy transfer takes place. Osborne and Porter have offered an attractive alternative (130). They point out that the Stokes-Einstein expression, Eq. (88) is no longer obeyed when the size of the diffusing species is smaller than the molecular diameters of the solvent. When the molecular diameter of the solute is sufficiently small in comparison to that for the solvent, the solute can *slip* past the solvent and the macroscopic viscosity is no longer a good approximation for the microscopic viscosity. These two explanations are not mutually exclusive, but further work is necessary in order to determine their relative importance.

It has been observed that good agreement is found for the calculated rates of quenching of fluorescence by oxygen with the observed rates when Eq. (87) is used, but not when the rates are calculated from Eq. (90) (132). Explanations similar to those offered by Osborne and Porter have been used to interpret the behavior of oxygen, a small molecule, in hydrocarbon solvents.

Thus it appears that a great deal of care must be taken when comparing k_q or k_q/k_r values which have been measured in different solvents, and that for accurate comparison of measured rates of diffusion with the calculated values, Eq. (87) must be used when Stokes-Einstein conditions are not met.

Other complications appear in the use of the Stern-Volmer equation when high concentrations of quenchers are used to deactivate a photoexcited molecule (133–136). When energy transfer is very efficient the quantum yield for product formation (or substrate disappearance) is only approximated by the usual expression

$$\phi = k_r/(k_r + k_d + k_q[Q]) \tag{91}$$

and static quenching must be taken into account. The quantum yield expression, in the presence of static quenching effects, is

$$\phi = [(1 - u)k_r/(k_r + k_d + k_q[Q])] + [uk_r/(k_r + k_d + k_{et})] \tag{92}$$

where k_r, k_d, and k_q have the usual meanings, u is the number of excited-state molecules which are born with a quencher as a nearby neighbor and k_{et} is the rate of energy transfer to nearest neighbor molecules. The appropriate Stern-Volmer expression is

$$\phi_0/\phi = (1 + k_q[Q]/k_r + k_d)(1 - \alpha u) \tag{93}$$

where all of the symbols have their previously defined meanings (135). Whenever the quencher concentration is low or whenever energy transfer is inefficient, the product αu is small, Eq. (93) reduces to the usual form of the Stern-Volmer equation (Eq. (83)) and a linear relationship between ϕ_0/ϕ and quencher concentration is observed. When $\alpha u \to 1$, a linear relationship between [Q] and ϕ_0/ϕ is no longer observed and the line will curve upward. In the limiting condition, $\alpha u = 1$, each excited molecule is surrounded by a quencher molecule, and deactivation processes now complete only with energy transfer to nearest neighbors. Under these limiting conditions the following equation is obeyed:

$$\phi_0/\phi = 1 + [k_{et}/(k_r + k_d)]. \tag{94}$$

Figures 9 and 10 show the Stern-Volmer plots for the quenching of the Norrish Type II reactions of aryl ketones. The fact that curvature is observed only in the viscous solvent *tert*-butanol adds support to Wagner's thesis that cage effects become important in viscous solvents and that energy transfer in nonviscous solvents is not totally efficient. It should be emphasized that curved Stern-Volmer plots will be observed only in the presence of high concentrations of quencher. For molecular quenching of long-lived excited states the quencher concentration will not be great enough to observe static quenching effects.

The Stern-Volmer plot will also curve upward if chemical quenching is superimposed upon the normal physical quenching (energy transfer). There is always the danger that chemical quenching will predominate rather than

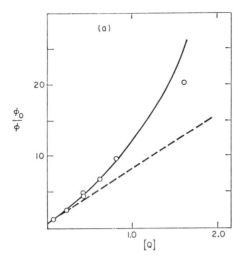

Fig. 9. Stern-Volmer plot of the quenching of γ-methylvalerophenone by 2,4-hexadien-1-ol in t-butyl alcohol.

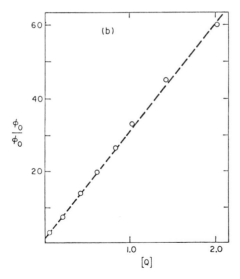

Fig. 10. Stern-Volmer plot of the quenching of γ-phenylbutyrophenone by pentadiene in pentane.

physical quenching. The appearance of the triplet products of the quencher is a good diagnostic test for energy transfer.

Another potential complication when using high quencher concentrations is that singlet quenching can occur for aromatic systems (137). Normally, triplet-state photoreactions of aromatic systems can be quenched by relatively low concentrations of quenchers and so singlet-state quenching is not usually observed under these conditions.

There are four basic types of plots that may be obtained when a Stern-Volmer analysis is applied to any given reaction. These four types are shown in Figure 11–14. The first linear correlation (Fig. 11) shows that there is direct competition between the reaction of a *single* excited state giving products and reaction leading to quenching of the excited state.

$$A^* \to B + C \tag{95}$$

$$A^* + Q \to A + Q' \tag{96}$$

The second possibility (Fig. 12) indicates that there are at least two different precursors leading to products or removing starting material. The Stern-Volmer plots for either olefin formation or ketone disappearance show curvature similar to that in Figure 12, indicating that there are two different excited states involved in these reactions. These states have been identified as the singlet (unquenchable) and triplet (quenchable) states (108). The modified Stern-Volmer equation (Eq. (97)) has been applied to a similar situation (138)

$$\frac{\phi_0}{\phi} = \left(1 + \frac{k_q[Q]}{k_r + k_d}\right) \Big/ \left(1 + \frac{k_q[Q]}{k_r + k_d} \frac{\phi_\infty}{\phi_0}\right) \tag{97}$$

where ϕ_∞ is the quantum yield for the given process at infinite quencher concentration.† A curved Stern-Volmer plot will also be observed when there are two different, but quenchable, states leading to products. The following reaction scheme will give a curved line for the plot of $\phi_0(A)/\phi(A)$

$$A^{T_1} \to B \tag{98}$$

$$A^{T_2} \to C \tag{99}$$

$$A^{T_1} + Q \to A + Q' \tag{100}$$

$$A^{T_2} + Q \to A + Q' \tag{101}$$

vs. [Q], but will give two different linear plots for the plot of either $\phi_0(B)/\phi(B)$ or $\phi_0(C)/\phi(C)$ vs. [Q] (Eqs. (98)–(101)).

† There is a basic similarity between Eqs. (93) and (97) since any curved Stern-Volmer plot may be represented as
$$\phi_0/\phi = (1 + (k_q[Q]/k_r)]/(1 \pm fcn[Q])$$
but the exact analysis of $fcn[Q]$ will depend upon the given kinetic situation (133–136, 138–140).

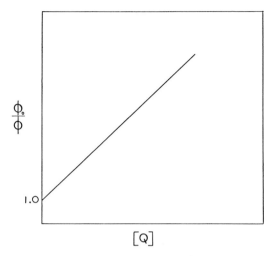

Fig. 11. Stern-Volmer plot.

The third possibility (Fig. 13) is that positive curvature will be observed. This case has been discussed previously and indicates either chemical quenching concurrent with energy transfer or signifies that energy transfer is not limited by diffusion rates at high quencher concentration. If curvature is observed, then energy transfer must be efficient (i.e., $\alpha \rightarrow 1$).

The fourth and least helpful possibility (Fig. 14) is that no quenching will be observed. This indicates that either the reaction is too fast to be quenched or that quenching is endothermic. The lack of quenching does *not* necessarily

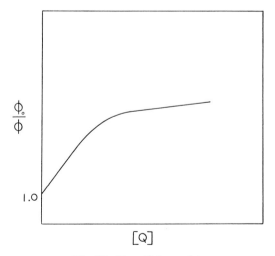

Fig. 12. Stern-Volmer plot.

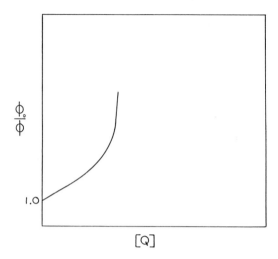

Fig. 13. Stern-Volmer plot.

give any indication of the multiplicity since some triplet-state reactions may indeed be too rapid for competitive bimolecular quenching. Also, the lack of quenching does not necessarily give any information with regard to the rate of the reaction. The singlet state reactions of aliphatic ketones are unquench-able (108,141), yet the available evidence suggests that they are nearly 1000 times slower than the triplet-state reactions of aliphatic ketones (105,142,143).

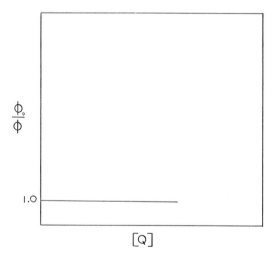

Fig. 14. Stern-Volmer plot.

4. The Intersystem Crossing Efficiency

The intersystem crossing efficiency, ϕ_{isc}, is the quantum yield for the spin inversion process $S_1 \rightarrow T_1$. Since the large majority of organic photoreactions occur from the triplet state, because of its long lifetime, the efficiency of triplet-state population is of fundamental importance. For example, if one observes a triplet-state photoreaction which proceeds with a chemical quantum of 0.2 the only statement that can be made, without a knowledge of ϕ_{isc}, is that 80% of the quanta absorbed lead to nonproduct-forming processes. However, if the ϕ_{isc} is known, then the efficiency of production formation from the triplet state is known. If ϕ_{isc} were found to be 0.2, the product formation from the triplet state is completely efficient and the efficiency loss must occur in the singlet state.

The rate of intersystem crossing is related to the quantum yield for intersystem crossing by Eq. (102),

$$\phi_{isc} = k_{isc}/(k_{isc} + k_f + k_s) \cong k_{isc}/(k_{isc} + k_f) \qquad (102)$$

where k_f is the rate of fluorescence and k_s is the rate of radiationless deactivation of the singlet state, usually assumed to be negligible in comparison to k_f. Thus in order to calculate k_{isc}, from ϕ_{isc}, or vice versa, the rate of fluorescence must be known. An approximate value of k_f can be calculated from the absorption spectrum by means of Eq. (103),

$$k_f = 2.88 \times 10^{-9} \bar{\nu}_m^2 \epsilon_m \Delta \bar{\nu}_{1/2} \qquad (103)$$

where $\bar{\nu}_m$ (cm^{-1}) is the mean frequency of the $S_0 \rightarrow S_1$ absorption band and $\Delta \bar{\nu}_{1/2}$ is the half-width of the absorption band in reciprocal centimeters (144).

5. Determination of the Intersystem Crossing Efficiency

The measurement of ϕ_{isc} is very simple and is based upon the sensitized isomerization of olefins (142,145,146). It is established that ϕ_{isc} for benzophenone is unity and Lamola and Hammond have found that all benzophenone triplets can be captured using moderate concentrations (0.05M) of conjugated olefins. With these facts, intersystem crossing yields can be measured by comparing the sensitized cis–trans conversion of a given olefin to that from the benzophenone-sensitized reaction. Since cis-piperylene, the

$$\phi_{isc}(S) = \% \text{ conversion (S)}/\% \text{ conversion } [(C_6H_5)_2CO] \qquad (104)$$

olefin usually employed, can quench the singlet states of aromatic hydrocarbons (137), the value of ϕ_{isc} at zero olefin concentration must be determined. This can be done by making measurements for a range of olefin concentrations and extrapolating to zero concentration. This will only be necessary for compound with long-lived singlet states.

The major requirement for this experiment is that *all* triplets must be captured by the substrate. In order for this to happen the triplet energy of the sensitizer must be higher than that for the olefin employed and the sensitizer must also be stable within the time period required for quenching. Unimolecular decomposition can often compete with bimolecular quenching. Experimentally, any triplet reaction of the sensitizer must be completely quenched by the olefin substrate.

6. The Ullman Color Test

Ullman and co-workers (147,148) have developed an elegantly simple color test for triplet energies of molecules with triplet lifetimes shorter than $\sim 10^{-7}$ sec and with triplet energies less than 64 kcal/mole. The test is based

$$(105)$$

$$(\lambda_{max} \ 544nm, \ \epsilon \ = \ 26,750)$$

$$(106)$$

upon Eqs. (105)–(109), where D^3 is the triplet state of some photosensitizer ($E_T < 64$ kcal/mole) and A is some quencher molecule. If the relative concentrations of **34** and D are adjusted so that each absorbs part of the incident light, then **35** will be produced by reaction (105) and destroyed by reactions (106)–(108). In the absence of the quencher A, a certain steady-state concentration of **35** will be built up depending upon the relative concentrations of D and **34**. If the quencher A is now added, both A and **35** will compete for the triplet sensitizer and the steady-state concentration of the red pyrylium oxide **35** will be increased relative to the sample without quencher. This assumes that reaction (110) will not occur. This assumption will be fulfilled only if the lifetime of A^3 is too short for energy transfer under the experimental conditions.

(35) $\xrightarrow[\Delta]{O_2}$ oxidation product (107)

(35) is the structure with C_6H_5 groups, O^+ and O^-.

$$D^3 + (35) \xrightarrow{O_2} \text{oxidation product } + D \qquad (108)$$

$$D^3 + A \longrightarrow D + A^3 \qquad (109)$$

$$A^3 + (35) \xrightarrow{O_2} \text{oxidation products } + A \qquad (110)$$

In order to estimate the triplet energy of any given quencher, the color intensity of an irradiated solution containing an appropriate sensitizer, **34** and the quencher is compared to that for an irradiated solution containing only **34** and the sensitizer. If the intensity is greater for the test solution than for the blank, energy transfer must have occurred from the sensitizer (D) to the quencher (A) and therefore the triplet energy of A must be lower than the triplet energy of D. If, for example, a color increase was observed when pyrene ($E_T = 49$ kcal/mole) was used as a sensitizer but not when phenazine ($E_T = 45$ kcal/mole) was used as the sensitizer, then the triplet energy of the quencher, A, must lie between 44 and 48 kcal/mole.

The beauty of this technique is that no apparatus is required other than the light source. The solutions of **34** (0.5–$1.0 \times 10^{-2}M$) and sensitizer are made up by trial and error until just visually observable concentrations of **35** are attained. The blank and the sample solutions are then visually compared for differences in color intensity.

III. PHOTOSENSITIZED REACTIONS

The theory of energy-transfer reactions has been extensively covered in the previous chapter, but a few remarks concerning the experimental problems should be made here.

The first requirement for an efficient triplet sensitizer is that its triplet state must be higher in energy than that for the substrate. The second requirement is that the intersystem crossing efficiency for the sensitizer should be relatively high. For high-energy sensitizers, acetone ($E_T \sim 75$ kcal/mole) and alkyl–aryl ketones ($E_T = 69$–75 kcal/mole) may be used. The intersystem crossing yield for all of these compounds is unity or very close to unity. Since the carbonyl triplets are very reactive, occasional complications arise due to chemical reactions of the sensitizer either with the solvent or with the substrate. These complications can be circumvented by using substituted benzenes (benzene, $E_T = 85$ kcal/mole) as sensitizers although the intersystem crossing efficiency for these aromatic systems is much lower than that for the carbonyl compounds. There is a wide range of sensitizers available with triplet energies under 70 kcal/mole. The most commonly used sensitizer is benzophenone ($E_T = 69$ kcal/mole), but triphenylene ($E_T = 67$ kcal/mole, $\phi_{isc} = 0.95$) is often preferred due to the chemical reactivity of triplet benzophenone.

A problem that can often be serious is the chemical separation of the sensitizer from the photoproducts at the completion of the reaction. This problem has been obviated by using solid, polymeric photosensitizers (149). The only polymer described thus far in heterogeneous sensitization experiments has been polyvinyl phenyl ketone ($E_T = 72$ kcal/mole), but many polymers might be profitably used for this purpose. In practice, the polymer is ground into small pieces and placed in a chromatography column. The substrate is dissolved in a hydrocarbon solvent and slowly passed over the solid, insoluble polymer. The two-phase mixture is irradiated with an external source and when the photoreaction reaches completion, the products are eluted from the bottom of the column.

References

1. W. Fleischhacker and F. Vieboeck, *Monatch. Chem.*, **96**, 1512 (1965).
2. P. Cerutti, K. Ikeda, and B. Witkop, *J. Am. Chem. Soc.*, **87**, 2505 (1965).
3. O. Yonemitsu, P. Cerutti, and B. Witkop, *J. Am. Chem. Soc.*, **88**, 3941 (1966).
4. G. Balle, P. Cerutti, and B. Witkop, *J. Am. Chem. Soc.*, **88**, 3946 (1966).
5. T. Tokuyama, S. Senoh, T. Sakan, K. S. Brown, Jr., and B. Witkop, *J. Am. Chem. Soc.*, **89**, 1017 (1967).
6. J. A. Waters and B. Witkop, *J. Am. Chem. Soc.*, **89**, 1022 (1967).
7. R. Srinivasan, *J. Am. Chem. Soc.*, **85**, 3048 (1963).
8. R. Srinivasan, *J. Am. Chem. Soc.*, **86**, 3318 (1964).
9. J. Meinwald and B. E. Kaplan, *J. Am. Chem. Soc.*, **89**, 2611 (1967).
10. J. E. Baldwin and R. H. Greeley, *J. Am. Chem. Soc.*, **87**, 4514 (1965).
11. I. Haller and R. Srinivasan, *J. Am. Chem. Soc.*, **88**, 5084 (1966).
12. M. Ochiai and K. Morita, *Tetrahedron Letters*, **1967**, 2349.
13. D. H. R. Barton, Y. L. Chow, A. Cox, and G. W. Kirby, *J. Chem. Soc.*, **1965**, 3571.
14. J. A. Barltrop and P. Schofield, *J. Chem. Soc.*, **1965**, 4758.
15. J. A. Barltop and P. Schofield, *Tetrahedron Letters*, **1962**, 697.

16. A. J. Kirby and G. A. Varvoglis, *Chem. Commun.*, **1967**, 406.
17. N. C. Yang, A. Shani, and G. R. Lenz, *J. Am. Chem. Soc.*, **88**, 5369 (1966).
18. G. R. Lenz and N. C. Yang, *Chem. Commun.*, **1967**, 1136.
19. X. A. Dominguez, J. G. Delgado, W. P. Reeves, and P. D. Gardner, *Tetrahedron Letters*, **1967**, 2493.
20. M. P. Cava and S. C. Havlicek, *Tetrahedron Letters*, **1967**, 2625.
21. Z. Koblicova and K. Wiesner, *Tetrahedron Letters*, **1967**, 2563.
22. K. Wiesner, I. Jirkovsky, M. Fishman, and C. A. J. Williams, *Tetrahedron Letters*, **1967**, 1523.
23. *Chem. Abstr.*, **63**, P 14816 (1965).
24. G. L. Lange and P. deMayo, *Chem. Commun.*, **1967**, 704.
25. B. D. Challand, G. Kornis, G. L. Lange, and P. deMayo, *Chem. Commun.*, **1967**, 704.
26. E. J. Cory, R. B. Mitra, and H. Uda, *J. Am. Chem. Soc.*, **86**, 485 (1964).
27. E. J. Cory and S. Nozoe, *J. Am. Chem. Soc.*, **87**, 5733 (1965).
28. P. Sunder-Plassmann, P. H. Nelson, L. Durham, J. A. Edwards, and J. H. Fried, *Tetrahedron Letters*, **1967**, 653.
29. R. Hoffmann and R. B. Woodward, *Acc. Chem. Res.*, **1**, 17 (1968).
30. E. J. Cory and A. G. Hortmann, *J. Am. Chem. Soc.*, **87**, 5736 (1965).
31. J. Fried and J. W. Brown, *Tetrahedron Letters*, **1966**, 1677.
32. J. Fried and J. W. Brown, *Tetrahedron Letters*, **1967**, 925.
33. M. Flammang-Barbieu, J. Nasielski, and R. H. Martin, *Tetrahedron Letters*, **1967**, 743.
34. P. E. Eaton and T. W. Cole, *J. Am. Chem. Soc.*, **86**, 3157 (1964).
35. K. E. Wilzbach and L. Kaplan, *J. Am. Chem. Soc.*, **87**, 4004 (1965).
36. K. E. Wilzbach, J. S. Ritscher, and L. Kapan, *J. Am. Chem. Soc.*, **89**, 1031 (1967).
37. E. E. van Tamelan and S. P. Pappas, *J. Am. Chem. Soc.*, **85**, 3297 (1963).
38. S. Masamune, H. Cuts, and M. G. Hogben, *Tetrahedron Letters*, **1966**, 1017.
39. S. Cremer and R. Srinivasan, *Tetrahedron Letters*, **1960**, 24.
40. See J. Meinwald and J. K. Crandall, *J. Am. Chem. Soc.*, **88**, 1292 (1966) and references within.
41. S. Masamune, *J. Am. Chem. Soc.*, **86**, 735 (1964).
42. D. M. Lemal and K. S. Shim, *J. Am. Chem. Soc.*, **86**, 1550 (1964).
43. N. C. Yang and D. M. Thap, *J. Org. Chem.*, **32**, 2462 (1967).
44. N. C. Yang, "Reactivity of the Photoexcited Molecule," *J. Polymer Sci. C*, **22** (Pt. 1), 145 (1967).
45. P. J. Wagner, *J. Am. Chem. Soc.*, **89**, 5898 (1967).
46. S. G. Cohen and S. Aktipis, *J. Am. Chem. Soc.*, **88**, 3587 (1966).
47. W. A. Pryor, *Free Radicals*, McGraw-Hill, New York, 1966, ch. 12.
48. C. E. Loader and C. J. Timmons, *J. Chem. Soc. Ser. C*, **1967**, 1457.
49. P. L. Kumler, Thesis, University of Rochester, Rochester, New York, 1967.
50. H. Labhayt, *Angew. Chem.* (Intern. Ed. Engl), **6**, 812 (1967).
51. P. Bladon and I. A. Williams, *J. Chem. Soc. Ser. C*, **1967**, 2032.
52. Y. Odaira, T. Tominaga, T. Sugihara, and S. Tsutsumi, *Tetrahedron Letters*, **1964**, 2527.
53. Y. Ogata, Y. Iazwa, H. Tomioka, and T. Nishizawa, *Tetrahedron*, **22**, 483, 1557 (1966).
54. D. I. Schuster and C. J. Polowczyk, *J. Am. Chem. Soc.*, **86**, 4502 (1964).
55. P. Cerutti and H. Schmid, *Helv. Chem. Acta*, **45**, 1992 (1962).
56. I. Moritani and N. Toshima, *Tetrahedron Letters*, **1967**, 467.

57. J. A. Marshall and M. J. Wurth, *J. Am. Chem. Soc.*, **89**, 6788 (1967).
58. P. J. Kropp and H. J. Krauss, *J. Am. Chem. Soc.*, **89**, 5199 (1967) and references cited therein.
59. R. Stoermer and H. Stockman, *Chem. Ber.*, **74**, 1786 (1914).
60. P. J. Kropp and H. J. Krauss, *J. Org. Chem.*, **32**, 3222 (1967).
61. W. M. Horspool and P. L. Pauson, *Chem. Commun.*, **1967**, 195.
62. W. Dauben, "Reactivity of the Photoexcited Organic Molecule," *J. Polymer Sci. C*, **22** (Pt. 1), 171 (1967).
63. J. Pusset and R. Bengelmans, *Tetrahedron Letters*, **1967**, 3249. For another recent study of this reaction see T. N. Huckerby, N. A. J. Rogers, and A. Sattar, *Tetrahedron Letters*, **1967**, 1113.
64. P. J. Wagner, *Tetrahedron Letters*, **1967**, 1753.
65. D. V. Rao and V. Lamberti, *J. Org. Chem.*, **32**, 2896 (1967).
66. M. S. Sander and D. J. Trecker, *J. Am. Chem. Soc.*, **89**, 5725 (1967).
67. A. Lamola and L. J. Sharp, *J. Phys. Chem.*, **70**, 2634 (1966).
68. K. Koyano and I. Tanaka, *J. Chem. Phys.*, **69**, 2545 (1965).
69. O. Buchardt, J. Becher, C. Lohse, and J. Moller, *Acta Chem. Scand.*, **20**, 262 (1966).
70. S. P. Pappas, B. C. Pappas, and J. E. Blackwell, Jr., *J. Org. Chem.*, **32**, 3066 (1967).
71. For recent work on cyclopentenone dimerization see P. E. Eaton and W. S. Hurt, *J. Am. Chem. Soc.*, **88**, 5038 (1966), P. deMayo, J. P. Pete, and M. Tchuir, *ibid.*, **89**, 5712 (1967), and J. L. Ruhlen and P. A. Leermakers, *ibid.*, **89**, 4944 (1967).
72. For recent work on cyclohexenone dimerizations see E. Y. Y. Lam, D. Valentine, and G. S. Hammond, *J. Am. Chem. Soc.*, **89**, 3482 (1967).
73. For recent work on coumarin dimerization see H. Morrison, H. Curtis, and T. McDowell, *J. Am. Chem. Soc.*, **88**, 5415 (1966), and C. H. Krausch, S. Farid, and G. O. Schnenck, *Chem. Ber.*, **99**, 625 (1966).
74. O. L. Chapman, P. J. Nelson, R. W. King, D. J. Trecker, and A. A. Griswold, *Rec. Chem. Progr.*, **28**, 167 (1967).
75. P. deMayo, unpublished observations.
76. J. A. Berson, Z. Hamlet, and W. A. Mueller, *J. Am. Chem. Soc.*, **84**, 297 (1962). For recent reviews of solvent polarity parameters, see C. Reichardt, *Angew. Chem.* (Intern. Ed. Engl.), **4**, 29 (1965), and H. F. Herbrandson and F. R. Neufeld, *J. Org. Chem.*, **31**, 1140 (1966).
77. A. A. Lamola, *J. Chem. Phys.*, **47**, 4810 (1967).
78. D. Rauh and P. A. Leermakers, *J. Am. Chem. Soc.*, **90**, 2246 (1968).
79. K. Mitteilung, *Z. Phys. Chem.*, **41**, 245 (1964).
80. R. N. Nurmukhametov, L. A. Mileshina, and D. N. Shigorin, *Opt. Spectry.*, **22**, 404 (1967).
81. For a review see S. K. Lower and M. A. El-Sayed, *Chem. Rev.*, **66**, 199 (1966).
82. P. J. Wagner, *J. Chem. Phys.*, **45**, 2335 (1966).
83. H. Morrison, H. Curtis, and T. McDowell, *J. Am. Chem. Soc.*, **88**, 5415 (1966).
84. D. O. Cowan and R. L. Drisko, *J. Am. Chem. Soc.*, **89**, 3068 (1967).
85. D. O. Cowan and R. L. Drisko, *Tetrahedron Letters*, **1967**, 1255.
86. P. A. Leermakers, H. T. Thomas, L. D. Weis, and F. C. James, *J. Am. Chem. Soc.*, **88**, 5075 (1966).
87. T. R. Evans, A. F. Toth, and P. A. Leermakers, *J. Am. Chem. Soc.*, **89**, 5060 (1967), see also C. Balny and P. Douzou, *Compt. Rend.*, *Ser. C*, **264**, 477 (1967).
88. P. A. Leermakers, L. D. Weis, and H. T. Thomas, *Compt. Rend.*, **87**, 4403 (1965).
89. J. K. S. Wan, R. N. McCormick, E. J. Baum, and J. N. Pitts, *Compt. Rend.*, **87**, 4409 (1965).

90. J. N. Pitts, L. D. Hess, E. J. Baum, E. A. Shuck, J. K. S. Wan, P. A. Leermakers, and G. Vesley, *Photochem. Photobiol.*, **4**, 305 (1965).
91. A. Bernas, D. Leonardi, and M. Renaud, *Photochem. Photobiol.*, **5**, 721 (1966).
92. O. Burchardt, J. Becher, and C. Lohse, *Acta Chem. Scand.*, **19**, 1120 (1966).
93. J. G. Calvert and J. N. Pitts, *Photochemistry*, Wiley, New York, 1966; (a) p. 645; (b) pp. 728–747; (c) pp. 780–788.
94. C. H. Nicol and J. G. Calvert, *J. Am. Chem. Soc.*, **89**, 1790 (1976).
95. E. J. Baum, J. K. S. Wan, and J. N. Pitts, *J. Am. Chem. Soc.*, **88**, 2652 (1966).
96. D. Gegiou, K. A. Muszkat, and E. Fischer, *J. Am. Chem. Soc.*, **90**, 12 (1968).
97. J. E. Leffler and E. Grunwald, *Rates and Equilibria of Organic Reactions*, Wiley, New York, 1963, pp. 321–342.
98. E. S. Huyser and D. C. Neckers, *J. Org. Chem.*, **29**, 276 (1964).
99. D. Bryce-Smith and A. Gilbert, *Chem. Commun.*, **1968**, 19.
100. R. S. H. Liu, *J. Am. Soc.*, **89**, 112 (1967).
101. G. Zimmerman, L. Y. Chow, and U. Paik, *J. Am. Chem. Soc.*, **80**, 3528 (1958).
102. S. Malkin and E. Fischer, *J. Phys. Chem.*, **66**, 2482 (1962).
103. G. Oster, L. Citarel, and M. Goodman, *J. Am. Chem. Soc.*, **84**, 703 (1962).
104. E. T. Kaiser and T. F. Wulfers, *J. Am. Chem. Soc.*, **86**, 1897 (1964).
105. P. Keller, G. Eggert, H. Wehrli, K. Schaffner, and O. Jeger, *Helv. Chim. Acta*, **50**, 2259 (1967).
106. A. W. Bradshaw and O. L. Chapman, *J. Am. Chem. Soc.*, **89**, 2372 (1967).
107. F. D. Greene, *Bull. Soc. Chim. France*, **1960**, 1356.
108. P. J. Wagner and G. S. Hammond, *J. Am. Chem. Soc.*, **88**, 1245 (1966).
109. N. J. Turro, *J. Chem. Ed.*, **44**, 536 (1967).
110. C. G. Hatchard and C. A. Parker, *Proc. Roy. Soc. (London)*, *Ser. A*, **235**, 518 (1956).
111. C. A. Parker and C. G. Hatchard, *J. Phys. Chem.*, **63**, 22 (1959).
112. G. B. Porter, J. G. W. Doering, and S. Kararika, *J. Am. Chem. Soc.*, **84**, 4027 (1962).
113. J. Lee and H. H. Seliger, *J. Chem. Phys.*, **40**, 519 (1964).
114. E. E. Wegner and A. W. Adamson, *J. Am. Chem. Soc.*, **88**, 394 (1966).
115. W. M. Moore, G. S. Hammond, and R. P. Foss, *J. Am. Chem. Soc.*, **83**, 2789 (1961).
116. W. M. Moore and M. Ketchum, *J. Am. Chem. Soc.*, **84**, 1368 (1962).
117. W. G. Leighton and G. S. Forbes, *J. Am. Chem. Soc.*, **52**, 3139 (1930).
118. K. Porter and D. H. Volman, *J. Am. Chem. Soc.*, **84**, 2011 (1962).
119. D. H. Volman and J. R. Seed, *J. Am. Chem. Soc.*, **86**, 5095 (1964).
120. J. N. Pitts, J. D. Margerum, R. P. Taylor, and W. Brim, *J. Am. Chem. Soc.*, **77**, 5499 (1955).
121. J. N. Pitts, J. K. S. Wan, and E. Z. Schuck, *J. Am. Chem. Soc.*, **86**, 3606 (1964).
122. T. R. Evans and P. A. Leermakers, *J. Am. Chem. Soc.*, **90**, 1840 (1968).
123. G. S. Hammond and P. A. Leermakers, *J. Phys. Chem.*, **66**, 1148 (1962).
124. P. J. Wagner and A. E. Kemppainen, Abstracts, 155th Meeting, American Chemical Society, San Francisco, California, 1968, p. 113.
125. W. G. Herkstroeter and G. S. Hammond, *J. Am. Chem. Soc.*, **88**, 4769 (1966).
126. W. R. Ware, *J. Chem. Phys.*, **37**, 923 (1963).
127. A. J. Fry, R. S. H. Lui, and G. S. Hammond, *J. Am. Chem. Soc.*, **88**, 4781 (1966).
128. K. Sandros and H. L. J. Backstrom, *Acta Chem. Scand.*, **16**, 958 (1962), and K. Sandros, *Acta Chem. Scand.*, **18**, 2355 (1964).
129. P. J. Wagner, Abstracts, 153rd Meeting, American Chemical Society, Miami Beach, Florida, 1967, R 118.

130. A. D. Osborne and G. Porter, *Proc. Roy. Soc. (London), Ser.A*, **284**, 9 (1965).
131. R. M. Noyes, *J. Phys. Chem.*, **65**, 763 (1961).
132. For a review see (a) E. F. Caldin, *Fast Reactions in Solution*, Blackwell, Oxford, 1964, pp. 155–156 and 280; (b) J. B. Birks and I. H. Munro, in *Progress in Reaction Kinetics*, Vol. 4, Pergamon, New York, 1967, pp. 251–252.
133. A. Weller, in *Progress in Reaction Kinetics*, Vol. 1, Pergamon, New York, pp. 187–214.
134. R. M. Noyes, in *Progress in Reaction Kinetics*, Vol. 1, Pergamon, New York, 1961, pp. 129–160.
135. P. J. Wagner, *J. Am. Chem. Soc.*, **89**, 5715 (1967).
136. J. Yguerabide, M. A. Dillon, and M. Burton, *J. Chem. Phys.*, **40**, 3040 (1964); **45**, 2719 (1966).
137. L. M. Stephenson, D. G. Whitten, G. F. Vesley, and G. S. Hammond, *J. Am. Chem. Soc.*, **88**, 3665 (1966).
138. E. F. Ullman and W. A. Henderson, *J. Am. Chem. Soc.*, **88**, 4942 (1966).
139. W. R. Ware and J. S. Novros, *J. Phys. Chem.*, **70**, 3246 (1966).
140. R. J. Campbell, E. W. Schlag, and B. W. Ristow, *J. Am. Chem. Soc.*, **89**, 5098 (1967).
141. N. C. Yang and E. D. Feit, *J. Am. Chem. Soc.*, **90**, 504 (1968).
142. R. F. Borkman and D. R. Kearns, *J. Am. Chem. Soc.*, **88**, 3467 (1966).
143. P. J. Wagner, *J. Am. Chem. Soc.*, **89**, 2503 (1967).
144. For a discussion of these calculations see ref. 132b, pp. 243–247.
145. A. A. Lamola and G. S. Hammond, *J. Chem. Phys.*, **43**, 2129 (1965).
146. R. B. Cundall and A. S. Davies, *Proc. Roy. Soc. (London), Ser. A*, **290**, 563 (1966).
147. E. F. Ullman and W. A. Henderson, *J. Am. Chem. Soc.*, **89**, 4390 (1967).
148. E. F. Ullman, *J. Am. Chem. Soc.*, **86**, 5357 (1964).
149. P. A. Leermakers and F. C. James, *J. Org. Chem.*, **32**, 2898 (1967).
150. C. Walling and M. J. Gibian, *J. Am. Chem. Soc.*, **87**, 3361 (1965).
151. S. G. Cohen and R. J. Baumgarten, *J. Am. Chem. Soc.*, **89**, 3471 (1965).
152. D. S. Kendall and P. A. Leermakers, *J. Am. Chem. Soc.*, **88**, 2766 (1966).
153. M. J. Cziesla, K. F. Mueller, and O. Jones, *Tetrahedron Letters*, **1966**, 813.

AUTHOR INDEX

Numbers in parentheses are reference numbers and indicate that an author's work is referred to although his name is not mentioned in the text. Numbers in *italics* indicate the pages on which the full references appear.

A

Aaron, C. S., 182(251), *283*
Abrahamson, E. W., 80, 136(11), 192(330), *277*, *285*
Abraitys, V. Y., 145(36), *277*
Abramovitch, R. A., 269(660), *294*
Achenbach, H., 164(146), *281*
Adams, W. R., 190(317), 249(551), *285*, *291*
Adamson, A. W., 330, *347*
Agosta, W. C., 224(448), *289*
Akasaki, Y., 252(578), *292*
Akinson, J. G., 164(145), *280*
Aktipis, S., 313(46), *345*
Alire, R. M., 72(146), *130*
Altman, L. J., 191(318), *285*
Amata, C. D., 53, *129*
Amin, J., 265(641), *294*
Anderson, J. C., 227(461), *289*
Anet, F. A. L., 108(217), *132*, 169(183a), 268(658), *282*, *294*
Anet, R., 268(658), *294*
Angus, H. J. F., 177(214,218), *282*, *283*
Aono, I., 203(354), *286*
Applequist, D., 188(289), 212(396), *284*, *287*
Appleyard, J. H., 188(293), *285*
Arnett, E. M., 179(237), 180(237), *283*
Arnold, D., 155(88), *279*
Arnold, D. R., 145(36), 150(56), 200(338), 201(344), 205(364), 214(409), 217(409), 218(409), 219(364), *277*, *278*, *286*, *288*
Askani, R., 148(43,45), *278*
Ateinmentz, R., 151(62), *278*
Ave, D. H., 151(67), *278*
Avery, E. C., 46(80), *128*
Ayer, D. E., 164(145), *280*
Azumi, T., 2(1), *15*

B

Babad, E., 163(143), *280*
Bachman, W. E., 222(436), *288*

Backstrom, H. L. J., 335(128), *347*
Badger, G. M., 267(651), *294*
Bäckström, H. L. J., 46, 47(81,82), 49, 114 (223), *128*, *132*
Baird, S. L., Jr., 76(164), *130*
Baker, W. P., 85(187), 86(187), *131*, 213 (398), 217(421), *287*, *288*
Baktschi, J. I., 257(601), *293*
Baldwin, J. E., 242(512), *290*, 298(10), 300 (10), *344*
Balle, G., 298(4), *344*
Balls, D. M., 153(73), *278*
Barborak, J. C., *278*
Barltrop, J. A., 160(119a), 207(373a), 214 (410), 254(588), 257(611),259(611,612), 272(678a), *280*, *287*, *288*, *292*, *293*, *295*, 300(14,15), *344*
Barrett, J. H., 170(190), *282*
Bartlett, P. D., 160(117), 162(117,136), 163 (117,142), 221(434), *280*, *288*
Barton, D. H. R., 242(511), 252(572), 269 (662), 275(688), *290*, *292*, *294*, *295*, 300 (13), *344*
Basinski, J. E., 155(87), *279*
Bauer, G., 269(663), *294*
Baum, E. J., 200(341), 215(415), *286*, *288*, 320(89,90), 321(95), 327(95), 328(95), *346*, *347*
Baum, J. W., *289*
Baumgarten, R. J., 217(425), 224(425), *288*, 312(151), *348*
Bayes, K. D., *289*
Beak, P., 265(639), *294*
Beaton, J. M., 275(688), *295*
Becher, J., 317(69), 320(92), *346*, *347*
Becker, H. D., 79(179), *131*, 213(399), *287*
Becker, R. S., 189(302), 265(640), *285*, *294*
Beckett, A., 34, *127*, 220(429), 222(429), 223 (441), *288*, *289*
Beckham, M. E., 243(518), *290*
Beekhuis, G. E., 190(308), *285*

N

U

Uda, H., 245(530,531), *291*, 304(26), *345*
Ullman, E. F., 60(136), *130*, 216(419), 223
(439,442,445), *288, 289*, 338(138), 342, *348*
Undec, J., 209(386), 210(386), *287*
Urry, W. H., 203(353), 256(598), *286, 293*
Usher, G. E., 209(386), 210(386), *287*

V

Valentine, D. H., 61(140), 79(171), 100(209),
130, 132, 163(141), 245(532), *280, 291*, 318
(72), *346*
Valvassori, A., 159(114), 162(114), *279*
Van Auken, T. V., 268(653), *294*
Vander Donckt, E., 276(696), *295*
Van Hemert, R. L., 34(50), *127*
Van Meter, J. P., *284*
Varvoglis, G. A., 301(16), *345*
Vassil'ev, R. F., 27(24), *127*
Vavilov, S. I., 45, *128*
Velick, S. F., 78, *130*
Vellturo, A. F., 254(589), *292*
Vernon, A. A., 188(294), *285*
Vesley, G. F., 2(1), *15*, 60(139), 65(139), 81
(139), 83(139), 103(139), 104(139), *130*,
161(134), 257(600), *280, 290, 293*, 320(90),
338(137), 341(137), *347, 348*
Vickery, B., 187(286), *284*
Vieboeck, F., *344*
Vinje, M. G., 156(92), *279*
Vo, K. P., 192(330), *285*
Vogt, V., 9(9), *16*, 60(131), 61(131), 99–101
(131), 118(131), 119(131), *129*, 160(127),
280
Volman, D. H., 264(629), *293*, 332(118,119),
347
Volmer, M., 83, *131*

W

Wagner, P. J., 50, 54, 70, 106(143), 109, 110
(220), 111, 112, *128–130, 132*, 159(116),
206(365), 214(410), *280, 286, 288*, 312(45),
316, 319(82), 327(45,64,108), 328, 333(108,
124), 334(45,108), 335, 336(135), 338(108,
135), 340(108,143), *345–348*

Walling, C., 60(133), *129*, 207(371), *287*, 312
(150), *348*
Walmsley, S. H., 29(36), *127*
Walsh, A. D., 135(5), 136(5), *277*
Walsh, T. D., 155(79a), *279*
Wan, J. K. S., 200(341), 203(356), *286, 296*,
320(89,90), 321(95), 327(95), 328(95),
332(121), *346, 347*
Ward, H. R., 177(215), *282*
Ware, W., 39, *128*, 335(126), 338(139), *347,
348*
Waring, A. J., 252(573), *292*
Warren, P. C., *290*
Warrener, R. N., 143(18), 165(151), *277,
281, 296*
Wasserman, E., 106(211,212), 107(211,212),
132, 269(664), *294*
Wasserman, H. H., 187(285), *284*
Waters, J. A., 298(6), 299(6), *344*
Watts, C. T., 266(646), *294*
Weber, G., 73, 78, *130*
Wegner, E. E., 330, *347*
Wehrli, H., 323(105), 340(105), *347*
Wehry, E. L., 95(203), *131*, 184(262,267),
284
Wei, K. S., 188(292), *285*
Weinreb, A., 40, *128, 129*
Weis, L. D., 319(86,88), 320(88), *346*
Weisbuch, F., 156(93), *279*
Weisgerber, G., 153(71), *278*
Weiss, A. C., Jr., *288*
Weizmann, C., 213(397), 222(437), 223(437),
287, 288
Weller, A., 336(133), 338(133), *348*
Welstead, W. J., 246(536), *291*
Wendler, N. L., 227(462), *289*
Wertzer, O., 162(136), *280*
Wetterman, G., 214(407), 217(407), 264
(635), *288, 293*
Wexler, S., 80(181), *131*
Whalen, D. L., 148(47), *278*
Whan, R. E., 72(146), *130*
Wheeler, J. H., *291*
Whipple, E. B., 150(56), *278*
White, E. H., 168(184), 169(184), *282*
White, J. D., 243(516), *290*
Whitear, B. R. D., 240(502), *290*
Whitham, G. H., 247(539), *291*
Whiting, M. C., 268(654), *294*
Whitten, D. G., 60(139), 65(139), 81(139),
83(139,186), 103(139,186), 104(139,186),

SUBJECT INDEX

A

Absorption, molecular, 2
Acenaphthene, 189
Acceptor, of excitation energy, 8, 18
Acetaldehyde, 203
Acetone, 204
  energy diagrams, 193
Acetophenone, 212
  phosphorescence spectrum, 95
  triplet energy, 92
Acetyl cyanide, 229
Acid halides, 228
Acridine, 276
Actinometers for quantum yields,
    benzophenone-benzhydrol, 331, 332
  ferrioxalate, 329, 330
  Reinecke's salt, 330, 331
Acyclic alkenes, photochemistry, 143
Aldehydes, aliphatic, 191, 193
    excited states, 191, 193
    primary process, 193
  alkyl, 203, 210
    formaldehyde, 203, 204
    unsaturated, 239–247
  aromatic, excited states, 194–198
Alkenes, 143–157
  acyclic, 143–145
    ethylene, 143–144
  alicyclic, 145–155
    medium- and large-ring, 153–155
    small-ring, 145–153
  excited states, 135–139, 171
  heteroatom-substituted, 155–157
  orbital symmetry, 143
  primary processes, 135–137
1-Alkyl butadienes, 160
Amides, 228
Anilines, 184, 185
Anthracene, 186–188
  energy diagram, 173
Anthraldehydes, 211, 212
Anthraquinones, 260–262
  phosphorescence spectrum, 95
  triplet energy, 92
Aromatic hydrocarbons, energies, 175
  quenching of fluorescence by dienes, 103
  tables of triplet energies, 92, 100

triplet quenchers, 105
Azides, 13, 268
Azines and related compounds, 264–272
Azobenzene, 266
Azobisisobutyronitrile, 266
Azocompounds, 266–268
Azulene, photoisomerization, 63
  triplet energy, 106, 116
  as triplet quencher, 106

B

Barrelene, 155
Beckmann rearrangement, photochemical,
    265
Benzaldehyde, 210
Benzene and catacondensed derivatives, 177–
    188
  alkyl, 179, 180
  aromatic halides, 185, 186
  energy diagrams, 173, 175
  excited states, 171–173
  phenols, aniline, and related compounds,
    184–185
  with small-ring substituents, 180–184
  sulfones, 186
Benzene epoxide, 166
Benzhydrol, 85
Benzil, phosphorescence spectrum, 95
Benzocyclobutanedione, 257
Benzocyclobutene, formation, 186
Benzocyclopentanone, 209
Benzonorbornadienes, 183
  photorearrangement, 151
Benzophenone, excited states, 6–8
  kinetics and quenching of photoreduction,
    85
  photochemistry, 216–219
  substituted, 219–223
  triplet energy, 92
  as triplet sensitizer, 44, 87, 88, 90, 91,
    108, 117, 120
Benzoquinone, 258–260
  energy diagrams, 239
  excited states, 238
  primary processes, 238–239
4-Benzoylbiphenyl, excitation transfer, 71